MY BEAUTIFUL WHITE ROSES

MY BEAUTIFUL WHITE ROSES

by

MICHAEL LECHNER

Published by the Smoketree Press
Levittown, Pa.

Manufactured in the United States of America

Library of Congress Catalogue Card Number: 75-169940

"IT HATH BEEN TOLD THEE, O' MAN,
WHAT IS GOOD AND WHAT
THE LORD DOTH REQUIRE OF THEE
    ONLY TO DO JUSTLY, AND TO LOVE MERCY
AND TO WALK HUMBLY WITH THY GOD"

Micah VI, 8

Foreword

How did this book come to be written?

In March 1948, in the library of Stamford, Connecticut, I browsed through a book about handicapped people who had managed to make something of their lives. One of these was St. Francis of Assisi, a victim of tuberculosis. Afterwards, I read several more books about his life. Then, I became curious about the reasons why a boy from a well-to-do home would leave it to live a dedicated life of poverty. What was the true story which led to this decision?

I wrote the first fifty pages on the theme. Then, I began to do more research and reading from available material. A persistent and nagging suspicion recurred, that there were too many gaps in this man's personal life!

Thomas of Celano wrote the "First Life" in 1228, just two years after Francis died in 1226, on orders of the papacy. There is nothing there about his father, mother or brother, despite the fact that they were still alive and could furnish all the facts about Francis.

Nothing of consequence was written for the next 100 years. Then a monk named Ugolino di Monte Santa Maria, wrote the book called "Fioretti". Again this was under Papal supervision. There is nothing biographical in the book and it is in the main stories of sweet legends about those near him.

Could it be possible, that, in a hundred years, nothing was written of a man whom historians call "the greatest Saint since Jesus Christ" and the "man who saved the Christian Church?"

During this period from Celano to Brother Ugolino, all writing of any kind was under Papal supervision. There was nothing of biographical value for the next 600 years! The only conclusion was that this was a deliberate and consistent effort, through the centuries, to destroy information about Francis' personal life.

Why . . . ? Because, the Roman Church of the 13th century could tolerate a Jesus Christ who was born a Jew and died a Jew, but could not tolerate another Jew who, historians say, "would save the Christian Church from falling apart."

Francis, by every act and expression, dipped into the lore and poetry and songs of the Hebrew poets, the Old Testament of his people and from his parents. Francis' tolerance and humility for all people had no sources in 12th century writing or theology.

Early paintings of the 13th century show Francis *without* the nimbus of sainthood, nor is he *wearing any crucifix in any* early picture. I researched for information in Lucca and Assisi and again found confusion. One set of historians of the 19th century claim that Pietro (Francis' father) came from Lucca. Another set of reknowned men claim that he did not!

In Assisi there is no record of his birth, baptism or any record of the marriage of his parents or any record of attendance at any church. In fact, the Library of Assisi claims that his mother's name was "Giovanna" and that "her family lived in Assisi for three generations." Yet, there is no record of this family or its name!

Other historians and the Catholic Encyclopedia state that her name was actually "Pica" and that she did come from Provence, France! *"Pica" is a girl's Hebrew name.*

Talk with the monks at the Church of San Francesco in Assisi and "they are not sure if he was born in Assisi or what year." Thomas of Celano could easily have stated in his book where Pica came from when he wrote the book. *She was still alive.* Was it because Provence was at this time the center of the largest intellectual population of Jews in the world?

Giotto (1266-1336) was the best painter of his time. He painted our earliest visual record of Francis, although these appeared about 70 *years after Francis died.*

Why did Giotto select Arles, in Provence, for his painting (Francis in Arles) rather than a hundred other cities? I think that Giotto gave posterity a historic clue which no writer could give. He selected Arles because Francis wanted to return and see the home of his mother Pica!

The painting shows Francis preaching to the monks and St. Dominic. In Francis' face could be seen the humility and love of mankind. The face of St. Dominic shows the hate and cruelty of the leader of the papal soldiers of Innocent III. This is the story which Giotto tells us in this painting . . . in Arles. (p. 248)

We can also see the pain and anguish in Francis' face, as he recalls the horror of his mother's youth.

It is an actual historical fact that Pietro chained Francis to a cellar post after he gave away a small bag of coins to the priest at San Damiani. Pietro Bernardone was a world traveler and salesman. He was a man of the world and knew the cities of Europe as he did his own back yard.

Would this man, with this kind of experience, the father of a tall, handsome son like Francis, chain him to a post for giving away a few coins? This man would laugh, if he paid many times this sum for the gambling debts of Francis.

There was then, a deeper and more emotional reason. It could only be the antipathy of any Jew for the oppression of the 13th century church and any small contribution would help it! Then again, why all the fuss (a historical fact) about the return of these few coins, that it required an appearance *before the Bishop of Assisi?* The only reason was to humiliate a Jew.

We see a record of this event in the painting by Giotto (p. 177) "Francis Gives Up His Inheritance." The expression on Pietro's face is not one of anger, but a worldly man seeing a ludicrous situation of his son undressing before an open court. Giotto shows us that the people were on the side of the parents of Francis, standing against the Bishop and the priests. Giotto tells us a lot of history.

Francis in his own humble life was a rebel and a radical against the most powerful "establishment" in all history, namely, the Holy Roman Empire. By his simple acts of humility and NON VIOLENCE he defeated the power of the Pope and the Kings of Europe.

They could easily answer violence with more violence, but *could not reply to humility with more humility!*

In exasperation, they made several attempts to have him burned at the stake for heresy!

Most all of the events are true. Volla and Vollo, the servants in the Bernardone household and Fra Baccione were created out of the times and could have lived in this period.

Failing all else . . . to convince the reader . . . SUPPOSING . . . just SUPPOSING . . . that St. Francis of Assisi was born and died a Jew . . . then this story will enfold. . . .

March 1, 1968   MICHAEL LECHNER
                                                         Levittown, Pa.

Acknowledgments

I am grateful for the use of these books for my sources:

First Life of St. Francis by Thomas of Celano
Saint Francis of Assisi by L. L. Dubois S.M.
Saint Francis of Assisi by William J. Little
Medieval Italy by Henry B. Cotterill
Italy in the 13th Century by Henry D. Sedgewick
The Mysticism of St. Francis by D. H. Nicholson
The Little Flowers of St. Francis by Raphael Brown
Among the Mystics by D. Fairweather
The Papal Monarchy by W. Barry
Selected Letters of Pope Innocent III by C. R. Cheney & W. R. Semple
History of the Jews by Solomon Grayzel
Civilization of Europe by Michael Grant
Europe and the Church under Innocent III by S. R. Packard
St. Francis by Howard Good
The Catholic Encyclopedia
The Jewish Encyclopedia
Encyclopedia of Religious Knowledge by Schaaf and Herzog
Blessed are the Meek by Kossak (from the Polish)
Life of St. Francis by Paul Sabatier
Tuberculosis and Genius by Lewis J. Moorman, MD
Heroic Lives by Raphael Sabatini
Mystics and Heretics in Italy by Emile Gebhart
Procedures of the British Academy re: 'Second Life' by Celano 1926
Studies in Mystical Religion by Rufus Jones
In the Steps of St. Francis by Ernest Raymond
Psychologie des Saints an essay by Henri Joly
Little Poor Men of Assisi by James Dobson
Life of Saint Francis by Father Cuthbert OSFC
History of Musical Thought by Donald N. Ferguson
Mysticism by A. B. Sharpe
Ideal of St. Francis by Hilarin Felder

xi

Mystical Element in Religion by Von Rugel
'*Liququtei Amarim*' by Rabbi Zalman of Liadi
Europe and the Jews by Malcolm Hay
History of the Jewish People by M. Margolis and A. Marx
Sabbath Festival Prayer Book by Rabbi Morris Silverman
The Pentateuch and the Haftorahs by Rabbi Dr. J. H. Hertz
Pictorial History of the Jewish People by Nathan Ausubel
'*St. Francis of Assisi* by Maisie Ward
'*Pirke Avoth*' the Saying of the Fathers
The Talmudic Anthology
Music in the Middle Ages by Gustave Reese
History of the Sound of Music by G. Abraham
The Saints by Baer in the publication Zion
Outline of the History of Music by Karl Nef
La Musique des Troubadours by Jean Beck
Music of 12th Century of Bernard de Ventadorn by Oxford Press
The Anthology of Jewish Music by Chemjo Vinaver. Copyright Edward B.
Marks Music Corp., N.Y.C. Used by permission.

Other publications and manuscripts in the New York City Library, Philadelphia Free Library, The Library of Yeshiva University, the Library of the St. Joseph's Seminary (New Rochelle, New York). The librarians of Assisi, Lucca and Perugia in Italy and the librarian of the University of Cairo, Egypt.

I am grateful to my son, Major Benjamin Lechner, M.D. for useful advice about medical information in the 13th century . . . for his skill with writing some of the musical scores in this book . . . and his patience in just listening to me talk about events in the dark ages.

Many thanks to these men for their time in reading and their comments about the original manuscript:

Mr. Stuart Rose, formerly senior editor of the *Saturday Evening Post* and *Ladies' Home Journal.*

Rabbi Maurice Eisendrath, D.D., LLD., (2), President, Union of American Hebrew Congregations, New York City.

Rev. George Wallace, S.M., PhD., Marist Fathers, Penndel, Penn.

Lawrence Feigenbaum, Ed.D., an executive with the New York City Board of Education.

Rabbi William Fierverker, Congregation Beth El, Levittown, Penn.

Rabbi Eugene Sack, D.D., Congregation Beth Elohim, Brooklyn, NYC.

The People in This Book

Francis Bernardone, born 1182, died October 3, 1226. *Saint Francis of Assisi in 1228,* also known as the *Troubador Saint.* His father was Pietro and his mother Pica and brother Angelo.

Clara (Clare) di Offreduccio, born January 20, 1194, Died August 12, 1253. *Saint Clare in 1255.* Her parents were: Count Favorone and Orotolana. Her two sisters were Agnes and Beatrice.

Pope Innocent III, born Lotario dei Conti de Segni in 1161. Elected Pope at age 37 in 1198. Left unique legacy (p. 255).

Cardinal Ugo Hugolin, born 1146, died in 1241 (Pope Gregory IX). Made Francis a Saint in 1227-1228.

Dr. Francis Jacobs, father of Pica Bernardone.   Angela, his sister.

Raymondin III de Bollene, Archbishop of Arles 1163 to 1181. Died in 1183.

Pierre Ier Isnard, Archbishop of Arles from 1181.

Benjamin Kolonymus, the friend of Francis' youth born about 1180. His was a great Jewish family known across France, Italy and Germany. Later a doctor with Abraham Maimonides in Egypt.

Bernard de Quintavalle, neighbor of the Bernardones, man of wealth who became the *First Companion* with Francis on April 16, 1209.

Peter Cattaneo, Doctor of Laws and Canon of Assisi, was the second to join Francis on April 16, 1209.

Gilles of Assisi, at eighteen became the Third Companion on April 23, 1209.

Rufino di Offreduccio and *'John' Capella* (the Hat) were also among the first twelve Companions of Francis.

Brother John and *Brother William* of England who actually returned with 1285 Christian slaves in the year 1189.

Bernard de Ventadorn, Pierre Vidal, Peire Cardinal and *Rambeau de Vaqueiras* were the noted composers and troubadors of this time.

Table of Contents

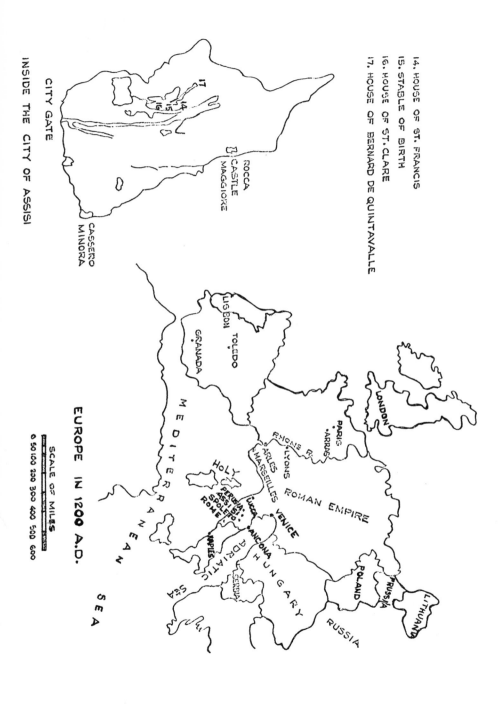

14. HOUSE OF ST. FRANCIS
15. STABLE OF BIRTH
16. HOUSE OF ST. CLARE
17. HOUSE OF BERNARD DE QUINTAVALLE

CITY GATE

INSIDE THE CITY OF ASSISI

ROCCA
CASTLE
MAGGIORE

CASSERO
MINORA

EUROPE IN 1200 A.D.

SCALE OF MILES

0 50 100 200 300 400 500 600

LISBON
TOLEDO
GRANADA

LONDON

PARIS
ARRAS

RHONE R.
ARLES
MARSEILLES
LYONS

ROMAN EMPIRE

HOLY
PERUGIA
ASSISI
SPOLETO
ROME
LUCCA
NAPLES
ANCONA
VENICE

HUNGARY

SERBIA

POLAND
PRUSSIA
LITHUANIA

RUSSIA

MEDITERRANEAN

SEA

ADRIATIC

SEA

MY BEAUTIFUL WHITE ROSES

Arles 1180

It was a sleety morning in January of 1180, when Pietro Bernadone boarded the ship bound for Marseille from Portsmouth, England. He wore the heavy coat and plain frock of the working priest. A broad-brimmed black hat kept whipping its rim in the wind. Behind him was a porter carrying Pietro's bundles and satchels of samples of soft goods. Despite his clerical garb, he was a salesman.

As Pietro walked up the gangplank to the boat a slight woman ahead of him stumbled over a crack in the plank. He moved quickly and caught her shoulders. He could not see her face in the winter gloom. All he heard was her voice, saying, "Thank you kindly, sir" in French, sweet and beautiful to his ears. "That water below looks very, very cold and angry to me."

Her clothes were billowing in the wind about her, so he could see little of the shape of her body. There was a timbre in her voice he would not forget.

As they came to the top of the plank, she turned to him smiling her thanks. He was desperately anxious to see the face which came with that voice.

Her eyes caught the priest's garb of Pietro. "Thank you for your help," her voice was kind, but there was an edge of coolness in it.

She called to a middle-aged woman ahead of her, "Aunt Angela, are you all right? Let us go to this part of the boat." She gestured to the rear of the heaving vessel.

"Yes, Pica," the older woman agreed.

Pietro became busy with his porter and his bags and lost sight of the two women.

He noticed that, mixed in with the travelers going to France, were about twenty soldiers carrying short swords and long bows. Some of the men carried an extra arquebus. Some porters near them were loading crates of arrows and bolts.

"What need for the army?" he asked one of the ship's officers.

1

"We heard there may be pirates floating around off yonder," he said, gesturing towards the English Channel.

"Pirates, this far north?" queried Pietro. The other officer shrugged and suggested that he say nothing to the women and the other passengers to alarm them.

As the ship started away from the pier, Pietro noticed two other boats also slipping away, settling into a loose triangle near each other. As they heaved into the ocean, swells drifted into a steady and rhythmic movement. He stood on the deck watching the shore melt into a gloomy mass.

Pietro always felt sad when he left these English shores. True, he loved his own warm Italian skies, the sweet smell of the cyprus trees and the rolling green hills near Lucca, in Italy where he lived. But, this English climate demanded sterner men to brave its raw weather. This kind of man he liked. In this year of 1180 there was too much to be done. He had often wondered if there was a restless energy in him which demanded that he see new people and places in England, France, Spain, Portugal and Sweden. The world was a big place and people needed his soft woolens for their clothing and homes.

He looked down at his priest's robe with distaste. That he a Jew, had to wear this disguise for his own protection! There was little respect for a priest, since he did not have to know how to read or write or need any education in religion. Although frowned on by the Popes, many of the priests were married and had their woman in the church quarters. Because of the easy life the priesthood attracted many criminals. They in turn used threats, superstition and fear to mulct contributions from people, especially the poor.

Pietro noticed that two priests stood aside from the crowd on the ship. They seemed like a good sort, so he engaged them in conversation.

At the outset, from long experience, he introduced himself as a Jewish traveler, selling goods in England and he was now returning to Lucca in Italy.

The two priests laughed at Pietro's garb, with sympathy, knowing full well the dangers on the road for any traveler, let alone a Jew.

The taller of the two men laughed as he remarked, "I guess our road robbers see a priest's habit and know they can get slim pickings indeed. At least from English priests."

"We carry very empty pouches," the shorter priest laughed. He introduced himself as Brother William, a simple parish priest of London Town. "And this, tall unfed gentleman," he pointed to his companion, "is

Brother John, Professor of Rhetoric at Oxford College. Born and bred in Scotland, Lord save him!"

"I hear that our brethren on the continent of Europe in the priestly garb do much better," remarked Brother John.

"Are you gentlemen traveling for your health?" asked Pietro.

The two priests laughed wryly. They told Pietro that they were on a money-raising mission to the continent, to obtain funds for the ransom of hundreds of Christian slaves captured by the Moslems in the Crusades.

Pietro learned that a Jean Matha, a priest in Provence in the south of France, had a vision about rescuing the slaves. He went to the Pope and asked to form a new order called the Trinitarian Brothers of Redemption. Most people in Europe did not believe in this mission.

Brother William had volunteered to help raise more money and his friend Brother John had asked if he could join him in this venture. So here they were, with empty pouches, on this mission to Europe to raise money for the rescue of slaves which most Christian folk said was another scheme of the priests to tax the poor people.

"Whenever we feel downcast, we have ourselves a bit of a songfest," smiled Brother William. "So what say you, Brother Pietro, would you join us?"

"For the benefit of yon lady and her companion," Brother John pointed with his chin towards Pica and her aunt Angela.

Pietro turned his head towards the two women, and a slight tremor of pleasure coursed through him, as he noticed that the younger woman had been watching them.

The two priests started to sing slowly, then more lustily as a slight wind created some movement of the overhead sails.

They sang:

O DIVINA VIRGO   (*anon.*)

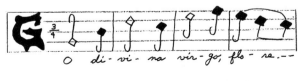

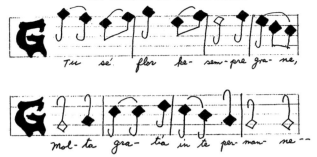

(Ref. from 12th Century Music by Reese)

"O heavenly Virgin, flower of every fragrance, thou art the flower that never fades, in thee is abundance of grace:"

Pica stood near the back of the ship, with her Aunt Angela. A twinge of loneliness tripped across her heart as she saw the tall priest who had helped her, talking with the two other priests. She noticed a strange thing —that when the two priests sang their songs, the tall man just stood there and smiled.

Suddenly there was a cry from aloft of "sail ho". Everyone moved to the side of the ship, towards where another was approaching rapidly. There was a sudden hush as the other ship struck out clawlike, awkward oars from its sides.

"They're making it move faster," Pietro thought to himself, and in the next breath the word, "pirates" slid out of his throat. For pirates gave no mercy and left few survivors after a raid.

There was a note of horror in the voices of the people on deck, when all eyes turned to their sister ships, there to help each other. They had turned away leaving them to become the victim and the bait, so they could escape! Pietro thought grimly that such was the Christian world where one would not try to help the other in great danger.

He reached down into one of his bags and drew out a short Roman sword. He had been trained by a soldier friend in its lethal use. This wouldn't be the first time he had defended himself and his property from robbers. But, this was the first time on the ocean against pirates.

Pietro looked around for the young lady with that beautiful voice. People were milling about and he wondered where she was. He didn't see her because a mild terror was surging across the passengers on deck.

The soldiers were getting a supply of arrows ready for their long bows, for distance shots across the closing gap to the pirate ship. The short stocky captain of their ship shouted to the soldiers, "Hold your shots and make every arrow count."

When a hundred feet of open water swirled between the ships, the pirate ship turned broadside to its victim. The soldiers let loose their arrows and each one found a mark. They reloaded and again the pirates fell all over their ship.

As the pirate ship closed fast, about twenty pirates jumped across the short gap of the two ships and were met by the soldiers, sailors and Pietro waiting for them.

Pietro dispatched one red-bearded pirate with a short sword chop into his body. Then turning, he met another man, striking him in the ribs as he ran by. He heard a woman shout behind him, he turned to meet another man attacking him from the rear.

Suddenly, the pirate stumbled. Through the edge of his vision, Pietro saw the woman push a long pole under the man's feet.

He swung and knocked the man unconscious with the handle of his short sword.

In a few minutes the battle was over. The pirate ship backed away, leaving the dead and wounded to their fate.

"You are *not* a priest." The woman's voice was happy with excitement and relief as she pointed to the tear across his smock which revealed his chest of chained iron links.

"No, I'm not," Pietro told her. "I'm a Jewish traveler who sells goods to people in England."

"Why the priest's dress?" she wanted to know.

"It's the only way a traveler can get about. Especially if he's a Jew. That makes it doubly hard. For then he is a victim of not only the thief but any Christian who wants his property."

"I haven't seen this in Arles, Provence, in France where I come from," she said.

"Perhaps, dear lady, you live a sheltered life," he chided her. "By the way, my name is Pietro Bernardone, late from the city of Lucca, in Italy. I live there with my older brother and his good wife. And you?" He took off his wide-brimmed hat and swept it under his bowing chest, in a mocking style.

"My name is Pica Jacobs from Arles, in Provence." She waited a few moments and smiled at him with her kind face, which held a twinkle of mischief in her eyes. "I'm an unmarried lady and my parents are Jewish too."

Suddenly they both stopped talking and looked at each other, finding something each wanted. Pietro in his long travels across Europe had met many maids in the taverns and the wives of business men who were charmed by his ready wit and gentlemanly behavior. These ladies were ready with their favors, willingly offered and gratefully accepted. Pietro had rested at many fountains and had quenched many thirsts. Never once had he met anyone like Pica.

She was above middle height, with a thin nose and long, round face. Her hair was the color of walnut surrounding a face which seemed to glow with a soft undertone of olive color under her flat cheekbones. Her mouth was soft and warm resting above a firm, narrow chin.

Pica saw a tall man, with curly light brown hair and tanned face, heavy lips and wide jaw. This man she knew wasn't afraid of people nor of life itself. He would meet each challenge as it came. A thrill of anticipation went through her as she looked into his dark knowing eyes.

Since he lived with a brother and *his wife*, she thought, he wasn't married.

"Oh there you are," a woman's voice broke their reveries. It was the short middle-aged woman behind them.

"This is my Aunt Angela," she told Pietro and introduced him to the older woman. She looked disheveled and her gray hair was blowing in the wind. One could read the anguish of the past hour in her face.

About them was the movement of people. Soldiers and sailors were tossing the bodies of dead pirates overboard. The badly wounded outlaws had their wrists tied and they, too, were dropped overboard.

A pirate at Pietro's feet was stunned, but not dead, from the blow on his head. Two soldiers tied his hands and his feet to a capstan on the ship. He would die on the gallows in a French courtyard.

"What brought you to England?" asked Pietro.

Pica told him that they had gone to England, to York to visit relatives and friends.

"Why I was in York to visit an old friend and financial advisor, Isaac of York," Pietro replied. "Why did we not meet? I can answer my own question, there are about a thousand Jews living in York, in this year 1180."

"Our paths did not cross," Pica laughed. "So I guess one should think of York as a large city, spread across the countryside."

"Again the Christian world is talking about a third Crusade," Pietro told the two women.

"Are the Jews of the world to face more murder and robbery as in the other crusades?" she asked. They both remembered that in each crusade, the soldiers attacked the Jews on the instigation of the monks and priests.

The Jews had property and they were easy marks because they had no official strength in any community.

"No, I don't think so," Pietro replied. "The Christians can get more by taxing us heavily." He told her about the Jew Tax in Lucca to force Jews out of the soft goods business.

"Why kill us? It is so much easier to get money out of live Jews than dead ones." He laughed without rancor.

"Do you know that the kings passed laws forbidding the payment of any interest on any loans. Of course this was aimed at the Jewish money lenders. Money lending, Pah! What a filthy business is this. Our own Talmud forbids it as a degrading thing. Yet what choice do Jews have?"

"Go into a trade, without the need for lending money," Pica suggested.

"Easier said than done," Pietro replied. "The Christians close all trades to us. The Guilds won't let a Jew into their groups. Jews can't own land in Italy and cannot employ a serf or a Christian. So, what are they going to do? Go into the only business not closed to them . . . money lending."

"What a horrible wheel around our necks." Pica thought aloud.

"There is another catch," Pietro told them, "the serfs belong to the baron of the local castle. Because they are technically part of the land or work on it, they became the serfs of the kings."

"We are not serfs in Provence, we are a free people there," Pica told him.

"True, but your French kings hold the Jews as their wards and 'protect' them. Of course by allowing the Jew to be a money lender, they in turn make the taxes high enough to allow the Jew to live and not squeeze him too dry."

Pietro decided to travel to Provence with Pica and her Aunt Angela. He bought a swift moving mare in Calais from a sailor who had won the horse in a dice game. He was glad to sell him to Pietro for a bargain price.

Pica suggested they name the horse Chancey, because he was a pawn of chance.

They were to travel by coach to an inn outside Arras and stay for the night. The next day they were to press on to Lyons, there they would take a boat down the Rhone River to Arles, in Provence. The journey would take about six days.

On the way to Arras the roads were rough and torn and the coach had to make several detours because of poor bridges over small streams. "They have money to spend for wars," the coachman told them, "but not a sou for good roads," shaking his head in Gallic resignation.

The coach approached two priests walking ahead of them on the road. The coachman made the sign of the cross over his chest and muttered, "Priests, a pest on them. They will bring me bad luck for the week."

As they started to pass them Pietro exclaimed, "Hold there, it's Brother John and William." The coach stopped. Pietro learned that they were on their way to Paris and had planned to travel as far south as Lyon, in their effort to raise funds for their mission to recover the slaves from the Moslems. They were happy to join Pietro, Pica and her aunt. At first they refused to ride in the coach and continued to walk alongside. But, Pietro warned that this would slow them up and that they would be caught on the roads at night. Only then did they consent to ride in the coach.

Pietro then got on his horse to make room for one of the priests. They reached a small inn in Arras just as it got dark. The fact that Pica and Pietro were not married created some confusion in the attitude of the innkeeper. It seemed that there were many travelers on the road and a lot of them were in this inn tonight.

When the five of them sat down at a table to eat, Pietro looked around to search for the people he often saw on his travels. He saw three other priests wearing the dark robes of some French order.

He and the two priests from England wore light gray habits. Pietro noticed that a man was in the corner of the room gently strumming a lute. He remembered that this was the famous Trouvére Pierre Vidal. He gave this information to the guests at his table.

After the meal, Brother John suggested that they have some after dinner entertainment. The two priests started to sing some hymns of Thanksgiving.

Soon a few more of the diners in the room joined them.

Pietro saw that the three priests in black kept on drinking from their mugs, paying little attention to the singing.

Brother William whispered something to Pietro, who arose and struck a heavy spoon on the table several times asking for quiet.

Pietro raised his voice so he could be heard across the room. He told the travelers how he had met the two priests at his table, on the boat from England. He asked the travelers to listen to the two priests and believe what they told.

Tall, lanky Brother John, late of Oxford College, then stood up and told the people about his mission to ransom the Christian slaves held in Moslem hands.

The people were generous when Pietro started the contributions in a small woven basket, with five silver sous. Everyone made some votive offering for their brethern in chains.

When Pietro came close to the three drunken priests, they laughed at him, one of them exclaiming, "You are worse thieves than we are. We at least do not hide our infamy with songs and lusty words." He turned his head away as did his companions and continued their drinking.

Pietro shook his head, remembering the large bag of coins one priest had in his wallet when they came into the inn.

The man called Pierre Vidal walked over to them asking politely if he could join them. He was received with joy and Pietro asked him to sing for the company.

Just about this time, a slight commotion arose in the corner of the room where the three dark-robed priests sat drinking. One of them forced the waitress to sit on his lap.

She objected to this behavior. The man then reached up quickly and tore her dress exposing one naked breast. The woman screamed. He let her go and she hurried away towards the kitchen.

A few minutes later, one of the dark-robed priests interrupted the singing at Pietro's table, with loud drunken messages. One of them attempted to mimic Vidal's voice.

Vidal then started to sing a song, which suddenly hushed the room into quiet attention:

(Ref. written by Roman de Fauvel. From Reese, "12th Century Music". The neumes are from the original manuscript.)

The room remained hushed for a few minutes, then two of the dark-robed priests arose from their table and walked on unsteady feet over to Pierre Vidal and his companions.

Pietro rose slowly to his feet, expecting trouble. One of the priests then took out a wallet from under his robe and asked Vidal if he would sell him his lute.

The trouvére laughed at him, asking if he had any gold sous. "For what priest has any gold?" he asked blithely, looking at the two companions in gray seated opposite him.

All of them laughed at this wry humor. The priest standing over them opened his wallet and showed them it was half full of gold coins. Pietro let go a short whistle in amazement. There was a small fortune there!

"Oh go along," the troubador smiled, "this must be your funds from the monastery. No, this lute is not for sale. This baby here," (he ran his hands over the lute with gentle care,) "has been with me a long . . . long time . . . She is like a little woman. On cold nights I take her to bed with me."

Everyone around them laughed, except the drunken priests. They were sullen as they returned to their table.

Pierre Vidal handed his lute to Pica and asked if she would sing something for them. She hummed a few tunes under her breath and then said for only those at her table to hear.

"And so many of my people died by the hands of these men and their brothers, I have a fine song for this occasion."

Then she sang,

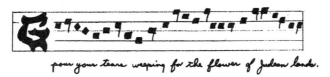

pour your tears weeping for the flower of Judean lands.

(Ref: from a liturgical drama about a slaughter of innocent Jewish children in the "Crusades" in Europe 11th century. The neumes were on the original manuscript.)

One of the three priests had his head on the table snoring loudly, the other two kept on drinking from their mugs.

Pierre Vidal in mocking tones and gesturing to them with his lute, then sang:

"Dear comrade, sleep no more, the bird I hear, who seeks

day, in accents clear sings his song and singing I hail you

Wake lest your jealous rival assail you; and soon ---

will come the mo - r - ning.

(Ref: note, from *Reis Glorios* by Guiraut de Bornelh Paris Bib. Nat. MS Fr. 22543 f.8)

The servant woman returned from the kitchen and was removing the empty mugs on the tables when one of the priests caught hold of her and said something into her ear. She angrily replied to him. The other priest arose and the two of them caught hold of her arms, as one held his hand over her mouth. They half dragged her to the rear room of the hostel. The door was shut with a bang.

A short man came out of the kitchen and moved as if to interrupt the abduction. Pietro could hear the innkeeper say, "Let be Vollo, let be, they are drunk. They could close this place anytime they want to. Let be Vollo."

The man nodded his head in resignation and returned to the kitchen with the innkeeper. No one tried to stop this wanton act, as if it was an accepted mode of the times. No one arose to help the woman, as if life was too cheap to bargain for it. No one's voice rose to say anything, as if a rustle in a forest could shake no leaves.

The next morning, just as Pietro and Pica were about to leave, they learned that the priest named Fra Baccione had lost his wallet of gold sous. He told the inn keeper that the woman, with them had stolen it. He demanded that she appear at once and be ready for eternal damnation!

Neither the servant woman, whose name was Volla nor Vollo could be found. They were gone, with their simple belongings and the heavy wallet of gold coins.

As Pica left the inn, she invited Brother John and Brother William to visit her home in Arles. She assured the two priests that their trip into Provence would help their cause. The people from Montpelier and Marseille would be generous. They promised to visit her soon.

On the way to Lyon, Pietro had to stop in Paris for several days to talk with some business friends. He and Pica stayed at the home of one of the friends.

On one of their sight seeing tours of the city, as they were crossing a bridge over the River Seine, a man and woman strolling ahead of them, struck a familiar note to Pica and Pietro. It was Volla, the servant woman from the inn and her husband, Vollo.

"Those priestly dogs, we had to teach them a lesson. Stealing from them . . . they stole the money too. Anyway, it was not stealing . . . they used my wife," Vollo said.

"Faugh," Volla said excitedly, "they were drunken beasts. They promised to give me a silver sou for the night's pleasure. But, I know their kind. With morning I would have gotten a wallop on the head and driven out of the room."

The woman asked Pica where she came from and boldly asked if she needed a pair of good strong servants for her household. Pietro made a wry motion with his head as if to negate the idea.

Then he looked at the pair and saw two strongly muscled, heavily boned people, who strangely looked like brother and sister, in height and facial structure.

Even their names, Volla and Vollo were strange ones. What Pica and Pietro liked about the pair was the fact that neither attempted to justify their stealing or condone it. This, too, was a mode of the times. There was something so earthy and warm about this pair that, almost together, Pietro and Pica agreed to accept them.

A few days later, Pietro and Pica reached Lyon and took a boat down the River Rhone towards Arles. Several times Pietro remarked how crystal clear the river was. They could see many sailboats and children swimming in the water as the ship glided along.

Since Arles was a seaport town, the wharves were filled with ships loading for trips out to sea and up the River Rhone, bringing goods from foreign lands and the wines, fruits, furs from the forests of Arles to the cities of Northern France and far off England.

When Pietro met Pica's father Dr. Francis Jacob, he was mildly surprised, how different the two were. Where Pica was tall and more heavy boned, her father was slight and shorter than his daughter. Her hair was a walnut colored, her father's was reddish blond. His nose was more aquiline, hers was wider at the nostrils.

Pica showed Pietro around their home and grounds. It was not a large house, but it had ample gardens. There was an area with pens for animals. Pietro learned that her father had attended the Medical School at Montpelier, then in his last year had decided to concentrate his studies on animal care.

The property reached down a slope towards the River Rhone. They sat on a masonry wall watching the slanting rays of the sun drift across the wide expanse of river.

On the other side of the property was the Cordeliére Monastery. Pica told Pietro that the Abbot had several times wanted to buy their property, but her father had refused to sell.

Pica was proud as she showed him her white rose bushes which some friends had brought from North Africa as small shoots in tubs of earth. She had cultivated and nurtured these plants until a whole corner of the garden wall held their beauty intact.

In his movement around the house, Pietro could see many evidences of learning and music. Many of the books and manuscripts were translations from the Arabic into Hebrew and French. Provence was famous in these years for its excellent translators who brought to France the learning and wisdom of the East. They also translated into Latin many books from Hebrew and Arabic.

Thus, the Jews of Provence brought to this most enlightened area of France, and all Western Civilization, for the first time broad sections of thought. They brought in books of mathematics, science, art and medicine and opened new pathways of understanding between the East and the West.

Vollo and Volla took over the household duties, with little pause, as if they had been there for years.

Pica had told her father about the invitation to the two priests, Brother John and William. He was enthusiastic about the priests' project and suggested that she invite many friends. A few days later the two men arrived and Pica sent out the invitations.

With a glint of mischief in his eyes, Dr. Jacobs told Pica to invite a heretic, Pierre Waldo, and Raymondin, the Archbishop of Arles. She raised her eyes in disbelief. Raymondin was the stronghold of the Roman Church in Provence. The Archbishop had been a participant in the Third Lateran Council of 1179. This Council had made new rules about the heretics in the south of France called the "Waldensians," named after Pierre Waldo.

She questioned her father about inviting these two men, so far apart in the world of religion, under the same roof.

Her father replied, it would make for an interesting afternoon to see these two men together. Raymondin had often come to this Jewish home of the Animal Doctor, because he liked to play chess with Pica. It was considered to be a woman's indoor game, but on one of his visits *"for good relations with the Israelites"* as he put it, he asked her to teach him the game.

He was a loquacious old gentleman and often spoke about events in his church as if the Jacobs were his own priests. He once boasted that he loaned the King of Aragon about 2000 gold sous at an interest rate of 50 percent. "And the fat king paid through his fat nose," he laughed aloud as Pica joined him.

He told them that there was a fiery young man at the Third Lateran Council (of 1179) who moved heaven and earth to get through heavy retrictions on the Jews. His name was Lotario dei Conti and he was not yet 20 years old.

"With three powerful Cardinals as his relatives, this young man will go far," Raymondin told them. "Who knows he may yet be the Pope someday, then he will surely be known as the 'wonder of the world'. He shook his head sadly, "Such force and brilliance to make the Jews smaller in the world. To what purpose?

"It was dei Conti who drove for the hated yellow badge for the Jews. It passed through the Council. But it was the Jew Yeheil, who is the financial advisor to Pope Alexander III, who convinced him to abolish this rule. For the Jew, or any person over 13 to wear this kind of badge, is not only a humiliation to a person's dignity but offers him as a target to any hoodlum to commit any kind of insult or bodily injury. This yellow badge was used by the Moslems to separate them from the Christians. Now he wanted this to be used against the Jews.

"Lotario dei Conti is related to all the rich and powerful houses and merchants of Venice. They want to eliminate their Jewish competitors and have all the business in Europe for themselves. The best way is to destroy the Jew. They plan this through Lotario dei Conti.

"Far worse than this, it separates people from each other. The Good Lord created all of us and we must live together in God's own world." He shook his head, "This is an evil thing, it is evil."

"Come Pica girl, sing for me your song about your white roses", he would ask. "This song soothes my heart in all the seas of troubles around us, sing girl."

Pica then would sing for him, her own song,

MY BEAUTIFUL WHITE ROSES

"My beautiful white roses each like a heart
With precious fragrance its petals part
   Bring all lovers a breath of life
Points new beauty in its sight.
   Each rose with gentle color rare   *(repeat)*
Dips this glory from the earth
   The petals float as soft as air   *(repeat)*
From far away its land of birth."   *(repeat)*

To the Jacobs' house that Sunday afternoon came about 75 people ready to listen and help the English priests. Most of the guests were Jews from Arles, Marseilles and Montpelier.

Vollo and Volla moved among the guests with huge trays of food and drinks, enjoying the party as much as did Pica and Pietro, with a freedom and good fellowship they had never experienced before.

They were quietly informed by Dr. Jacobs, that, although they had the status of servants in the family, it was the Jewish custom to treat them as part of the family. This was their home, each of them was an equal partner in this household in the work to be done and respect for each other.

The two servants were greeted warmly by Brother John and Brother William, who tactfully did not refer to their last meeting in the inn in Arras.

Pierre Waldo came and moved amiably among all the guests, as did the famous composer Bernard de Ventadorn who was visiting in Provence and could not miss a good party where he could display his talents.

Father Jean Matha, who lived in Provence, came to join the two brothers from England. It was Father Matha who had a vision that he should do something about redeeming the Christian slaves, and asked these two priests to help this project of recovery.

David Kimchi was an old friend of the family, a famous Jewish translator who lived near Arles. He had written many books as did his father before him, bringing the wisdom of the East to the European world of letters.

Pietro saw how easily Dr. Jacobs moved among his guests, a liking for people written across his face with a ready smile and good humor. Pica helped in the kitchen and served the guests on the terrace and in the garden. When people admired her white roses, her face beamed with happiness.

With the arrival of Raymondin III, the Archbishop of Arles, there was a momentary hush of respect for the dignity of this fine old man. He introduced a thin, youngish man as Pierre ler Isnard, the Canon of St. Tropheme, and said he had "to blackmail him to get him out of the monastery."

The old Bishop laughingly told the people around him, "Since there are so many of my Jewish friends here, this young man will probably be the next Bishop of Arles, when St. Peter calls me to his throne." He laughed as he put him arm around ler Isnard.

He pointed to Father Jean Matha, "Ah, my good Father is here to enjoy Pica's good food. I trust we will have no visions here today." He joked with the embarrassed priest.

The Father introduced Brother John and Brother William to the old Bishop who greeted them warmly. He saw Pierre Waldo across the room. "Come over here, you young heretic." His voice was joshing and easy.

Pierre Waldo already commanded a wide following of thousands of well wishers who called themselves "Waldensians" and other "Albigensians" across France, Germany, Hungary and England. He approached the Bishop, seated in an armchair which he made into a throne by his presence and manner.

Waldo approached quickly as he was bidden and knelt, kissing the ring on the old man's finger. The Bishop nodded his head slightly to the younger man. Ler Isnard straightened up and moved slightly from the Bishop.

"Now, don't get your hackles up, Isnard," the Bishop told him. "Mother Church has a wide bosom and can suckle all her children, both good and bad ones. See, she has two Pierres at my side."

"Which would you say I was?" smiled Waldo. "A good one or a bad child of Mother Church?"

"Men like you are trying to destroy our Church." interposed ler Isnard.

The room became quiet, as Pica looked fully at her father. A slight frown crinkled her face. He shook his head slowly.

"I did ask his Holiness Pope Alexander for permission to translate the Holy Bible into the vulgar language, namely French, Waldo said. "This was granted. Is it wrong for more Frenchmen to know and love our Holy Scriptures? Before, only a few priests knew it because the Bible is in Latin. And many of our Jewish friends like David Kimchi, here. We are all of us Frenchmen."

David Kimchi added smiling, "You gentlemen know that old story of the priest who told his congregation that 'God gave us the Bible in Latin because He knew no French'."

This brought on general laughter and relieved the tension in the room.

"Yes, but you went on beyond this," ler Isnard's voice was incisive. "You preached against the priests and the fountain of the Holy Church." He directed his angry face at Pierre Waldo.

"A good son can talk about his father, with dignity and respect," was Waldo's quiet reply. "There are good people, not wicked ones nor are they heretics who want the Holy Church to be cleaner and purer in spirit. Is it wrong for us to plead that the priest who ministers to the ills of the poor be himself capable morally and in spirit with the founder of all Christians, our Lord Jesus? Is it wrong for us to ask that this priest know how to read and write? Instead he preys upon the superstitions of the poor and the illiterate, mulcting from them the little possessions they have, in the name of Our Father, when they themselves disobey every commandment of the Holy Scriptures?"

"Not all of us can be University graduates and scholars like our two holy brethren from England," the Canon replied smiling.

"Ah well, I came here for a quiet afternoon of good talk and of course some music," complained the old Archbishop, "And we get into these endless discussions about our faith."

He gestured with his hand to Bernard Ventadorn to come closer, "And I see our good friend and music writer, a competitor of yours, Rambeau de Vaqueiras is also here. Come closer and let me greet you."

As the two men approached the old man, they knelt in obeisance and stood up together, smiling at each other.

"And how is her Highness the Queen from Aquitaine," asked the Bishop kindly of Ventadorn. It was known through all of Europe that the Queen had brought him into her court (in Paris) of King Louis VII and heaped honors on him and his musical compositions.

"The queen finds new favorites with each new season," was the reply. "I am now traveling a bit to see more of our beautiful Provence. The court restrains, one might add. The glamour of courtly processions lends little time for contemplation and careful thought for new compositions."

"I know indeed," sighed the Bishop. "But enough of meandering into other realms," he waved his hand at Ventadorn and de Vaqueiras. "Would you two favor us with some of your songs. Of course it may not be to your dignity to sing your own melodies. I know that the troubador lets the jongleur do the singing for him. Then let our dear Jewish daughter, Pica be your jongleur."

"No, your excellency, Rambeau and I will sing this one together, if the Lady Pica will lend us her viélle and a lute." They then sang this ancient melody together:

Then Vaqueiras asked to sing this one alone:

(Ref: old 12th century Christian melody)

"As men may be crippled through their sins, so may they be made whole again by faith."

Rambeau de Vaqueiras raised his hands and said, "Since we have gathered here today, not to listen to us demonstrate our wares, but another more holy purpose, I would like to hold us for a while with this old Gregorian melody of Jesu, forsaken and dying on his cross," he then sang,

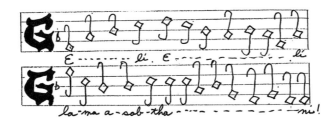

He moved away.

Brother Williams walked to the place left by the troubador and said, "God, Oh God, why hast thou forsaken me? Is the cry of all people everywhere and especially those Christians who are held captive in the Moslem lands. There are several thousand there. And now I must ask my brothers, the Jews of Provence, to help us recover these human souls."

"The old Gregorian who wrote this melody made a slight error. Jesus knew only the Aramaic not the Hebrew word for 'forsaken' which should be 'zava . . tanni . .' Not 'asabtanni' . . . You will forgive me, I can't forget that I'm a school teacher."

"Slavery as it was known in the Roman and Greek society was not a part of Jewish life at any time in history. The Jew abhorred slavery as he would the plague. The few slaves permitted were only for payment of bad debts or a judgment of a court. But, by ancient Jewish law the slave must be freed in a year of Jubilee or at the end of seven years.

"Allow me to be erudite from the ancient Hebrew text of the Old Testament in Exodus XXI, 26, "Vehee yahkeh ish ess ain ahvdoh oh ess ain," and if the master strike the eye of a bondsman and destroy it, or smite the bondsman's tooth . . . or the loss of a limb . . . then he must be given his freedom. This is the law of the Book. This was true of any heathen slave.

"Always the slave was treated as a human being, not a chattel or an animal.

"As far back as the Old Testament, Jews have been kind to people in distress. In our travels Brother John and I have found that the Jews have been most generous in London, Paris, Montpelier and many other cities in France. I trust you will be most generous in your giving at this time."

Pietro Bernardone began to move among the guests with a large woven basket, collecting silver and gold coins from the guests. He was ostentatious as he put in his own five silver sous into the basket. As he went around every person made valuable contributions to this cause.

Archbishop Raymondin told Pietro that he carried no money with him but would make his contribution later. Pierre ler Isnard put in a single silver coin. Pietro looked into the canon's face and saw a slight tinge of disdain for the proceedings. The words of the two priests returned to Pietro, 'that Christians would not believe this venture could ever be successful'. He saw that disbelief in this priest's face.

Without counting it, Pietro turned over the contents to the two English priests, who then spilled the coins on a large table and counted out almost 80 sou raymondin, which could rescue about 200 slaves.[1]

The old Bishop told Dr. Francis Jacobs, slyly, "I remember that in the

[1]In 1189 Brother John and Brother William after many hardships returned to Europe with 1285 Christian slaves. History of Slavery—1860.

Old Testament in the 'parshe Ki Thessa' in Exodus the ancient rabbis talk of the payment of the shekel as a means of atonement in advance. Let me see how the Hebrew goes, "Vayedahberr Adonai ehl Moshe laymore, kee sisso ess rosh b'nai yisroel lif ked vonossnuh ish kopoor naph sho la Adonai biffkoed ohsum vehlo bohem nehfesh bifkoed ohsum."

"And the Lord spoke unto Moses saying, "When thou takest the sum of the children of Israel, according to their number, then shall they give each man a ransom for his soul unto the Lord, when thou numberest them, that there be no plague among them. . . ."

Dr. Jacobs replied to the Bishop that this half shekel was a payment of an atonement before the *soldier* went into battle. In this way he gave notice that he was to take life not in murder but in the heat of battle.

"But, right now," the Bishop continued, "are not you Jews paying 'kopoor,' the ransom for your own souls, not those of Christian slaves?"

"You know that our Rabbis interpret this to mean atonement of the *soldier* not the *civilian*. After any battle the Jewish soldier would have *no* great songs for victory, as the Romans and the Greeks would celebrate. Instead they would go to the ancient Temple in Jerusalem and pray to God for forgiveness and bring gifts to the altar of God," said Dr. Jacobs.

"Your excellency remembers what the Talmud tells us," David Kimchi added, "that the angels started to sing when the Egyptians were drowning in the Red Sea, as the children of Israel crossed over ahead of them. God, may His name be blessed, told the angels to stop singing, 'My children are dying and you are singing?' By this God then meant that all of us, Christians and Jews, are indeed His children."

"It has always puzzled me," interposed Pierre ler Isnard, his voice smooth, "why the Jews talk of atonement and the far-reaching aims of Judaism and yet when Moses was gone only forty days, they made Aaron, the brother of Moses, make them a golden calf. They wanted no mighty spirit of an unseen God. They wanted to see a real idol. It could have been made of wood or stone or gold."

Dr. Jacobs raised his hand and said, "The Jews had been living in a slave land for more than 250 years. They were not ready to be a free people. Aaron was forced into an agreement with these people because he wanted to buy more time until Moses returned from Mount Sinai. He thought that by asking men as well as women to give their gold rings and their trinkets, they would laugh at his request. I think that history proved him wrong. People always have money to buy false gods like the golden calf, in every age of mankind. For purposes of evil money can always be found. But, for good purposes there is neither time nor money available."

"In a way," said Pierre Waldo, "Am I not trying to save our Holy Christian Church?"

"How so, by trying to destroy our people's faith, with more heresy?" interposed Pierre ler Isnard.

"No, I am trying to bring to the Church a fresh spirit," replied Waldo calmly. "Much as Jesus brought to the Jews 1180 years ago. In a true sense He did not intend to found a new religion, but induce a new spirit in the old Jewish faith in Adonai."

"Do you want to convert to the Jews?" asked ler Isnard. "Many Christians have been burned at the stake for just that. In fact," he turned towards the English priests, "one of your brethren met that fate just recently."

David Kimchi added, "Yet Christians are converting to Judaism by the hundreds, because they can find no spiritual faith or healing from Rome."

"God is infinite" said Waldo. "Men of good will cannot believe that Jesus was the Son of God. To my people He was the son of a Jewish carpenter named Joseph and his wife named Mary. Jesus was a man of great ability and prophecy and he remained a Jew all His life."

"This is outright heresy," muttered ler Isnard under his breath, "And one day you will burn for this."[2]

"There is another important difference," said David Kimchi as Archbishop Raymondin III sat back in his chair enjoying this joust of thoughts across the room. "How can the Christians believe that a thoughtful man could accept the death of Jesus over 1,180 years ago for the vicarious atonement of the sins he will commit next week or next year, for that matter last week?"

"This is the mighty principle of Christianity," said the Bishop," that every being on earth can find absolution from his sins upon the body of the Christ. Else he has no anchor in the wind. His soul and his ship of life will founder upon the sea of living."

"Yet, isn't this an easy way out for a man after he had sinned or to give him a philosophy for living a good life?" persisted David Kimchi.

"No, it is not an easy way," ler Isnard answered. "Every man knows that he will be punished in the after life by going to the hell fires of satan for eternity.

"This is our weakness and yet our strength because no other religion can offer this to all men, wherever they may be. It is our weakness, because men

[2]Waldo later *was burned* at the stake for saying this.

cannot and will not reach with their hearts to the heavens to pray and talk with God. They do take the easier way and reach only to the body of Christ. This is not enough.

"This was one of the discussions at the Lateran Council of 1179, when some of the princes of the Church said, 'take away vicarious atonement and our whole structure of Christian theology would crumble.' For this reason the idea of the 'Wafer' as the body of Christ and 'Holy Wine' as the blood of Christ was discussed at length.

"We let you Jews rely on an unseen God, we bring our God right into the palm of the hand of the Christian. He can feel and drink into his own body and soul the essence of Jesus who died for him. What more can a simple soul ask?"

"The Jew and *only he alone* must atone for his transgression," said Dr. Jacobs sadly. "It is most convenient for the Christian to declare that Jesus died for man's sins. This is like watching two lovers making love in bed and finding some thrill from that. It would be more proper in the nature of life that a man live his own sex life, not through the vicarious thrill of seeing others.

"By the same thought, a man must pay for his *own sins*, then there is no vicarious substitution. This kind of vicarious substitution is creating a sexual degeneration of Christian man. My colleagues at the Montpelier Medical School can vouch for this truth."

David Kimchi waited as silence weighed the room after Dr. Jacobs' words settled into the minds of those about him. "Your excellency remembers the passage about Jacob and his dream of the ladder to heaven?" asked Kimchi.

"You mean that men can reach with their thoughts and hearts to heaven itself?" the Bishop replied. "In Jacob's dream, he saw angels going up and down the ladder to heaven. Our ancient scribes were trying to tell us that men can reach to God himself. This is contrary to all of our Christian teachings. This is why Jesus died on the cross to be the spokesman for all mankind."

"This thought," said Kimchi," and the constant repression of free thinking, for all men are not alike, has created an internal fear in your Christian men and women, not of God but a hate for the Holy Church. This repression has throttled the writers and artists to give free expression to their minds. Your Excellency, in the past thousand years of Christianity, what giants have you nurtured or created? What men has the Christian Church made from *its own clay*? After all, Peter, James, Paul and Mark and Jesus himself were all Jews.

"Perhaps you would want to name one man, St. Augustine. Yet he did not appeal to the universal man of all faiths as did these first twelve men. Where in the last thousand years has Christianity created such men as our prophets like Moses, Abraham, Isaiah or Jacob, such powerful writers as Maimonides, poets like Ibn Gabirol, Yehudah Halevi or Kolonymus? Let us be frank, your Excellency, the Roman Church you have today is not the kind of church which Peter and Paul wanted for you. You have built huge buildings of stone and mortar, but where have you trapped the spirit of man?"

"We have trapped him in obedience to our will," replied Pierre ler Isnard. "The first rule of our Church is strict obedience to its tenets. They must have faith without reservation. Otherwise all civilization would be destroyed. Christianity is the mortar which holds it together.

"Once again," the old Archbishop intervened, "enough of this talk, let us have some more trouvere music. Bernard de Ventadorn," he signalled to the poet, "Would you kindly present some of our best. . . . ."

Pica played the vielle, while the composer sang some of his songs.

AMORS, E QUE-US ES VEJAIRE?

(Ref: from Songs in Provencal by Ventadorn, arranged by Egon Welles, Oxford Press, London.)

Love, what is your opinion?
Can you ever find a greater fool than I?
What do you think? that I ought to be a lover
And go on without finding grace from my lady?
Whatever you command me to do
I'll do it, for I must.

Ventadorn and Pica both stood tall together, with long tresses glinting in the afternoon sun. Pica would play the strings and then sing quietly along with the composer.

Pietro stood aside, watching, with often troubled eyes, noting how easily Pica held helself in such company. He looked about him. There was great wealth here, men of science and business, a few rabbis, teachers, writers, translators, and many more vocations in this gathering.

Here was a household of Jews, yet it drew into its folds the Archbishop of Arles and his next successor! This was the kind of world which was Provence in the year 1180.

The room was quiet as Pica and Ventadorn sang his melodies together.

Later another troubador and composer named Peire Cardenal came into the Jacob's home. He was greeted warmly by many of the people there because he was bold in his songs about the greed and ignorance of the clergy.

He was a tall man of middle age. There was a smile on the face of the Archbishop as the man knelt in obeisance. Cardenal made a slight upward gesture of his thumb as he rose to his full height above the seated old man. Ler Isnard did not miss the gesture, which was a reflection on the celibacy of the priesthood, which every one knew was seldom obeyed in those days.

If the old Bishop saw the gesture, he ignored it and asked the composer to sing one of his songs.

"What kind of a song?" the troubador asked. "Shall it be about love, death, or something to tingle the mental juices?"

"As usual," the old man replied. "Your biting wit has an edge to it. Sing what you will, your satires on the church are well known to all of us. Sing on, this is a free household."

The troubador borrowed the lute from Pica and sang this song:

SIRVENTÉS DE PEIRE CARDENAL

"A new poem wants to begin, that I will say on Judgement Day,
And if to the devil it delivers my soul.
I will cry out, "My Lord, have pity"
I will cry out that "I have suffered greatly in the world."

"Keep me, if it pleases you from torment.
I will only cry out to the One who draws me from nothingness
And reprimands me for my faults."[3]

After he finished the song, Pietro could see the white anger on the face
of Pierre ler Isnard. He also noted the smiles of amusement on many of the
faces of persons who could understand the satire and the bite of the words.

"This is the kind of heresy in every Jew home in Provence," said ler
Isnard quietly to the Archbishop. "How long can we tolerate this? Since
I am to be your successor, may I suggest to Your Excellency, that since our
friends the Jews have so much money to help Christian slaves in far distant
lands, perhaps they could better serve our Christians closer to home?"

The room suddenly became hushed into an awkward silence.

[3]This song of satire and others like it cost Cardenal his life. He was killed by the
Dominicans. Song is found in La Musique des Troubadors by Jean Back, Henri Laurens,
Editeur, Paris.

"Let us consider," the priest went on, savoring the effect of his words. "What do we need closer to home than Palestine? Ah yes, the Bridge de Crau on the way to Aix. It is in need of considerable repairs. Shall we say 40 sous for each Jewish family in Arles?"

A collective groan sounded across the room, with many voices in protest, including the old Archbishop. "Very well," ler Isnard conceded with a magnanimous gesture of his arms. "Shall we say, the tax with Your Excellency's approval of course, shall be 20 silver sous on each family?"

Again the groan was heard across the room. "Shall I return to 50 sous?" ler Isnard asked, a glint of hard vigor in his face. He nodded his head, "Then it is agreed," he turned to the old Bishop. "See, our Jewish friends will find the money to help us rebuild this fine old bridge. They have given their consent."[4]

As they left, the Archbishop said slyly to Pietro and Pica, "I wish I could marry you in the Cathedral, but the law forbids me to marry Jews. Unless, you two children want to turn Christian? We could give you two a mighty wedding?" he said kindly.

When they refused politely and smiling, he nodded his head. He then raised his open palms over their heads. "Be blessed my children. God will bring you fine sons to make you both proud of them." The old man waved a farewell to Dr. Francis Jacobs.

For the next few weeks, Pietro traveled around the cities in Provence selling his woolens and silks and taking orders for future deliveries to this area.

In the market place of Montpelier he met merchants and travelers from all over the known world, come to do business in this ancient city near the Meditteranean Sea.

Arles and the region of Provence exported wines, olives, grapes, apples, cherries and many kinds of nuts. They also exported many kinds of furs like bearskins, a cat animal like the lynx, wool and goat cheese and the hides of a black wild pig found in the forest above Arles.

Pietro met dark-skinned men from far-off India, selling spices and silks; Arabs from the Levant selling fruits, figs, wines and jewelry; men from the far north countries selling furs and woven materials. He also met Frenchmen, Germans, Englishmen, Italians and Portuguese, each intent on buying and selling.

[4]In the Library of Arles it is recorded that this amount was fixed on all Jewish families for this repair work.

Among them he found a natural camaraderie and exchange of ideas from over the seas and nations, forgetting any barriers of race or religion. They had common goals for exchanging the goods and the products of their countries. Some of them brought books from their lands for the able translators in Provence to replenish the dryness of intellectual thought which was beginning to stifle Europe at this time.

Pietro met two local physicians who had been at the Jacobs house that Sunday afternoon for the appeal for funds. They greeted him warmly and invited him to join them for lunch at a local inn.

He learned that the Montpelier Medical School has been established with Jewish money and was famed all over Europe for the fine quality of its teachers and the renown of its pupils. Most of the physicians in Provence were Jews and their Christian colleagues used any device to deride them.

For instance, Moses ben Maimon (Maimonides), who was the physician to Saladin and his family (he was the sultan of Egypt and the conqueror of two Christian Crusades to Jerusalem) had made many studies on the use of herbs for the cure of skin diseases.

Maimonides had written about these cures to many of his fellow Jews in Provence, giving them details and methods of application. The Jewish doctors had used these compounds and been derided for their use by their Christian colleagues, who claimed that Maimonides was an Arab and a Jew not to be trusted.

The good doctor had made studies of lung ailments and their treatment which the Jewish doctors used with success. This enraged the Christians more and they sought to have laws passed restricting the Jewish doctors.

Pietro learned with some amusement that some high-placed clerics, who were most vehement in their charges against the Jews, used Jewish physicians for themselves or their families. He found the same pattern among the ruling classes.

To his surprise Pietro learned that Jews had settled in Provence more than a 1,000 years before, built synagogues, schools for learning the Torah and charity organizations to help the poor. Most of their occupations were as doctors, translators, writers, and men of science. Some also were engaged in farming and agriculture, making wines and weaving.

Pietro had been taking orders for fixed prices of delivery to Provence, Germany, Spain, and France. On his return to Lucca in Italy, where he lived with his brother, Paul, and his wife, Mirianne, he found to his dismay that the Christian merchants in Lucca and Venice had forced imposition of a heavy tax called the Jew Tax on all woolens and dyed goods. This was in addition to an earlier one.

In the year 1180 most all the weaving and dying of soft goods in Europe and Sicily was in the hands of the Jews. The Northern Italians had forced this kind of extra taxation on Jewish products to destroy them so they could fully control all the production in Europe.

Strangely enough the Talmud considered the business of weaving and dying as the lowest kind of occupation and frowned upon it as degrading.

This was a period of serfdom, created by the Christian rulers to obtain cheap labor for husbanding the farms and the fields of growing food. These same rulers considered the Jews as their own special serfs, to be treated as potential sources for income and taxation. They forbade any of the clerics ruling over the Jews because they were the property of the crown and not to be molested.

With the new and heavier Jew Tax, Pietro estimated that he could not meet his orders for goods. He then returned to Provence to inform his buyers of this state. Pica was sympathetic and kind about his troubles. She asked him to take her to the home of her friend Abraham Kolonymus, whom he had met on the afternoon of the appeal. He and his wife had a new-born son named Benjamin and Pica had some gifts for him.

On the way Pica told Pietro that, across Europe in France, Italy and Germany, many writers rabbis, teachers, physicians and poets were named Kolonymus. She told Pietro that the Abbot of their neighbor, the Cordeliére Monastery, had once again asked her father to sell his property to the Church. The doctor had refused.

They spent most of the day at the house of their friends, which was about ten miles away from her home. They took turns holding the lusty boy Benjamin in their arms. Abraham Kolonymus was a teacher of science in the local school and his wife Hannah was a fitting mate for him. They were a happy couple and challenged Pica and Pietro to follow them soon to the altar and produce sons like Benjamin.

On the way home Pietro and Pica agreed that it was a good Jewish home in the finest traditions of the Talmud and the spirit of God. It was night by the time they reached Arles. They could see a bright light ahead of them. As they came closer to their home, they saw that it was on fire. The flames were licking at the wooden structure and the inside was almost gutted.

The howls of the animals in their pens and the birds in their cages were shrieks of fear in the night. A small fire was burning in nearby trees. As they approached the rear of the house Pietro saw a dark-skinned monk tossing furniture and pots of flowers from the garden into the fire. Another monk near him was doing the same.

Pietro jumped off of his horse and ran towards the house. Raising his clenched fist he drove it into the face of the dark-skinned monk, who he learned later was called the "Arab". The other man was called the "Sicilian." Pietro hit him on the shoulder with a heavy stick. Both men ran off howling deprecations at him.

Pica and Pietro then made their way to the front of the house and met a tearful Vollo and less reserved Volla. The two servants had gone into town a little earlier leaving Dr. Jacobs and his sister Angela alone in the house. When they returned they saw the two "monks" setting fire to the house.

They were told the "Arab" had pushed Dr. Jacobs back into the burning house when he tried to escape. They did not see her Aunt Angela and were told she also was trapped inside. The town's night watch made a feeble attempt to save the house and soon there was little left but a few smoking walls. Both Dr. Jacobs and Angela were dead.

Someone had entered the rear pens and left out the birds and animals to roam freely into the night.

Pica and Pietro stayed that night at the house of one of their friends. The next morning, two hooded monks came to the door of the house and arrested Pietro for striking a monk. He was to be tried by the Archbishop in a trial to be held in the monastery. No lawyer could represent him, because this was an ecclesiastic court. He was to be held in the monastery of Cordeliére.

Pica was grief stricken by this turn of events. In the company of some friends she went to the home of the Archbishop of Arles, Raymondin III. At the door she was told that the old man was ill and in bed and could see no one.

For the first time in her life Pica knew what it was to be utterly and completely alone. There was a sudden desolation of the mind and spirit which sank deeper into her soul, searing it with the pain of grief and despair.

A few hours later Abraham Kolonymus arrived with his wife. For the first time, Pica's well of reserve broke and the tears spilled over in the arms of Hannah.

Since the Archbishop was ill, they decided that the best thing to do was to visit the abbot of the Monastery and ask for his help. They drove her there. The monks at the door would not allow her to enter the gates. They told her to return the following week.

Pica tried to enter the monastery every day and each time she was turned away. This went on for three weeks. She made as many attempts to see the Archbishop without success. Finally, one morning she alone was allowed to enter through the gates.

Inside the gloomy, cavern-like walls, she felt as if this was an unreal, world of the nether regions. She was kept waiting in one of the small rooms for more than two hours. Then one of the hooded monks motioned to her to follow him.

She was led into a larger room and saw at once that Pietro was seated in a chair, in the center of the room, with his hands tied behind his back. She tried to run towards him but was stopped by the monk who had brought her into the room.

Pietro gave her a smile, but she could see welts on his face and could sense that his body had been beaten as well. He seemed to have aged about ten years in the last three weeks.

She turned her head as another monk entered the room and sat behind a low lectern and waited before speaking, as if savoring each moment of absolute power over them. She recognized the deacon, Pierre ler Isnard, who had visited her house only a few weeks ago . . . . yet it seemed like another age to her.

From the gloom of the shadows in the corner of the room, a third monk arose and read the charges against Pietro *in Latin*. The look of dismay on the face of Pica and Pietro brought a smile of recognition and total mastery on that of the deacon.

"Well, I'll help you poor children," ler Isnard smiled to them. "By all the rules of Canon Law, the charges should remain in our holy tongue, however, in this case since I know you both as friends. The first charge is that you are now keeping in your employ one Volla and a man named Vollo. This is forbidden by the 3rd Lateran Council of 1179. No Jew may employ a Christian. We know that this has been observed more in the breach than in reality. However, this is the Law."

"Next, you have allowed heretics to make mock of the Holy Roman Church in your home, to our displeasure. Another Law is the fact that no Christian may use a Jewish physician for any needs, even including an animal. This is the Law of the Physicians of Arles. Your father, may his soul find repose, disobeyed this law."

"Next, during all these months in which you resided in Arles, you Pietro

Bernardone, never once entered a synagogue nor a church for prayer to your God. This therefore, brands you as a heretic and you lose all protection from the Duke of Provence and come into our hands for trial."

"Last, but not the least of your crimes, you struck at two of our monks in anger and to do bodily harm. So much so, that you broke the jawbone of one whom we call the "Arab" and battered the shoulder of one called the "Sicilian."

The priest then stood up, pointing his arm and finger at Pietro. "Now we take Jurisdiction as a court Christian," his voice rose. "When you struck one of our monks, you struck at Mother Church. This we will not allow. You Jews live in Provence only at our sufferance. You will do as *we* wish and obey *our* laws."

Pietro tried to rise from his tied chair and made as if to answer him. Ler Isnard held up his hand in silence, "All rules of the civil courts do not apply here in these holy grounds. Only canon law does apply. In this case you are not allowed to reply. We have all the known facts, none of which you can deny. You cannot swear on our Holy Bible. So, you cannot tell the truth in this court."

Ler Isnard sat down, his hand under his chin, holding the room and its shadows trapped in silence. A few sounds, low and garbled, were drawn from his throat, as if inside the man a debate were in progress.

"I know that you are both friends of our Archbishop and I want to rule with the same kind of justice in his stead. I therefore rule that since you have committed all these crimes against the Church and the State that you Pietro Bernardone shall lose your right arm in payment for these injuries," ler Isnard said.

Pica ran from the restraining arms of the monk who tried to stop her, towards Pietro, holding him in her arms like a trussed child. She kissed his face and tried to clean the bloodied welts on his face with her kerchief. At the same time she made small animal sounds of pain and misery for both of them.

"If you object so much, then I will declare," ler Isnard said, "the judgment which I thought of in the first instance would also include the fingers of the left hand as well. So that for the rest of your life you Pietro Bernardone, will never again strike a brother of the Church."

The cry of dismay which came from both young people seemed to please the man. "Of course, all can be forgiven by an indulgence to the Church."

Pica and Pietro waited with their breaths caught in their thoughts.

"A respectable gift to the monastery would be deeply appreciated and acceptable. For instance, young woman, you are the sole heir of your father, the late Dr. Jacobs, may his soul find repose. It is within your power to deed over as a gift, all the lands and alas very little property, which belonged to the deceased. Such a gift would enable this monastery to expand its facilities which are much too small for our growing needs. It is for you to decide."

She nodded her head without any hesitation. Ler Isnard, as if anticipating her decision, reached behind him and brought out some legal papers, written in Latin, on to the lectern. In a moment she was near him, signing her name in several places and watched as he sealed the wax with his ring.

Ler Isnard nodded his head and a monk untied Pietro. "Mother Church most heartily accepts your most generous gift. May your marriage be a happy one and bring you many fine children," ler Isnard told Pietro and Pica.

As they left the monastery, Pica walked towards the gutted house where she had been born and lived all her life. Here was buried the memory of her father and her Aunt Angela, lost forever in the ashes of their home.

Suddenly, she started to cry, "Oh my beautiful white roses, gone forever." She leaned over on the shoulder of Pietro and sobbed. They turned to leave with their friends Abraham Kolonymus and his wife.

They were never to see these grounds again. Almost thirty-three years later their son Francis Bernardone, would visit this place.[5]

A week later, Pica and Pietro Bernardone were married in the home of Abraham Kolonymus, by the local rabbi. Many of the friends of her father came to the simple wedding ceremony, since nothing elaborate could be arranged because of the recent death of her family.

The day before the wedding, Pica asked Pietro if he wished to call off the marriage. She told him that she had no worldly goods, no more than the clothes she wore and had no dowry of any kind. All their fortune, their books and music and other precious things were all lost inside the burned house.

[5]Today the Cordeliére Monastery still stands. . . . Since 1360 only a few sturdy walls remain, with no roof to support. At high tide the River Rhone drifts closer, making the ground soggy and limp . . . the stone retaining walls at the river's edge are broken.

There stands Cordeliére, a gaunt testimonial to spiritual and moral decay . . . the open walls like mute, pleading arms reaching towards the skies, begging God to return again.

The once clear waters of the Rhone River, where Pica as a child, swam and played . . . is now polluted with filth.

The proud forests above Arles, the mighty oak, fir and juniper, each a proud sentinel to God's handiwork . . . are all gone.

God gives and man destroys.

Pietro assured her that they would make their way in life, that he would provide for her and keep her safe from harm, and asked her to have faith in him. They would not live in Provence as they had planned, but would return to Lucca, in Italy.

After the wedding ceremony, David Kimchi, on behalf of the Jews of Arles, presented the couple with a dowry of 100 sous. This was an ancient custom among Jews not to allow the orphan to marry without a proper dowry.[6]

As they turned, leaving Arles, Pietro and Pica could see the tall steeple of the Cathedral Hotel de Ville built of cold stone and timbers, piercing into the sky behind them.

They rode towards Lucca passing through Salon, Aix en Provence, Brignoles, Frejus, and Cote d'Azur.

[6]By today's standards a sou is worth about two deniers of about $5 each.

Lucca 1181

When they arrived in Lucca, at his brother Paul's house, they were greeted warmly by him and his wife Mirianne. There too, bad news awaited them.

Most all of the money the two brothers had was held on deposit by the Jew Aaron of Lincoln in England, through letters of exchange. This was a means by which Jews could prevent robbery on the road or travel from one country to another.

When Aaron died suddenly, King John appropriated all the money Aaron held, on the pretext that King John needed the money to fight a war.

The two brothers were virtually ruined. Pica offered her dowry to tide them over their troubles.

To add to the troubles of the Bernardone brothers, more stringent rules were imposed on the Jews trading with woolens and woven goods. The Bishop of Lucca in that time was Guglielmo Guinitinga, who wanted strictly to observe the 1179 dictum of the Third Lateran Council to suppress the business operation of the Jews. He was related to the Guininga family which had many bankers and merchants, who were anxious to eliminate competition.

By every device of taxation and suppression they were driving out the Jew from his monopoly of the textile industries in Northern Italy. The only opportunity for them to exist was to travel far outside the limits of Italy. This would require a lot of financing, which the death of Aaron of Lincoln had cut off.

By chance, Pietro and Pica were walking in one of the local parks, when they met another young couple, also strolling along a wooded path. The man was heavy set and the woman had dark olive skin. They were friendly and struck up a conversation.

They introduced themselves as the Count Favarone di Offreduccio and his wife Ortolana Sciffi and they lived in Assisi, which was near Rome. The Count was sympathetic about Pietro's troubles and suggested that they meet another time and develop possibilities for helping each other.

Pietro noticed how easily Pica and Ortolana gravitated to each other and this he felt was the reason that the Count would try to help them.

A few days later, Pica and Pietro paid a visit to the Count. He had money to invest in risk ventures and would finance Pietro in the sale of woolens and clothing materials on a partnership basis. Pietro would be the silent partner and let the Count's name and money work for them. Since he was a Christian, the harsh laws against the Jews would not apply in their venture.

It was Ortolana who suggested that they come to live in Assisi, where she owned a house across the street, from their home. The house was not too large but the street floor could be used as a warehouse for their goods and the upper floors for living quarters.

To Pietro and Pica this was indeed manna from heaven—to find a home and new friends with an opportunity to build a sound business, with no Jewish restrictions on his back. They brought their few belongings with them to the small house in Assisi.

In the year 1181, the life and mores of Assisi was free and liberal in its attitudes toward the Jew and his Roman Catholic neighbor. People respected each other's beliefs, they dressed alike and enjoyed the same kind of entertainments and simple pleasures of life.

In Assisi, the Jew could own land and engage in any pursuit without suppression. The men would hold horse races with pennants flying and the younger men would have foot races through the streets. They played a game similar to tennis, with stones, eggs, and large nuts.

There was no Jewish community in Assisi and no rabbi. But, in Viterbo, about 35 miles away, and Ancona, about 55 miles, and throughout all of Umbria, Jews had already been settled for several hundred years. In Pesaro, a seaport near Assisi, there was a flourishing Jewish community at the time.

It was Ortolana who introduced the Bernardones to the well-to-do in Assisi. One who lived near them was Bernard de Quintavalle. He was a tall, handsome, cultured man of wealth and position. He gradually fell into the habit of visiting them and learned to enjoy the singing of Pica, who had not forgotten any of her Provencal songs and melodies.

Volla and Vollo easily adopted the customs of the city and made their own quarters in the basement of the house. Pietro was especially grateful for the couple's being in the house since most of his business was in England, Germany, Portugal and Spain. He would be gone for long periods of time.

On one of these long trips in 1182, Pica went into labor with her first child. She had been in the cellar warehouse checking some bales with Vollo when she felt the first pangs. She sent him for the local doctor, who was away and could not be found.

Vollo became frantic and went to Bernard de Quintavalle, who obtained a mid-wife. When they got to Pica she was being soothed by the ministrations of Volla, across one of the bales of woolens. Vollo tried to carry Pica in his strong, burly arms, but she started to go into the last stages of labor.

Assisi 1182-1194

They then used the bed of Volla and Vollo, in the basement. It was there that the first son of the Bernardones was born. She named him Francis after the memory of her father, Dr. Francis Jacobs.

There was an ancient tradition among the Jews, going back almost 2,000 years, that the soul of the dead would find no peace until a child is named for him. This tradition Pica meant to keep.

It was almost a week later that Pietro finally arrived from across the Swiss Alps. He had been held up for days by robbers preying on travelers in that region. As he held the lusty blond boy in his arms, he vowed to Pica that he would be home when their next child was born. He hoped that he always would not have to go off on such long trips away from their home in Assisi.

They asked Bernard de Quintavalle if he would be the Godfather to their new son, to which he readily agreed. He promised to teach the boy all the skills of riding a horse and the use of weapons for his self defense.

About two years later, another boy arrived to Pica and Pietro. He was also a lusty young blond-haired boy. They named him Angelo, after the memory of her Aunt Angela.

As the two boys grew older, it was Bernard who taught them to ride ponies, then horses and to use small wooden swords and lances. He took them into the woods, teaching them the names of trees, the leaves, the flowers across the wide Umbrian plains and to observe the various kinds of tints in the rocks and soil. He taught them how to swim in the lake near Assisi.

He noticed how Francis could see tiny details of color and the actions of birds and animals on the move, which he himself had missed.

Pica was an excellent musician on the lute and the mandola. She taught the two boys how to play them and to cherish the instruments. They learned how to read and compose music and she taught them the poetry and songs from Provence. With these, they learned the melodies of their faith and the Hebrew paens to God.

When Pietro would return from one of his long journeys across Europe or to England, he would bring many fine presents for the boys and Pica. There were stories to relate about people in high places, about events in many cities and news from many lands which the traveler of those days would know.

The Bernardones knew how to laugh and sing together as a family. Often, in his early years, Francis would compose some childish ditty, which would be solemnly presented before the family and received with dignity by all members. Together, they would often compose a musical play story, for their amusement or for some of their neighbors.

Then once again, Pietro would have to tell the stories and news from many cities in Europe which he knew as well as he did Assisi.

Pica soon found that Angelo cared little for the music and preferred reading a book. Francis, however, loved the songs of the troubadors and quickly acquired the knack of using the strings as a gentle background for the melodies Pica taught him. He had a good, full voice and knew how to put lilts into the words which gave them a special flavor. This was the art of the troubador.

When Francis was about 12 years old, Ortolana gave birth on January 20, 1194, to her first child, whom she named Clara. The little girl was called by this name and "Clare." She was a sturdy, light-haired girl. When Pica took Francis to visit them, he insisted he wanted to hold the new baby in his arms.

Looking at his tall body and strong arms, Ortolana allowed him to hold the little girl, who grasped his forefinger in her tiny fist and made small sounds of pleasure. Even after he placed her in the crib, she held on to his finger and it took some of his young strength to unclench her fist.

Pica tried to teach Francis at home in secular studies but found it difficult to make him concentrate on his work. He much more preferred to be walking outside under the trees, or riding his horse into the Umbrian plains or playing his lute.

Bernard suggested to her that she send Francis to the church school of San Giorgio, where he would be exposed to books and learning of the period. He would also be able to meet other boys of the well-to-do families of Assisi. She could then be selective about his religious training and reading materials.

Most of the work done in the school was in Latin. Francis had no affinity for the language and refused to learn anything. Because he was not a Catholic, the priest-teachers could not discipline him with threats.

Francis took away with him a continued dislike for the priests which lasted him a lifetime. This was one of the forces which led him on an adventure to Christian Sainthood.

Although Francis and his brother Angelo looked like their father Pietro Bernardone in coloring and height, they were as different in personal likes as two strangers. Where Francis was sensitive about people, animals and nature around him, Angelo cared less about people and was more interested in books and the operation of their father's business.

Francis was immaculate about his clothing and dress. Body cleanliness was a fetish with him. His brother was careless about his clothing and his cleanliness. Where Francis would wash his hands or his body with any sign of dirt, Angelo would wait until he found time to do what was necessary.

Francis could sit for an hour looking at the sky, watching some wheeling birds or sit at the edge of the lake watching the ripples dancing. Angelo had no patience. "He was too practical," Pietro often said of him, "for such nonsense!"

Lucca *1195*

When Francis was 13 years of age, "he had reached the age of manhood," Pica had told him and he was ready to be Bar Mitzvah. That is, "be brought before the congregation as an adult".

Since there was no rabbi or synagogue in Assisi, where such a service could be held and the Bernardones had few friends in Rome, the decision was made to go to Lucca.

There was no synagogue in Lucca either, but the several hundred Jews who lived there made temporary quarters in a warehouse for the Sabbath and High Holiday services.

They would go to the house of his Uncle Paul Bernardone and his wife, Mirianne. Just about this time Benjamin Kolonymus, the son of their friends in Provence, came to visit with them and was invited to make the journey to Lucca. Volla and Vollo went along to help with the housework.

The Bernardones also invited Bernard de Quintavalle, their neighbor and friend, to attend the services for Francis.

When Pietro had been in Regensburg, Germany, a month earlier, on one of his frequent selling trips, he met Rabbi Jehudah Halevi and a Jewish singer of ballads known as Suesskind the Meistersinger. He suggested to them that they should visit Lucca about this time, because it was likely that Pietro and his family would be there.

Pietro also asked the rabbi if he would lead the Sabbath services. Paul and Mirianne were gracious hosts to the rabbi over the Sabbath and put on a festive table that Friday night for all the guests.

Francis would always remember the sight of Pica and Mirianne, with lace shawls over their heads, intoning the prayer of lighting the Sabbath candles and enfolding their arms over the tiny flames towards their bodies.

"They are bringing in the Sh'Cheena, the Spirit of Sabbath, into this household," whispered Pietro to Angelo and Francis who stood near him. All the men near them stood with covered heads watching the holy tableau.

Both women intoned slowly, "Boruch atah adonai elohenu me-

41

lech ho'ohlum asherr kidsho'nu be'mitsvosaff ve'tzevonu lehadlik shel shabbos . . ."

"Blessed are Thou O Lord, King of the Universe, who hast sanctified us by Thy commandments and commanded us to kindle the lights for the Sabbath."

Then each woman prayed in silence, their lips moving in devotion, asking the Lord of the Universe to bring health and sustenance to their homes.

At the table, Rabbi Jehudah told them that he was a cousin of the famous Rabbi Yehuda Halevi (and named for his memory) who was the well-known writer and poet. He was known over Europe for his work with the Zohar, the book about the mysticism in the Jewish religion. When this Rabbi was about to enter the gate into Jerusalem in 1150, an assassin killed him.

Pica remembered that in Provence there were many legends about the Sabbath, which was a great gift from God to all people everywhere. The pagans did not rest on the seventh day. In fact there was an ancient story she had heard, when she was a little girl, that two angels would accompany each Jew on his way home on Friday night. One was a good angel and the other was an evil one.

If the house was clean and ready for the Sabbath, the good angel blessed the house and the evil one must say "Amen".

If the house was *not* ready for the Sabbath, then the evil angel curses the house and the good angel must say "Amen".

The ancient Cabbalists put this legend into Hebrew Poetry and music, the rabbi mentioned. He then turned to Pica and asked her if she had heard the "Ufros Oleynu" in Provence. It came from the thirty-first chapter of Exodus.

Pica had heard it sung in the Synagogue at Montpelier in Provence and the chant was very ancient. The Rabbi helped Pica and the two of them sang this together:

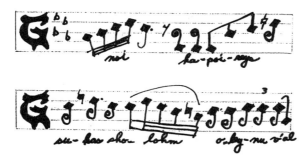

"Yea, spread over us the tabernacle of Thy Peace. Blessed art Thou, O Lord,

Who spreadest the tabernacle of peace . . ."[7]

All of them sang after-dinner songs from antiquity. Some traced the longing of the Jews for their heritage and return to Israel and its glories of the past.

Then, the Meistersinger was asked to offer some contribution in the evening. "After all," said Pietro with a smile, "You are the most professional singer of us all." They all laughed at this.

The Meistersinger apologized that this was Friday night and he could not use his lute. Pica then supplied him with his key notes to get started.

He hummed a few notes, as if to himself, then explained to them, "this is called Sh'Chuloah Achuloh, which means "Wasted and Desolate". It was written by the poet Solomon ibn Gabirol, when he was thirty years old, when he lived in Spain. He died in the year 1050. The music is from ancient sources which have come down to us through the years."

[7]From Anthology of Jewish Music by C. Vinaver.

"Wasted and desolate, why dost thou weep?
 Doth thy heart more despair than that thou wait?
 My end is delayed and my darkness not ended
 Be hopeful, poor one,
 For soon I shall send an angel to pave My Way,
 And on Mount Zion shall I anoint My king!
 The Lord is king and the Lord hath been King
 Tell unto Zion that the Lord will be King
 Behold thy King cometh unto thee."

After this song, Benjamin asked the Rabbi if he knew the melody for 'Kol M' kodeysh Sh' vee', (Who Sanctifies the Seventh Day). The rabbi replied that he did. Benjamin told them that his ancestor named Moses ben Kolonymus had written this poem in Mayence about the year 990. The Rabbi guessed that the music had come down to them through many years of folklore. They sang together:

(from Anthology of Jewish Music by C. Vinaver)

"Whoever sanctifies the Seventh Day as befits it,
    Whoever guards the Sabbath piously, not to desecrate it,
Great is his reward according to his deed
    Each man to his camp and each man to his standard."
Later that evening, this quotation from Rabbi Halevi was to remain with
Francis all his life. From the Pirke Avoth, The Sayings of the Fathers, "Better is one hour of repentance and good works in this world than the whole
life of the world to come. Come see how great is Charity. Ten strong things
exist in the world: a mountain is strong, but iron breaks it; iron is strong,
but fire softens it; fire is strong, but water puts it out. Water is strong, but
clouds bear it along; clouds are strong, but wind spreads them out; wind is
strong, but the body of man withstands it; the body is strong, but fear
breaks it; fear is strong, but wine overcomes it; wine is strong, but sleep
dispels it; sleep is strong, but death overcomes it. But Charity rescues even
from death."
    There were many more quotations bandied about the table that night.
Another that Francis remembered was: "When a beggar stands at your
door, the Holy One, Blessed be He, stands at his right hand."
    Later, Pietro asked Suesskind the Meistersinger, "You be charitable to us.
You travel over Europe. What news of the moment?"
    "You know that I perform like a trained bear," he replied sadly, "doing
my stints to amuse the lords and the ladies of the lands. I'm getting tired
of all this travel. Perhaps one day we will have theatres in large cities, like
the ancient Greeks. People would then come from far places to see good
performances. Yet, I find that more and more these ladies and lords are
surprised that being a Jew, I do not have horns in my head. No offense to
you Ser Bernard," he turned towards the Christian de Quintavalle, who
smilled.
    "This is the price all of us pay, for being Jews in a most Christian world."
Paul Bernardone told them. "Here, in the city of Lucca, we have several
hundred Jews able to build and support a fine synagogue. Yet, we must hold
services in an old warehouse. The orders from Rome are that we cannot

build a better place than any church in town. It must not be a single mille higher. Then to cap it all, we may not build within sight of any church."

"Is this the written law?" asked Rabbi Jehudah. "Can't you appeal to the Archbishop? You know for the past hundred years the Popes have issued at least twenty Bulls permitting the Jew to worship in peace and that they ·cannot be baptized by force . . . "

"True, Rabbi," enjoined Paul, "but each Bishop no matter, how small the community makes up his own rules, most of them depending on the amount of gold he can squeeze from us."

"So, why not buy him off?" asked Pietro.

"He has too much money as it is." Paul replied. "The Guininga Family controls everything. They are as rich as Croesus and they can demand donations to the church, even the price one must pay to get buried and have a mass said for some poor Christian. The Bishop wants to observe the strict letter of the Third Lateran Council which tried to supress us more than ever."

"Do you know that I can't hire a domestic worker, if she is Christian, because they prohibit a Jew and a Christian from living under the same roof," interposed Mirianne.

"They don't enforce this rule in Assisi," Pica observed.

"This is because each town makes its own rules," Pietro offered. "In Assisi we are more lucky than most towns because of a liberal Bishop. In other towns the Jew is at the mercy of any particular fanatic or pietist who demands that the rule be enforced.

"Look what happened in England in 1189 and 1190. The Jews loaned money to the churches who couldn't get any from their own bankers. They also loaned money to the Lords of the land. The Jews were taxed by the government to make up heavy losses by the king. The Jews then were forced to raise their interest rates. Like a vicious circle this lead to the massacres of Jews in 1189 and 1190. The first thing the criminals did was to go after the bonds held in safeboxes. When they got these, they burned the house and killed the owners to destroy all the evidence. Along the way they also killed hundreds of men, women, and children for no other crime than that they were Jews—people who had nothing to do with this money.

"So the government in England set up a new system of filing and registration of all bonds of debt, to be kept by the government in order to protect itself, for a future source of revenue, rather than the Jewish men who made the loans. The government itself was a silent partner in the higher interest rates and the massacres as well.

"Do you know what King John of England will do? He will order an entire town of all Jewish men, women and children to be put in jail until they raise a ransom which will be called a Jew tax, is paid. They must remain in jail until this money is paid in full. In fact this is how I met Pica. She was coming home from paying part of this ransom she paid in London. The money was contributed by Jews in Arles."

"This is why, in our sacred writings," Rabbi Halevi told them, "it is your sacred duty before God, for every Jew to ransom his neighbor."

"All of us have suffered at the hands of the Christian Church," Pica's voice reminisced slowly. "Do they think they can blot us out, like a small boy holding his hands before his eyes? Each time they strike at us, they kill their own Jesus once again. Each Christian, when he hates a Jew hates his own God that much more. Then they cover it up with beautiful and bigger churches to atone for their sins."

She suddenly forgot the company around her and the others were silent, sharing with her in compassion a few treasured moments as she sang in a low voice, her own song, "My Beautiful White Roses." (Francis had heard it many times.)

On the way to the synagogue the next morning, Paul Bernardone told them that he had bad news. The Bishop insisted that the Sabbath service could not be held unless one of the local priests were allowed to give a sermon to the Jewish congregation.

"No one to appeal to?" asked Pietro, anger showing in his face.

"Yes, if you can run to Rome and back in an hour," was the reply from his brother.

"Is this another test of our humility?" asked the Rabbi, as they walked in silence towards the house of prayer. "Remember the story they tell in the Yebamot of Rabbi Gamaliel who was aboard a ship when he saw another one sink. On this ship was the famous Rabbi Akiba. When he landed, there was Rabbi Akiba in the school. He told me, 'that he seized a piece of heavy wood and when a wave came, I bowed my head before it.'

"We can learn two lessons from it, namely, when the wicked assail you or trouble comes, you incline your head and you will be rescued. The other is that everyone can be rescued if he is near dry land." Then Rabbi Jehudah laughed, "We are all on dry land, so we have nothing to fear." The others joined him laughing.

Later that morning, Rabbi Jehudah stood up before the small congregation gathered in this makeshift synagogue in the warehouse. The odor of woolens, skin and hemp hung like a drifting, pungent wave over all of them. Each one moved closer to his neighbor, ashamed and humbled in their discomfort.

In the rear of the synagogue stood two monks and six soldiers, who were armed and arrogant in these strange surroundings.

After a brief service, the rabbi reached behind him, turning and moving the embroidered curtain aside on the small Holy Ark, holding the Torah, the five sacred Books of Moses.

He touched the curtains tenderly and gently moved it so he could reach inside to enfold the sacred scrolls in his arms. Turning to the congregation he sang an ancient Hebrew melody "Vayéhee binsoah h'oraohn . . . . . ."

"And it came to pass, whenever the Ark started, Moses would say, Arise O Lord and let thine enemies be scattered, let those who hate Thee, flee before Thee. Out of Zion shall come forth Torah and the word of the Lord from Jerusalem."

The congregation joined him as he sang, the walls rang with their voices, reaching across the centuries, pleading to God, singing in Hebrew.

"Boruch sheh'nosan Torah leh'omoh Yisruel bickdush oso . . . ."

"Blessed be He in his holiness who gave the Torah to his people Israel . . . ."

The congregation stood up as he gently drew off the velvet covers of royal purple colors and golden decorations, of intricate weave over the sacred scrolls.

He stood holding up the scrolls in his two hands, "This is the Torah proclaimed by Moses to the children of Israel, at the command of the Lord. This was written more than 2,000 years ago." He bowed slightly, as if making obeisance to these holy words.

In the rear of the room one of the soldiers was mimicking the rabbi in a high falsetto voice.

The rabbi continued, "Bestow on us the good gifts of Thy light and accept our prayer in mercy . . ." Again the voice of the soldier mimicked him.

Then the entire congregation joined with the rabbi, first singing softly, then in ever increasing crescendo, "Loh ahl ehnush rohitz nooh . . . . ."

"Not in man do I put my trust, nor do I rely on any angel but in God in heaven, who is the God of truth . . . . ."

Again the congregation was pleading to their God, singing with joy, capturing in the melody the anguish of the years, weighted by the presence of the priests and the guards corrupting their communion with God.

The sacred scrolls were then placed gently on the covered table and then rolled open to the portion to be read.

"On this Sabbath day we will read the Holy Script as was written by the scribes of Moses about 1,000 years before this Christian era," said the rabbi.

"We are a people of the Book and our religion is one of the Spirit." These last words caught Francis' memory and he repeated them slowly in his mind. "We are a people of the Book and our religion is one of the Spirit."

He knew he would not forget them, nor the events of this day. Nor, would he forget the words, "Not in man do I put my trust . . . but in God who is in heaven. . . ."

One of the guards in the rear moved and his sword scabbard clanked against some metal. The noise rang into the rafters as foreign to this Sabbath ritual as they were.

At this latest deliberate outrage, Pietro quickly lifted himself out of his seat, followed by Francis and Angelo. Although the boys were 13 and 11 years old, they stood tall and strong, close to their father's shoulders.

The three of them moved quickly to the rear of the room and approached the six soldiers.

A smirk appeared on the face of one of the soldiers, who reached for the short sword at his side. Pietro moved, feinted to the man's left, as Francis moved against his midriff. With Angelo behind him, they pushed the soldier back into the men behind him.

One of the monks stepped between them, snapping out, "For shame John, this is a holy place. To start trouble . . . tze . . . tze . . . You know better. Go back to your seats," he told the three Bernardones.

After a few moments of hesitation, the soldier took his hand off his sword. Pietro and the two boys returned to their seats.

Rabbi Halevi beckoned with his hands and Francis, together with his friend Benjamin Kolonymus, walked up to the rostrum, in front of the Ark.

Because Francis had learned no Hebrew, he stood alongside his friend, who was to read the portion of the week from the Torah. Then Benjamin made the prayer for the Haftorah, the reading from the Prophets, singing the melody with depth and a lilting voice.

"Boruch ahtoh Adonai elohenu melech ho'olum. . . ."

"Blessed art Thou, O Lord our God Ruler of the Universe, who has selected good prophets, taking delight in their words which are spoken in truth. . . . . ."

After Benjamin was finished with his reading and chanting, he returned to his seat and Francis remained on the rostrum. The rabbi then returned the Sacred Scrolls to the Ark, singing chants heard more than 1,000 years ago. He then closed the velvet curtains and nodded his head to Francis.

Francis stood up before the congregation and spoke the only language he knew, French, the tongue spoken in 12th century Italy.

"We have read from the Prophet Isaiah, Chapter 52 and 53. In my own way I will tell you how I feel, the things I feel this day, which is holy to me and to my parents. I am truly grateful to my dear friend Benjamin Kolonymus who helped me today read the Haftorah.

"I could not learn our ancient language because there was no one to teach me in Assisi and there are so few of our people there. In the opening passage the Prophet Isaiah tells us that we owe everything to God.

"He that created the heavens and stretched them forth; He that spread forth the earth and that which comes from it; He that gives breath to the people in it.

"To open the blind eyes
To bring out the prisoner from the dungeon
And them that sit in the darkness of the prison house
Hear ye deaf
And look ye blind, that ye may see.
Who is blind, but my servant?
Or deaf as my messengers that I send?
Who is blind that he should be my servant . . ."

The voice of one of the monks in the rear of the synagogue interrupted the boy's confirmation speech as he shouted aloud, "That is it, you are all blind. You are the blind ones," as he walked rapidly to the front of the congregation, facing it.

Francis turned to the rabbi behind him, his face questioning. The rabbi who was standing, slowly sat down in his chair, his arms open in resignation, to an overbearing shame. His face mirrored this shame for his people, made aliens in their own house of worship.

Francis stood tall staring into the face of the monk, as they confronted each other. His sturdy body was ready to battle for his dignity. Then he slowly stepped off the rostrum and walked to his seat next to his brother Angelo. As he sat down, the younger boy patted him on the thigh and whispered, "good fellow."

Pietro stared at the face of this monk, searching his memory, for this man looked familiar. The man took out a white scull cap, which he put on his tonsured head. The monk's name, Pietro recalled, was Fra Baccione, who lost his wallet at the inn almost fifteen years ago.

"See," the monk said to the Jews gathered in front of him. "I respect this house of worship and wear my 'kipot' like the rest of you. I know this is the custom of my brothers the Jews." His voice became unctious and smooth. "I took my vows from the teaching of the Apostle Paul, who, like you was a Jew and also a Rabbi.

"Saint Paul lived in Tarsus and knew Jesus in His ministry. In truth, He wanted, as did Jesus, to make the Jewish religion more to the liking of God. So you see, the Christians are in truth as much Jews as you are.

"But, this young man," he pointed to Francis seated below him, "did not read from the Prophet Isaiah, who goes on to say,"

They are all of them snared in holes
And they are hid in prison houses
They are for prey and none delivereth
For a spoil and none sayeth, 'Restore'
Who among you will give ear to this?
Who will hearken and hear for the time to come?"

"You see," the monk Fra Baccione went on, "your own writings tell you that you are blind to the coming of the Son of God. . . ."

Some of the congregation in the rear of the warehouse tried to leave and were stopped by the soldiers at the door who refused to let anyone leave the building. Many of the people crowded into the rear portion, refusing to sit in their seats, as the monk went on with his harangue. They were held by the weapons of the soldiers.

"They murder and steal from us," said Pietro to Pica and Francis. "They humiliate us and drive our faces in the mud and they still want us to love and join them."

Pica held up her hands to silence her husband, as the monk pointed to the Bernardones.

"You are indeed the blind ones. You will be punished," he moved his palm in a gesture of the priestly blessing. "I know what you Jews do in the privacy of your homes," he waited relishing the sudden moment of silence, waiting for his next words.

"You despoil the wafer of the Host," he smiled down on them. "Just because you Jews do not believe in your own God, you still refuse to believe in Jesus our Lord. He is in the wafer of the Host and many of you stab it with pins and knives to make it bleed. Yes, you want to crucify our Lord again, you stab it to repeat once again the thrust of the spear by the Roman soldier, as our Lord was dying on the cross."

He smiled benevolently at them, "but one day we will make you pay with your blood for making the Host bleed again." The monk Baccione then sat down in the empty chair next to Pica and Bernard.

Rabbi Jehudah stood up on the rostrum, his arms open in pleading.

The other monk sat next to his fellow. As Baccione sat in his seat, he ran his left hand up Pica's thigh. She stood up and his hand continued up her thigh towards its apex. Bernard also arose and exchanged his seat with her. As he sat down, his buttocks struck the monk across the knees.

The congregation, soldiers as well as monks, were hushed into silence as the red-haired rabbi's voice lifted in depth, slowly blending the odors of the warehouse, their humiliation and the arrogance of the interruptions as he chanted a melody none had ever heard before, in Hebrew.

"Hinini hay'unni mimahs . . . ."

"Behold, In deep humility
I stand and plead before Thee, God on high:
O hearken and give heed to my prayer.
Though unworthy of my task,
Though imperfect too, and filled with awe,
I bow before Thy holy presence here,
To crave compassion for my erring folk
O God of Israel's patriarchs,
Their children's children send me as their voice,
To supplicate Thy pardon and Thy grace,
To ask Thy mercy, Thy continued love.
Though unworthy of my mission, Lord,
Though I stand not flawless in Thy sight,
Condemn not my people for *my* faults,
Consider but their virtues, righteous Judge.
Forgive us *our* iniquities,
And turn our afflictions into joy.
Thou great exalted God who hearest prayer
Hear ours and bless us with life and peace."[8]

Francis was caught by the sight of the monk who sat next to Fra Baccione, who was bent over, his body wracked with sobs, as if he suddenly realized that the rabbi was praying *for him also*.

The Rabbi raised his arms in a final benediction and said, "I will now chant a prayer usually reserved for the High Holy days, but this is a special day in all our lives."

He sang this melody one time, the congregation then repeated it *twice* singing it with gusto and verve.

a-do-noy a-do-noy ael ra-chum v'i-cha-nun

---

[8]Translation from prayer book by Rabbi Morris Silverman. Written by unknown in Early Middle Ages.

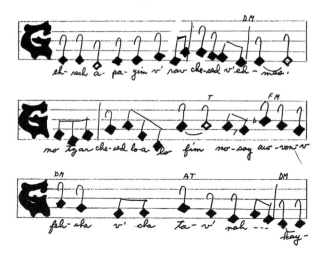

eh- rech a- pa- yim v' rav che-sed v'eh - mes.

mo tzar che-sed lo-a- lo fim no-say aus-von-iv

feh-sha   v' cha   ta - v' nah --- hay-

"The Lord, the Eternal, is a merciful and gracious God, slow to anger and abounding in a loving kindness and truth; keeping mercy for thousands, forgiving iniquity, transgression and sin and aquitting."

This ended the Sabbath Service and the congregation left the warehouse turned into a synagogue for the day.

"Sometimes, I think the world has gone mad," said the Meistersinger as they continued their walk to the home of Paul Bernardone. "The goyim, with an apology to you Ser Bernard, think that we Jews not only stick pins into a tiny bread wafer but that we also kill children at Passover time and use their blood for the pascal lamb on our door posts."

The Rabbi explained to Bernard de Quintavalle that the mark of the pascal lamb on the door post would enable the Angel of Death to pass the home of the Jew, when they were slaves in Egypt under Pharoah. "Now, our Christian brethren *can believe,* can actually believe that we can do this to children!" His voice caught the horror of this thought.

Pietro told them, "It was in Blois in 1171 and in Paris in 1180 and the same in the massacre of York in 1190. In each city hundreds of Jews were killed for this vile accusation."

"They even make a 'saint' of such a death," the Rabbi added. "In Norwich, England, in 1144 a child was lost, then killed by some animal or a madman. The people of the city murdered all the Jews in the city. Then to cap it all they made a 'saint' of this child William."

"This must be a mad world indeed," repeated the Meistersinger.

At Paul Bernardone's house the guests kept coming and going all afternoon. When the sun had set, the Rabbi wanted to conduct the late or

Min'Cha Service. Looking around he could see only nine men, he needed ten men for a "minyan" or a congregation.

"This includes you too," he patted Francis on the shoulder, "since early morning, you are now counted as an adult male. We still need ten men for our 'minyan'."

He looked around the room as if expecting another guest. His eyes lighted on Bernard de Quintavalle and he shook his head.

Francis saw the motion and asked, "why not?"

"Shall we cheat ourselves or the Lord?" he asked in a mock whisper, "we need a male Jew," he whispered to the boy.

"Again, why not?" asked the boy.

The rabbi turned to Bernard and asked if he would consider himself as a Jew to make up the quorum required by ancient law. The other nodded his head in appreciation of the situation and dutifully put on the skull cap the older man handed him.

The Min'Cha service was short and simple in its prayers, the rabbi read the words in Hebrew, then translating them, "Elohai n'tzer leh shonee meh rau. . . ."

"O Lord
Guard my tongue from evil and my lips from speaking guile,
And to those who slander me, let me give no heed,
May my soul be humble and forgiving unto all.
Open Thou my heart, O Lord, unto Thy sacred law,
That Thy statutes I may know and Thy truths pursue.
Bring to naught designs of those who seek to do me ill."

The rabbi then bowed his head in silent meditation. After the sun had set and the moon could be seen in the night sky, they gathered around the table on which a candle, twisted in a gay waxen glory, was lit. The rabbi chanted a simple prayer over a cup of wine which he held in his fingers.

"Blessed are Thou our Lord for the fruit of the vine." He turned to Francis, "This day you will never forget."

The next morning, Rabbi Halevi stood up at the breakfast table and told them that the Lady Pica had asked him to give Francis some parting advice before he went on his journey.

"What can any man, be he rabbi or layman, tell young men in these days and troubled times. We Jews have lived at peace with our Christian neighbors for almost a thousand years. We have been able to talk with each other about our religions like grown people. But, across the lands, stemming from fears within the church, spilling into crimes and the murders of the Crusades, floats over all of us a horrible angel of death.

"The Roman Church has just found out that people can think and have bodies which contain eternal souls. People want to believe and love God, but the Church not only puts a price on this, but restricts this love of God to the *how* each one can worship Him."

The red-haired rabbi stopped and looked down on the boy's uplifted face, held, as all of them were, by the emotions caught in this man's voice.

"Well, like the Patriarchs of old would tell us, 'walk humbly with God.' Walking humbly with God does not mean like the humility of the sheep or the cow. They do not know or understand God. An arrogant man cannot do this, because he thinks only of himself. If God were in this room, like a good father, He would want us to walk with dignity, respect and pride in ourselves and those about us.

"Walking with God means that a person will find inner strength within himself to create and do wonderful things *here on earth*. For after all, our days are numbered in this world. What will any of us do with them? And you Francis, *what will you do with them?*"

Ancona 1197

The seashore of Ancona, Italy, along the Adriatic Sea, was very rocky but the air was clear and salty. Many people of wealth owned homes near the edge of the Sea. Jews had lived in Ancona for centuries before this, now no Jew could own land there, because the local ecclesiastics and the Church had placed such high land taxes. Since the Bernardones lived as neighbors with his financial supporter in Assisi, Count Favorone di Offreduccio, they were able to buy adjoining properties. A handshake between the two men, was their agreement that one side would always belong to the Bernardones.

One afternoon, when the sky was overcast, all of them sat around on the covered piazza of the Bernardones. Francis was then about 15 years old and his brother Angelo was two years younger. Near him was Benjamin Kolonymus, now 17, and Rufino, about Francis' age, who was the nephew of the Count and the son of the Count's brother, Scipione di Offreduccio.

Slightly away from the boys were the Count's daughters, Clara, then about 4 years old and her sister Agnes, about a year younger. Near them sat their mother, Ortolana, knitting some scarf.

Another boy, named Gilles, who was about Clara's age, sat on the floor watching the two girls dressing their dolls. His parents were farmers, but his mother worked as a domestic in one of the nearby homes in the summer. He came to visit the children, sitting and watching them like a friendly mastiff.

Clara kept darting her eyes at Francis, admiring his bright golden head and his tall sturdy frame. Her mother glanced at her and saw the child's dancing eyes. She had often remarked to her husband, the Count, that "Clara had the eyes to drive the devil himself." The Count had answered with a laugh, "She could make the devil run with his tail between his legs and like it. That's our Clara. We had better marry her off early or she'll have every young jack in Italy at our doors."

Then he told his wife that Pietro Bernardone was making enough money from his, Favorone's investments, to pay a handsome dowry for his two daughters, Clara and Agnes. Perhaps there might be another little girl some day? Good God willing.

Ortolana could not help listening, as did Clara to the conversation of the older boys. Someone had asked what kind of careers they wanted out of life.

Benjamin was telling them that he wanted to study to be a physician under the guidance of Moses Maimonides, who was then the house physician for Al-Kamel, the Sultan of Egypt. This great doctor and writer had a son named Abraham who was also planning to be a doctor and the two boys were to study under the care of the older man. Since the father was a kinsman, Benjamin was to go to Fostat (now called Cairo) later this summer.

Francis told them that he wanted to be a great soldier and plan and execute fine strategy in battles. The Jews of ancient days had great soldiers like King David, King Saul and the Maccabees. There was something exciting about risking one's life in a battle and in war. After all, what greater price to pay than one's life for a noble cause?

Rufino thought he would like to be a handsome knight leading the ladies to balls and big social events.

Angelo wanted to be a great merchant, who would make contracts for selling lots of goods to people all over Europe.

Francis half-turned and saw that Gilles and Clara were watching and listening to their talk.

"And what do you want to do?" asked Francis of Gilles. He blushed with the eagerness which the very young feel, when an older boy has shown him some attention. His blunt nose seemed to crinkle in his heavy and thick face as he looked up with doting eyes.

"I don't know," Gilles replied. "But, someday you will tell me, won't you Francis?"

The older boy nodded his head and smiled, little realizing that their paths would meet again in about 13 years in a dramatic adventure to last through many centuries.

"How about you?" Benjamin chided Clara, "Do you want to be a great lady some day like your cousin, Rufino, will be a great knight of the Empire?"

The little girl paused and her brown eyes seemed to dip into her four-year-old mind, searching for a good answer. Then, her eyes lit up in happy expectation, as she replied, "Yes, I know, I want to marry Francis."

The three older boys laughed at this sally. Her face became serious and alarmed.

"You'll wait for me, Francie. Won't you wait for me?" she pleaded.

"Sure, sure." he replied, with the soothing voice which a fifteen-year-old would use for the prattle of a four-year-old girl.

"Why do you want to study with this man Maimonides?" asked Rufino of Benjamin, "and go all the way to Egypt. I heard it's a land of sand, hot as Hades and lots of flies."

Benjamin laughed in agreement, "That is so. But firstly, he is a kinsman of mine and second he is one of the greatest physicians of our day. This man is using herbs and other kinds of help which have changed the name of medicine from witch doctoring and wild guesswork to the Art of Medicine.

"People for the next hundred years will benefit from his experiments and discoveries."

"Is he an Egyptian?" queried Rufino. "You would have to learn the language. It is difficult to know."

"I have begun to study some books which Abraham sent me," replied Benjamin. "It is an old tongue, a mixture of Persian and Arabic. Since I know the language of Hebrew, learning another is not too difficult."

"Some of us, I would say most of us, in the princely homes in Italy," Rufino told them, "think it is below our dignity to even learn to read and write. We leave all that kind of work to scribes and clerks. So why should we bother?"

Suddenly Clara interrupted them with, "My nana taught me to sing a German song." Then she hummed a children's *'viegenlied.'*

"See, my dear little cousin has big ears," Rufino laughed. "She doesn't miss a trick. You'd think, there she is playing with her dolls and lo' and behold, she hears everything that is said by others."

The little girl continued dressing her doll. This time her sister, Agnes, who was three years old, remarked aloud, "I want to marry Francie too. Can't I Francis?" she inquired, looking up at him, her small arms wide.

"You can't marry him," her sister Clara reproved. "How can you, if *I am to be married to him.* Two ladies can't marry the same man, you silly."

"Are you sure?" the little girl asked without belief.

"Two ladies cannot be married to the same man," opined Ortolana, their mother. "Anyway, this is a long way off. And then again, not so far away. I was married when I was 17 years of age to your father the Count. It is not too far away."

"One of the nice things about living in Egypt," Benjamin told them, "is the fact that a man can have as many wives as he can support. Saladin, who was the Sultan, before this one, had about twenty wives."

"Oh, that's for me," laughed Rufino, "I think I'll go with you to the land of Egypt. On second thought, no. There are too many flies and too much hot sand for my liking and easy ways."

"Isn't this the Saladin who defeated the Crusaders and yet allowed the Christians to visit Jerusalem?" asked Francis.

"Yes, this is the same man," replied Benjamin. "Do you know which physician Saladin sent to tend Richard the Lion Hearted?

"It was Maimonides, who helped cure Richard the King of England when he had an infection from a bad wound. Saladin was a cultured and thoughtful man. He was generous with his Christian enemies, when he could easily have destroyed them.

"As a military general, you could well study his military tactics, Francis, and see how brilliant he was."

"One of the reasons they lost was," Francis suggested, "Saladin was only *one general* in command of a *single army*. The crusaders had seven armies ruled by seven different kings, each one wanting the spoils but doing nothing to work together as one fighting mass."

"And they were fighting among themselves," remembered Rufino. "You would imagine, that, fighting for a cause like regaining the Holy City of Jerusalem, the birthplace of our Lord Jesus Christ, would be sufficient to join them together as brothers in a common cause."

"Strange, you mentioned Jesus of Nazareth," Benjamin told them. "When he lived in Nazareth, his name was Joshua in Hebrew, the son of Joseph and Miriam. His father was a carpenter, and I understand there were several other children in the family. During his lifetime he was known as Joshua but later *the Greeks* made the name into Jesus and that is how he became known to us today. Because there is *no such word as Jesus in the Hebrew language or in the Aramaic.* History does not tell us what ever happened to the other children or to his father Joseph."

"We may be the descendants of those brothers and sisters, of Joshua or Jesus," Francis suggested. "It's something to think about."

"Joshua or Jesus came along just at the right time. If he had lived fifty years earlier or fifty years later, the time would not have been right," Benjamin told them. "At this time, there were many people who foretold that the world would come to an end, soon. There was one type of book written called the Apocalypse. The author of this book is forgotten. The word Apocalypse means, a 'revelation of the unknown'. Part of the Book of

Daniel in the Bible, is really an Apocalypse, because it tries to tell how God in some future time will punish the sinful nations and save the pious ones. During the first century before the Christian Era and the hundred years after the death of Jesus there were lots of books written about the destruction of all mankind.

"One of the oldest and most interesting of these books was by a man named Enoch. This was probably an assumed name of the real Enoch, who was the patriarch who preceded the Flood. The Bible tells us that "*God took Enoch*", which means that this *man never died*. In this book Enoch tells how sin and wickedness will finally disappear from the earth and a great era of happiness will then descend on all mankind. God would send one of His anointed, the *Messiah, to redeem Israel* from the oppressor and all humanity from degrading sin. This was written in images and descriptions of God's judgement and the Era of Peace which would follow the coming of the Messiah.

"The Jews at the time of Jesus liked to read this kind of book and others about their ancient heroes like King David, the wisdom of Solomon, the greatness of Moses as a leader and a soldier. As a religious people the Jews felt that for many centuries God would not tolerate the cruelty and wickedness of the Romans, Egyptians and the Greeks and the Syrians. God had promised the Jews that they would be teachers and leaders of mankind. Instead they were treated as a conquered people by these same Romans and Syrians. The Jews knew that they were morally superior to these nations, yet these nations were making them feel small and powerless.

"The only way they could explain this was that *their generation* was not worthy of God's promise, while the generation of King David *was worthy*.

"The ancient prophets believed that eventually the Gentile world would come to see how great the religion of Israel was and *join with us*. The prophets thought this would be a natural course of life. The only way many of them thought to save the world from degradation was for *God Himself* miraculously to come here and improve the world."

"The world was ready then for the coming of Jesus," said Rufino, "so why did not the Jews follow Him?"

"Many of the Jews did, like all your first twelve apostles," Francis said. "There were millions of Jews who lived in and around Israel who actually *never saw or heard of Jesus*. There were about 6 million Jews who lived outside the Holy Land who never heard of him."

"You know," Benjamin smiled, "the lord of the manor is not great man to his servant, nor is the prophet great to the people near him. Can anyone show me a *single bit of proof* that Joseph, the father of Jesus, ever became a Christian? Is there any true proof that *his mother Miriam*, or as the Romans named her Mary, ever became a Christian? Jesus had brothers and sisters. Did they become Christians?

"We Jews do not tend to worship men as people, we can only obey and respect one God. The Jews were oppressed by the Egyptians, the Greeks and the Syrians for a thousand years before Jesus was born. These other religions have gone from the face of the earth because they believed in *substitutes for the one God*. They turned their worship to idols and stone statues. Now, the Church of the Romans and the Greeks substitute the Wafer of the Host for the body of Jesus and drink wine like it was His blood. God must be a unity of One and cannot be divided into any messengers or any sons or any saints or angels. The Jewish religion, which Jesus learned as a boy, needed no substitutes and each one could pray directly to God."

"Yes, but Jesus was resurrected and came back from death," Rufino told them. "Isn't that proof of his divinity?"

"None of us were there," suggested Benjamin softly. "So, I have no answer for you. Supposing *this was true*, that Jesus was resurrected and came back from the dead. We Jews have already believed this for two thousand years, this was the test of man's reaching for God, by being just and pious in this life, to earn eternal life in the world to come. But, Judaism is based on more than this. Jewish life is based on Charity, which was completely foreign to the ancient Greeks and the Romans. A famous rabbi once said, "The world rests on three things: Torah, which means study and observance of moral laws; Worship, which means the Temple or Synagogue, and acts of Charity."

"Didn't Jesus say to his followers," Rufino said, " 'if you would be perfect, sell all you own and give the proceeds to the poor and come follow me,' or something like that. There is one foundation of Christianity, that is, helping the poor with charity."

"At my confirmation in Lucca," Francis remembered, "rabbi Jehudah Halevi told us that 'He who tries to give and do charity is granted money by God to do it.' But, the best one he told us was, 'Greater is he who persuades others to give than him who gives.' Come to think of it, that is a big order."

Outside it had begun to rain heavily, although the air was warm. Little Clara walked closer to the older boys and asked Francis, "Where is God?"

The older boys looked at each other bemused. Rufino was ready to brush her away, with the impatience of a fifteen-year-old, and was stopped by a gesture from Francis.

"God is all around us, little sister Clara," he informed her gravely.

"In this very room?" she inquired, "or perhaps outside in the rain?"

"The rain comes from the clouds high in the sky," the boy told her. "Of course that means it comes closer to God. Who knows, He may be out there in the rain right now."

She suddenly ran out from the piazza into the pouring rain. Lifting up her arms, her small bright head sparkled with the slanting rain dancing over her face. Her mother Ortolana moved quickly to the edge of the bricks lining the floor, but was caught in silence, as all of them were, by the sheer joy in the little girl's face, as she reached up to the sky with her small arms outstretched, "God is touching me," she cried out, "God is touching me."

Francis, seeing that her mother was held, waiting, ran out into the rain to bring Clara back to shelter. She caught his two hands in her own and started to dance in circles with him. The boy started to laugh and tossed his head with sudden abandon which the little girl had stirred in him.

He joined her, dancing in short steps, his long legs to match hers, in that pouring rain, while the others stood on the edge of the piazza watching the two of them.

"Come on in," shouted Benjamin to both of them, "You'll catch your death of cold."

"There speaks the future doctor," Francis shot back at him laughing. "Anyway, the rain is warm and soft to the touch. Come on out, those of you who love the rain and dance your sins away."

Soon, they were joined by Rufino and little Gilles. All of them danced in a circle in the heavy warm rain. Benjamin and Angelo stood aside, amused smiles on their faces, which only the young can portray for their friends, who suddenly have gone slightly mad.

The next day, the sun came out bright and hot, toasting the sand and the rocks across the beach. The four boys, Francis, Rufino, Benjamin and Angelo, swam out a distance into the ocean, their lithe strong bodies moving cleanly through the surf. They lolled around, floating, letting the warm ocean currents move their young bodies gently in the swells.

They raced into shore, like young dolphins, dipping and swooping at each other and rolled into the tiny beach, panting. They lay quietly, exhausted for a while, their chests heaving. This was a tiny beach surrounded by heavy rocks. Near them on chairs sat Pica and Ortolana. Clara was building sand castles with Gilles.

"Yesterday," Rufino remembered, "I asked you if your new teacher, this Doctor Maimonides, was an Egyptian?"

"No, he isn't," replied Benjamin. "He was born in Cordova in Spain in 1135 and lived there with his parents until he was about fourteen. His father was a local judge of the Jewish city. Their family had to leave Spain with thousands of other Jews who then went to North Africa. The boy Maimonides then studied with his father in Hebrew, the Torah and the Jewish poets.

"When he was about 23 years old they had to move again. They wanted to go to Palestine, but couldn't because of the Crusades. So they made their home in Fostat (later called Cairo, Egypt). He and his brother David went into the business of importing precious gems from India and Ethiopia. His brother David died in a shipwreck, so the work of supporting the family fell on him. At the same time he studied to become a physician, and he won such fame that he became the house physician for the family of Saladin, the Sultan of Egypt. Then he helped save the life of Richard the Lion-hearted, King of England, who wanted him to become his personal doctor. But, he wanted no more wandering in any Christian lands.

"Far more than being a physician, he became a great writer and voice in the whole world by his books explaining Judaism to the Jews and the world. This is the man who will be my teacher."

The boys lay quietly, soaking in the warmth of the Italian sun, content to rest and think about what Benjamin had told them. Across the mind of Francis raced his agility in diverting the spear hurled at King Richard the Lionhearted by the Arab enemy. Across his thoughts was the accolade of thanks granted to him by this noble king, the ideal of all the youth of Europe.

"Yet, England is ruled by his brother King John," said Francis. "Isn't it strange that two brothers can be so different?"

"I guess God makes a different mold each time," Rufino laughed. "In this case, he must have thrown it away as a bad one never to be repeated. He is a cruel king, this John."

"Come to think of it," suggested Francis, "I guess all life has many kinds of opposites. We have day and night, we have life and death. God created the world from chaos, so He had to use all the materials He had at hand."

"Where did he hide the devil?" asked Rufino.

"He must have hidden him out of sight," laughed Benjamin.

"But, the devil is here," insisted Francis. "Hidden or not, he is around us waiting to pounce on any of us."

"Here, see for yourself," said Rufino, lifting one of the larger rocks showing them the teeming life moving around in the wet sand. "Turn any kind of rock over and you can surely find the devil's handiwork. Who said it was hot in hell. It must be cold and clammy, like this wet rock."

"God created Good and Evil," Benjamin told them. "In the creation of the world, He looked at what He created after the fifth day and said 'it was good'."

"Let me see if I remember this," Francis said, "the first day was chaos and God created the heavens and the earth. So he said, 'Let there be light' and there was light and he divided the light from the darkness, calling it night and the other he called day."

"Then on the second day?" asked Benjamin, smiling to his friends.

"On the second day," volunteered Rufino, "he divided the waters from the firmament from those beneath it and there was heaven."

"Very good," said Benjamin, "and the next day?"

"I know," said Francis, "And God said, 'let the waters under the firmament be gathered into one place, and let the dry land appear.' He called one the land and the other the seas."

"Now, your turn," Benjamin pointed to Rufino.

"Let me see," ruminated the boy, "We are not at . . . the fourth day? Ah yes, God said, 'Let the earth put forth grass, fruit trees and herb yielding seed and other seed upon the earth, right?"

The older boy nodded, smiling to Francis, "We just finished the third day. Did any one of you think of all this *in the day we now have,* from sunset to sunset. Could all this happen in that time? What do you think?"

"God could will anything," Francis replied slowly, "by just thinking about it. Lots of things we can't understand because we are only mortals. What we see and can do is only as far as we can touch or smell."

"What do you think?" the older boy turned to Rufino.

"I go along with Francis," was the answer. "God could do anything."

"But, in science we can question without disrespect to God," Benjamin told them. "Many scientists believe that these 'days' mentioned in the Bible are not the kind of days we know but periods of time. They could be a year, or a million years in time."

"This would prove that God is infinite," Francis suggested. "He is without any beginning or any end. This is a lot for us human beings to understand."

"Let's go back to the creation of the world," Benjamin laughed, "before we get into more philosophy about God. We are now at the fourth day."

This was met by silence from the other two. "Well, I'll tell you," he suggested, "Days and nights. Does that help?"

"I remember," added Rufino quickly, "lights in the firmament to divide day from night and signs for the seasons and the days and the years. God made the two great lights, the greater one to rule by day and the lesser one at night with the stars. There was evening and morning. This was the third day."

"On the fourth," went on Francis, "God made the waters swarm with all kinds of living creatures and sea monsters and let fowl fly above the earth and everything that creepeth. He said they should multiply to each its own kind."

"Then on the fifth day," Rufino remembered, "He made all the beasts and the cattle and all the creeping things on earth."

"Man should not feel so proud of himself," Francis said laughing. "God waited until the sixth day, after all, he must have been tired to create man. God made the beasts and even the tiny bug and the flea on my horse *all ahead of man.*"

"Yes, the poor man," suggested Rufino, "all alone in the world, with no one to talk to, not even the beasts in the field. The world must have been a very quiet place with no women around." He threw his voice in the direction of Pica, Ortolana and Clara, amusement in his tone.

The older women looked at the boys and smiled in recognition of his sally.

"The nice thing, the Bible tells us," went on Francis, "is that God made man and woman in his own image and then blessed them. Here at least we started out with an eternal blessing. And then God saw everything that He had made and behold, 'it was very good.' And there was evening and there was morning, the sixth day."

"Doesn't this single statement in the Bible," Benjamin turned to Rufino, "contradict the theory of the Church of original sin of man?"

"Man himself became evil," Rufino replied, "when he ate the forbidden fruit in the Garden of Eden. It needed the death of Jesus to make atonement for this original sin."

"But thousands of years went by," replied Benjamin. "In all that time

"There could be no original sin," Francis interposed, "Because God saw man waited for Jesus to come along?"

His handiwork and said it was good."

"Jesus died to atone for all the sins of mankind," Rufino went on.

"But, God created *both good and evil,*" continued Benjamin. "Then He gave man a choice which one to select. At the same time He created life and death, night and day, hate and love. All these He created, so mankind needs no one to atone for its sins. Man can atone for his own sins, no one else. Otherwise you make a substitute in atonement. It was not the intention of Jesus when he preached in Palestine, to make *someone else* atone for a person's own sins.

"The Church has built up a false premise and thousands of people refuse to believe this. Many of them like the Waldensians want to remain Christians, but only believe that Jesus *was a prophet, not the son of God.* Many other thousands are turning away from Christianity and worship stones, the sun and the moon and the stars."

"For a thousand years," Rufino said, "the Jews and the Christians have lived peaceably side by side. Only in the last fifty years have they begun to kill and burn Jews. What happened? Perhaps I can answer my own question. Was there anyone in all the world more tolerant than Jesus, the Jew. A good, clean, tolerant Christian Church would also be tolerant of the Jew, who were His own people."

"In some ways we Jews miss a leader like this," Benjamin said. "The chance to follow one man, who has become a Godhead for millions of people. There is something so glorious and enchanting about this. It makes life so much simpler and easier to live with."

Rufino asked him why he did not become a Christian and do some cleaning up inside the Church.

Benjamin laughed, "Oh no, we Jews can speak with philosophy about any religion because ours is the grandpa of religions. The Christians and the Moslems have taken their roots from the Jews."

"Is that one of the reasons why you want to go back to Palestine?" asked Francis softly.

"I'll be near the Holy Land," replied Benjamin slowly. "Even the Koran says that the 'People of the Book' will return! Right now it is a wasted desert which no one dares to occupy, almost like an empty house waiting for its true owner to come back. It is like a haunting spirit and the crying soul of its people waiting for the body to return. One day please God, we shall return to our homeland. For wherever the Christian Church rules, the Jew cannot find any peace."

Assisi 1202

"Let me help you, Francie," the little girl looked up at her tall companion, admiring his strong face and the glints of gold dusting his hair with the warmth of the Italian sun. She could see the beads of sweat on his round, muscled chest and arms.

"Sure thing, little sister Clara," Francis looked down from the strength of his twenty years at the nine-year-old girl standing beside him.

He saw a sturdy body, dressed in short colored trousers and tight jacket which young girls wore in this year of 1202 in Assisi, Italy. He admired the way she stood up to him. "Like a young tree," he thought to himself.

Her hair was a reddish blond, hanging to her shoulders and he could touch the strands of gold mixed in at the ends. A high forehead accented the bright, warm eyes, which often led people to do her bidding gladly. Her nose told the world that hers was a blood line of Roman rulers who had controlled a world for centuries. She bent over, her shoulders firm and strong as she started to lift a basket of small stones. Around them was the bustle and movement of hundreds of people working on the wall of Assisi, preparing for war with the nearby city of Perugia.

Another boy came closer to them. "Hello, Cousin Rufino," her voice trilled off to the other. He was shorter than Francis and darkly handsome. People in the town said that the two cousins looked more alike than did Clara and her sister Agnes.

Rufino Offreduccio was slight of build and was staggering under a large rock, on top of a heavy cloth on his shoulders. As he tottered slightly, Clara made a motion to help him. Francis stepped in and supported the burden easily.

"Thanks Francie," Rufino said gratefully as the afternoon sweat crept on his forehead.

Francis bent over and took her rocks quickly. He was startled at the weight of the basket which she had brought him. She glanced up at his face and a smile washed her face, lighting the brownish glints in her eyes, as she

68

always did when she looked up at Francis. After all, her mother had said many times that he was her true brother of the spirit, not in the flesh. But, her brother he was indeed.

The two boys walked away, their steps wobbling with the load of the rock, towards the wall which was being repaired. Clara recalled her first adventure with Francis when she was three years old and he was almost 15.

She had toddled into the sea waters of the beach in Ancona. The waters of the Adriatic Sea could get vicious at times.

A shallow though strong wave had trundled her into the sand. With the water spilling over head, suddenly the warm and friendly sun became a world of noise and salty, choking darkness. Her eyes caught something bright in the water and felt herself drawn into the sunlight again. She had not swallowed any water and she had remained alert. Her first glance was that of the boy's forefinger. Her next glance led her to his tall, sturdy body and the long firm arms of the athlete. At that moment, despite her youth, she discovered Francis as a man in her life.

"All right little sister?" she heard him ask. He started to grasp her under the arms to walk her out of the surf.

She wriggled away from him. "I want to stay in the water," she told him. She shook her head, still holding on to his finger, smiling up at him in that most ancient of all signs of young womanhood. "Don't tell Mama," she said. Clara did not ask people, even at this age. She told them.

"May I call you my brother Francie?" she had asked him. He had looked down at her body arching up to him, from the worldliness of the fourteen-year-old, giving assent to a 3-year-old girl. Thus, an ancient rite of the male lord was offered and accepted. "Only if you let me call you 'little sister Clara'," he chided her. "But for now, we best sit on the beach and I will build for you a castle, a truly beautiful castle of sand, fit indeed for King Arthur himself."

They walked out of the breakers, with her small hand in his larger one. As both of them built their castle of sand on the rocky beach of Ancona, using drift wood and small stones to reinforce the structure, he kept weaving a story for her.

The story he told was about a beautiful princess who lived in a far away land. She was looking for her brother and could not find him. He entwined his story with bits of lore about this make believe land, with bright colored birds and the nests they built high up in the tall trees.

She listened and was held more by his voice than the story itself. The tones made music in her ears. She would not forget this scene. Far into her mature years, when the nights were weighted with a terrible loneliness, she would cherish these early moments with fond memories. And so their friendship and love began that afternoon, on this sandy beach, to last them through a lifetime. That love was to spill over into millions of souls for the next 700 years.

*　　*　　*

Now, the city they both loved was at war with her neighbor, Perugia! Everyone had to repair city walls.

Assisi was a city-state, which controlled its own destinies. There were many such municipalities in Italy which the Pope wished to destroy. Assisi wanted to remain free of such domination.

When Lotario de Conti became Pope Innocent III at the age of 37, he was the youngest one to be elected to the Throne of Peter. He had three of the most powerful Cardinals helping him because they were his near relatives. The young Pope also had the wealth of the Venetians behind him, because they were in his family!

The vote was unanimous in the College of Cardinals. This was on January 8, 1198. Yet, it was not until February 21, 1198, that the young Pope was finally ordained as a priest! On February 22, on Sunday he was consecrated as a Bishop!

One of his first acts as Pope was to convince the Prefect of Rome, a man named Peter, to resign and recognize the Pope as the supreme authority. He also induced Senator Scottus Paparoni to resign his powerful position in the city government of Rome. Now the young Pope had the entire city of Rome, its civil as well as its ecclesiastic forums, in his hands.

Pope Innocent set himself up as the liberator of Italy from the foreign rule of the German kings, who at that time ruled over Italy and the Sicilies. He then conquered Spolleto and Perugia, destroying the city-state civil authority. So they became part of the patrimony of St. Peter.

When the German Emperor Henry VI died in 1197, Innocent somehow convinced Queen Constance, who was reigning in behalf of her young son Frederick, to appoint the Pope as the Guardian of the young king. When she died, shortly later (November 27, 1198) of some unknown malady, her will specified that this guardianship was to continue!

Now, the Kingdom of Sicily was in the Pope's hands.

Innocent III then began a systematic drive, for the first time in Western civilization, to control *all* the temporal, civil and political and ecclesiastic power in Europe. He obtained feudal lordship over the kingdoms of Aragon, Portugal, Hungary, Sicily and soon over England and Ireland.

He dominated the kings of France and interfered in the operation of every dukedom and most especially in Provence. (There, in a few years he was to send in his army of Dominicans in the Crusade against the Albigensians. They destroyed a civilization over 1,000 years old and slaughtered tens of thousands of Christians and Jews.)

"We in Assisi are a free people," Pietro told his family one night before the war started, "which Innocent wants to crush. He had only been in office a few months, when he sent his Bull named Mirari Cogimar to Assisi on April 16, 1198, threatening us with war and all dire circumstances. To Innocent any free people is a threat to him personally. All over Europe they call him the young 'Wonder of the World'. This man truly believes himself second only to God Almighty here on Earth."[9]

"Now he and his Venetian relations want to dictate who can do business in Europe," Pietro went on about the war.

"They will become the moneylenders and the bankers for all the kings and merchants in Europe. They will stop, at any cost, anyone they please from doing business. Because the full power is in their hands.

"In 1189 and 1190, the Venetians helped start the riots in England to crush the Jewish bankers and burned the notes of all the debtors. Do you know who will suffer the most from the power of this Pope? The Jews will. He will use this power to drive them out of existence. Yet, we in Assisi are like the Jews of old, we are in the way of the conqueror. In ancient days the Jews were in the way of the Egyptians, the Assyrians and the Romans.

"The conquerors had their pagan gods and their idols. The Jew had his one God, 'Adonai'. A conqueror cannot have any other god than his own, one that he can touch or move at will."

"Then we must fight to the last man to win this war with Perugia," Francis promised vigorously.

"It sounds very good," Pietro suggested, "but the Perugians have heavy Roman equipment and much better soldiers and generals in the pay of the Venetians. They want Assisi and we cannot stop them. I have paid a heavy share, as a Jew. I have paid an extra heavy share of taxes, for the

[9]Innocent's letter to the Archbishop of Ravenna dated March 1198 . . . "the liberty of the Church is nowhere better served than where the Roman Church obtains full power both in temporal and spiritual matters." His letter to King John of England, April 21, 1214, ". . . and over all He has set one who He has appointed as His Vicar on earth . . . so all men should obey His Vicar and strive there shall be one fold and one shepherd. . . ." "All secular kings for the sake of God, so venerate this vicar that unless they seek to serve him devotedly they doubt they are reigning properly" from Selected Letters of Pope Innocent III by C. R. Cheney and W. R. Sample.

defense of these walls. Since I cannot work on the walls like other citizens, I must send you in my stead. It will be to no avail."

Assisi had lived at peace with its neighbors for so long that the city fathers had never expected it to be attacked by one of its nearby sister cities. Since the city had some heavy walls and was high on a hill, it would be safe, they thought.

The army from Perugia arrived and one of its generals asked the city of Assisi to surrender. This was refused and they attacked. The small local army, the local boys and the citizen volunteers used stones, spears and swords to defend their city.

They were no match for the trained soldiers and the superior forces of the Pope's Army.

Because they had refused to surrender, about twenty boys were to be held in prison, as hostages, until "damages" would be paid in full by the people of Assisi to the city of Perugia for the cost of the war.

A Captain of the army then asked the boys to "give their word as gentlemen" not to escape from the wagons which would transport them to the city of Perugia. He told them that they would be held only a short time, until "certain matters would be corrected" and then they would all be freed soon.

It took less than a day to march to Perugia from Assisi. The boys, led by Francis, sang marching songs and kept each other's spirits high. They laughed and told jokes about each other. To most of them who had never been away from home very long, this was like a picnic and an adventure.

They were brought to an old castle outside of Perugia and all the boys were shown into a large room in the basement, used for storage and wine aging.

Not until they heard the heavy clank of the sliding bolt in the thick wooden door did they realize that they were trapped!

Francis sat down on the cot, which would be his bed and looked around him at the dank, brown, sweaty walls of their prison. Now, he felt much as the animals would in his grandfather's cages in Arles. For the first time in his life, like all the other boys, they were trapped in a stone cage!

Frances looked around him to see who were his companions and fellow inmates. There was Captain Gentile, who had been very friendly to the boy several times during the battle; Parao, the Duke's son; Rufino Offreduccio and Giovanni di Capella (so named by Francis because he always wore a hat even to bed and when he bathed!) There was Paulus, the son of a Count, and many others.

Since they had no means for outside excercise, the boys would wrestle with each other, tumbling over the hard stone floors, creating in turn many broken noses and lost teeth.

They would hand wrestle, when the more violent form bored them, in the style of the Ancient Asiatics, with arms to arms and face to face on the wide table which served them all.

Parao, the Duke's son, got a small dagger into the room. They played a game of hitting targets on the wooden door and into a circle on the floor, with different kinds of twists of the arms and throwing it overhead and underfoot.

At the end of several days, Pietro arrived with Angelo, bringing several hampers of food which was greeted by the boys with loud cheers. A louder cry of joy went up when they saw the mandola which the father brought for his son.

Father and son went into a corner of the room and Pietro told him that their stay would be longer than he thought. The Perugians had set up a very high price for their "damages." It could not be raised in Assisi and would almost bankrupt the city.

He was trying to fill these outrageous demands by asking many of the wealthier citizens of Assisi to issue letters of credit from the bankers in Rome, who were owned by those in Venice. But these bankers wanted interest rates of over 40 percent.

He told Francis that Pica, his mother, was very depressed by his being caged in this stone tomb. She would sit by herself singing songs of her youth on her harp and lute. Pietro feared for her health if Francis stayed away too long.

Francis asked his father to tell Pica to write to him.

A week later he received a letter from his mother.

Dearest Son,

Your father told me not to write anything which would depress you anymore. My dearest Francis, who so loved the fresh clean air of the outdoors, who loved the trees and the birds flying across the skies, must by some trick of cruel fate be bound inside of your stone castle in Perugia.

My only cry to you is to trust in God. He knows what is in your heart and that you are the victim of a cruel tyrant in Rome.

My father once read a story to me about a famous Rabbi Phinehas who told this: A King left his country and returned after a long absence of many years. When he came to the palace his own sons did not recognize him. They looked at other dukes and princes searching for the face of their father.

The king told them, "I am your father, they are without power in this land! God says the same thing. Do not turn to angels and saints, they have no power to help you. Turn to me, for I am your father."

We have not trained you too well in our religion and the traditions of my fathers before God. It is our fault not yours. So that now, in an hour of great need for God, you may not know how to pray to Him.

Like the bird in the sky then, let your soul soar to heaven, through the thick walls of your prison, reaching with your heart and your being to Him who sees all things and knows every cranny of each one's heart.

When the hours are truly lonely, you have the mandola and locked away inside you is the music I have taught you for all your years since you were ten. Bring out all the fine music with your voice, let others hear you, so they too can find peace, as I trust and hope you will, until you return home to us safe and whole again.

I have enclosed a few pieces of music, which you have heard and may remember. Play them often and play them well.

Your dearest mother, who waits for your early return from Perugia.

Pica

A PSALM OF DAVID

"The Lord is my light and my salvation!
 Whom shall I fear?
The Lord is the stronghold of my life;
 Of whom shall I be afraid?

In august, when the leaf falls from the
bush and dies with the slightest wind,
the flower does not last,

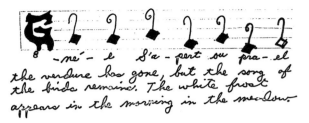

(In August, when the leaf falls from the bush and dies with the slightest wind, the flower does not last, the verdure has gone, but the song of the birds remains. The white frost appears in the morning in the meadow.)

Francis liked to reread the letter from his mother and did so several times. This seemed to annoy Giovanni the "Hat" and he would make some slighting remarks about the 'Hebe' loving his Mama and being a "mama's boy."

Francis ignored the comments and was silent. This infuriated the other still more. Once he made a mocking dance around Francis, with some of the other boys warning him to stop.

As Francis continued to read the letter, suddenly Giovani reached and grabbed it and made a dance waving it over his head, making motions to tear it up and wipe his pants seat with it.

Francis threw himself on Giovanni, trying to protect the letter from being destroyed. This started a fight. The two boys were strong, with pent-up emotions and built-in weeks of imprisonment goading them on.

The others made a circle, watching them. No one tried to stop the fight because any pair of them could have been on that floor battling each other. Each one found an inner satisfaction in the blood spattered on the faces of the two who were fighting.

They fought for almost an hour, the battle moving from one to the other. Finally, they were so exhausted that they just sat down on the cold stone floor, looking at each other, with panting chests, wracking their lungs for air.

Suddenly Francis started to laugh. The other paused a moment and added his laughter to the scene. He reached behind him retrieving the letter and handed it to Francis.

Once a week, after due payment to their guards, the boys were allowed to have a few prostitutes come in and relieve their tensions. This was done openly, in the large room, so all could watch.

One day when this occurred, at the same time a priest from one of the nearby towns came to visit with them. Parao invited him to "join the festivities and use one of the girls." The priest told him that he would accept the invitation, but he required more privacy than this open room.

Parao insisted and the priest just as adamantly refused. Some of the boys took this as an insult to them as well as the prostitutes and went about removing the robe of the priest including his loin cloth, leaving him nude except for his sandals, which he begged the boys to let him have.

Parao then slung the robe over his head and added a cowl to partially cover his face. After calling the guard he got out of the door.

In about ten minutes he was back, shoved into the room by an irate guard. He looked down at his fancy leather shoes and laughed aloud. It seems that he had almost gotten away, when one of the guards noticed the fine shoes which he wore, under the priest's meager robe. Back he came to their common prison.

But, the guards were so angry at the laughter of the boys at this stunt, that they were forbidden to have any prostitutes for a month.

The boys' anger at Parao continued in grumbles and outright threats to him and his safety. He showed them his knife several times, warning them that any more threats would result in some 'loss of skin.'

Almost two weeks had gone by and they were still forbidden to have any of the girls. Many fights broke out among them.

Then one day, Parao's sister, Pulca, came to visit him. She was a tall, Junoesque young woman, well endowed, who came in with swaying hips and wide flouncy skirts. One of the young men came near them in a corner and complained bitterly to her about the stunt played on them by her brother.

She looked up at him pertly and offered to be a "better substitute than any whore in Christendom" for her brother's friends, of course.

Out of respect for her dignity and position in society, several of the boys would act as a screen around them. However, at her insistence, they had to face forward away from the cot. She slyly remarked that, "they could peek a little."

Parao then demanded that Francis "give them some soft music for this noble sacrifice to the God of Love." He strummed his mandola in a fanfare of sound then sang for them this song which his mother had sent him:

re- ter- ner Lors me
te tro- ver Lar- ge

vou- droi- e se- jor- ner
qui ne vous- ist con- ter

gre- ust porc et buef et

When I see winter return, then I would
find lodging, if I could find a
generous host who would charge me

mou- ton, mou- tony, fai- sany

et ve- noi- son, Gras-

-ses ge- li- nes et

cha- pons Et bons fro- ma ges

en gla- con.

nothing, who would have pork and beef
and mutton, ducks, pheasants and venison,
fat hens and capons and good cheese
in baskets.

(When I see winter return, then I would find lodging, if I could find a generous host who would charge me nothing, who would have pork and beef and mutton, ducks, pheasants and venison, fat hens and capons and good cheese in baskets.)

Then, Francis sang this song, with such a wail and melancholy in his voice that it brought waves of laughter:

(This was a 12th century song of lament by Daniel to Darius written by the students of Beauvais, France.)

Francis had the wit and the satire to play this melody at this time.

After this act was completed, several of the boys asked her to be gracious, also to them. She agreed to select five more lovers. As she walked around the room, flouncing her skirts, she paused near Francis. She shook her head saying firmly she would have no 'Hebe' inside of her.

Francis laughed at this sally. He continued to strum his mandola, as the acts of fealty and love went on for the next few hours. During this time, some of the boys who were not chosen would slink off into a corner and perform the oldest acts known to them and to them alone.

The next day, one of the boys in a general conversation about the clothing girls wore under their dresses, stated that the garters of Pulca were pink. Another one insisted they were blue. This started a long argument, with one group insisting it was one color and the other claiming it was another.

Angered, one of the boys struck the other in the face. A few minutes later, somehow, Parao's dagger was plunged into the first boy's chest and before the end of the day he was dead!

With some meager ceremonies, he was buried in the courtyard outside the castle prison. No one could fix the blame for the use of the dagger and its final path of death.

The prison guards shrugged their shoulders with Gallic aplomb. They told the prisoners "a pox on you all." They then allowed the prostitutes to return.

On several occasions Francis noticed how cruelly the prostitutes were treated by some of the boys. Once, one of them struck a poor creature in the face several times and threw her out of the room bodily, with her clothes half off. It seems that she had commented about his body odor. No one stirred to help her.

Another almost beat a girl half to death, without any of the other boys interfering to save her. She had refused his demands to kiss his naked body. Men as well as boys treated these love partners as low creatures. The oldest profession was trapped in the customs of the times. Only ladies of equal rank were treated with dignity and respect.

Assisi 1203

Then one day Francis received a letter from his father.

My dear son Francis,   March 10, 1204

As a traveler in Europe and England I have learned with dismay that the Fourth Crusade which was preached by Pope Innocent III with such fervor and high ideals for the Christians to conquer Jerusalem was instead sent to Constantinople in Greece.

The news over all of Europe is that the main reason Innocent III was elected Pope with no *single dissenting vote* was so that his Venetian relatives could control all the business of Europe and destroy all their competition. They sold the needy French Barons a "Bill of Goods." They did not give a tinker's damn about the differences between the Roman and the Eastern Greek Churches. To them, this was a way of having everything in Europe. All the boats taking the Crusaders to Palestine were theirs!

To every person who knows the facts, Innocent III knew about this attack and approved it. So, Christians murdered Christians in cold blood and more than 30,000 men, women and children were slaughtered in Constantinople. The streets were running rivers of blood from the murder of innocent people.

For all the world, the Pope wanted to be boss of "One Christian Church" and he was to get it any way, at any cost. This was the nature of the man. He did not measure cost as long as it would satisfy his own lust for ambition to be the *"second one to God on earth."*

Why do I tell you about this vain and ambitious Pope? Because we Jews are alone in Europe. We have few friends in high places now. We are like a small ship in an angry sea and we get tossed here and there on the waves, at the whim of rulers and Popes.

If the Christian world learns to live at peace with each other, then we

Jews will in turn have some measure of peace. If they constantly destroy each other in violence, then we get in their way. (We spoke about this in Assisi, it seems ages ago.) Like a mad bull, they attack us, for no other reason, that in the heat of battle, anything that moves or stands still must be struck.

I am still working for the ransom money to get our boys back home. Money these days is only available from the Venetian bankers who with pity in their faces and tears in their eyes ask for 100 percent interest on their loans. And they killed Jews in Paris because they wanted 8 percent interest!

I hope with God's help to raise this money soon, so we could have our boys home again.

I saw young Miss Clara Offreduccio the other day and she sends her kind wishes to you. She is growing tall and will be soon a beautiful lady. She will make someone a fine wife one day.

> Your father,
> Pietro Bernardone

Francis was seated on the cot as he read this letter. Next to him was Rufino, who asked to read the letter for news of the world. As Francis moved to hand him the paper, he started to cough and his body was wracked by shivers.

Rufino in kindness put his arm around his friend's shoulders holding him until the shivers subsided. He then looked down on the letter and noticed a spatter of blood in tiny brownish spots.

Francis told him that he had seen them before, for the past three weeks and perhaps he was sick. Rufino talked with one of the guards, who knew Francis and often appreciated his songs and a few gifts of his food.

Two days later, a doctor from the castle came down to the prison room and examined the naked chest of Francis, thumping on his back and on his rib cage, listening to sounds with his ear pressed close to the boy's chest. He murmured something under his breath and left the room.

A few hours later he returned with one of the guards who took Francis out of the prison into the castle, where he was placed in the bed of a room in the servants' quarters. He was told that he had a lung disease which caused the spit of blood.[10]

Francis had to give his solemn word as a gentleman that he would not

---

[10]Later generations would know this as tuberculosis.

escape. Otherwise, he would have to be chained to the bed post. He could not return to the prison room with the other boys, because the doctor felt that they could get the same sickness.

He advised the boy to get into the hot sun and allow it to bake upon his chest to dispel "the spirits inside his lungs."

A month later, almost to the year, Pietro came to Perugia and told him the boys were to be released, since the ransom money had been raised. He and many of the citizens of Assisi had agreed to make payments far into the future, to make up the sums demanded by Perugia.

Pietro came with a carriage. Pica and Angelo were with him. They helped Francis from his bed to save his strength. Pica suddenly burst into tears of remorse at her son's illness. Pietro cursed the name of Pope Innocent III, and wished all the demons of hell to fall upon that man for all he did to mankind and to the Jews especially.

At home in Assisi, with complete rest and Pica's good food, the coughing spells of Francis receded. They seemed to return at times when he became upset about something.

After several weeks, Pietro encouraged Francis to go out with his friends. He told the boy to outfit himself in new clothes and mingle more with his "rich friends."

Francis was always popular with the young men of Assisi, because he had a ready wit and could play the mandola like a troubador. He rode his horse well and in the races outside of Assisi with the other young bloods he made a good showing. They played games of hitting hard boiled eggs over an upright rope hung between two high poles. (Something like modern paddle ball)

In this game they would also use nuts and small stones. The girls would often join the boys in these games. They would imitate the knights of King Arthur's Round Table in holding tourneys on horseback using long wooden staves wrapped on the ends with heavy woolen cloths. They would ride swiftly through the streets of Assisi mounted on gaily decorated horses, blowing bugles and horns.

In the evening the boys would gamble with a form of dice called "odds and evens" and named Zara. This kind of game required a passive form of violence, and Francis, not being violent by nature, would lose heavily to the other boys.

Several times, Francis would ruefully tell his father, Pietro, that he lost money gambling and owed debts as much as 50 marks. His father would make a face of concern, then laughingly pay the boy saying, "Better to pay for this than for your prison."

Then began a period of the Revels, which became an annual event for the young people of Assisi. They would dress up in their best finery and hold courts named after one Ambrose. They would strut around in their fine clothes, dancing in the streets, making love to the girls and giving each other all kinds of funny gifts. They would often have contests to see who could make up the most humorous gift for a boy or girl.

Francis won a prize with a box, wrapped in golden cloth and tied with ribbons. When it was opened, two white doves flew out of the box, with long stringers of thin ribbon dangling from their feet. At the end of the ribbons was a small sign which read, "catch me if you can."

One evening they asked Francis to play some dance tunes. Then the revellers chose him to be King of the Revels and Pulca, the sister of Parao, the Duke's son, as the Queen.

She wore a long gown brocaded with golden threads and low cut, so that her breasts protruded from the bodice. Seated on the thrones near each other, she remembered her taunt in the prison of Perugia and invited him to partake of her rite in her boudoir.

Francis laughed, reminded her about not having any "Hebe inside of her." He had not changed one bit since that day, he slyly informed her.

She retorted that it was a lady's privilege to change her mind and that, as king he could make any demand which must be obeyed by the queen, "his noble slave."

As King, Francis appointed himself as the "Noble Troubador of the King's Court" and made them sit around in a large U as he entertained them with songs of the times.

"Let all those who are in love come and dance, the others not! The Queen ordains it. All those who are in love! Let those who are jealous be driven with blows from the dance . . . . . ."

" . . . Let all those who are in love come and dance, the others not!"

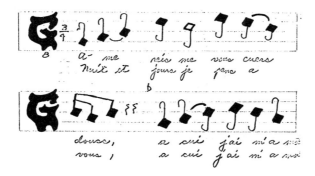

(Gentle heart, could you love true
   Heart to whom my love I've tendered?
Night and day I think of you
   Gentle heart, could you love true?)

Then Francis saw that Clare and her mother Ortolana were standing at the edge of the crowd listening to his songs. Gesturing with his mandola, recognizing them and singing to Clare, as if she stood alone:

(It was in May, sweet time and gay
When all is fresh and gleaming
I rose to play and took my way
To where a fount was streaming.
Where blossoms bright hedged fruit trees white
I heard a VIÈLE entrancing.
Before my sight a gallant knight
and noble maid were dancing.)

Later that evening, he walked alone with Clara towards the outside gate of Assisi, holding hands, their eyes drinking the soft brilliance of the starlit sky above them.

"You sing so beautifully," Clara sighed to him. "You touch all who listen with words of balm."

Francis laughed. "You make me feel like a professional jongleur. Believe me, I'm not."

"Yet," she replied slowly, "you make everyone feel as if you were singing for them alone."

"Let me tell you little sister Clara," he shook his finger amusedly at her, "that is the trick, we jongleurs have to entice our ladies fair into our web of evil hands."

"Have we not gone long ago away from 'little sister Clara'?" she asked. "And you have no evil hands. You have nice hands."

"Has our little girl truly grown up, to be so serious?"

"Must I remind you, Francie," she said, "that little girls do grow up and think of many things."

"I am twenty-one years old and you are just about ten," Francis told her.

"My mother was betrothed when she was twelve," Clara retorted. "Girls get married in Italy and France at twelve and thirteen years of age. This is our custom, silly."

"My mother was married when she was nineteen," Francis said.

"Your dear Pica waited too long for her Pietro," she replied.

"And I need not wait too long," he bent down looking into her face. "Dearest Clara, would you truly want to marry me?"

"All my life since that day on the beach in Ancona," she told him. "I remember when we sat on the porch in Ancona when you were about fifteen and that day at the walls of Assisi."

"You asked me to wait for you . . ." he finished.

"Mama tells me I held your finger when I was in my baby crib," she laughed, "so you see I have a long claim on you."

They both were silent, their thoughts and eyes reaching over the Umbrian Plain, towards the shadows of the mountains, dipped far off in the night sky. Assisi stood high in the plain and the clear stars over their heads seemed to cluster and sprinkle jewels of light bending shadows into silhouettes and odd patches below them.

"My papa is as old as you would be with my mama," she said suddenly breaking their silence.

"You have twisted your words," Francis laughed with her.

She came into his arms as he held her closely to himself. They kissed slowly and tenderly. He held her off gently, then she came again into his arms.

"Truly, Francis," she said into his ear. "I have waited for you all my life and now I shall not let you go."

"Yet, today I am King of the Revels," he told her, "and Pulca awaits me in her boudoir to partake of her favors. She demands this as her right."

"That is for you to decide, my king and my lord of the realm," she bowed down to him in mock obeisance. "I am but your lowliest slave, too, who awaits your bidding. Beat me, flog me with whips," her voice was serious, "but O Lord, love me unto eternity."

They fell into each other's arms, laughing at their sallies, happy in the sheer joy of being near each other.

He then suggested that they go home, since it was late and Ortolana would worry. As they slowly walked home together, she asked him, "Will you always love me, Francis, the way I love you?"

He handed her a small gold pin of a bird in flight. "Until the end of time," he promised her solemnly.

Since he was King of the Revels, he and the others, who were his "Knights of the Court" decided that they would have a fete called the "Garrison" the next day.

A long stockade was built of wood. This was then covered with long lengths of cloth which he got from his father's warehouse.

Twelve girls of the best families in Assisi were to dress in fine white cloth, and be waited on by 12 handmaidens, who were to protect and shield them from the attackers. (Clara was too young for this.)

Ten or twelve boys also dressed in white were to attack this haven of the "Virgins," without force or violence. They were to use only flowers and ribbons as weapons. The handmaidens were to return the fire of the "weapons," until there was the blowing of a rams horn signalling the end of the "war."

They would all then march through the streets singing songs, dancing in pairs or inside a circle. By arrangement they would visit the homes of the "virgins" and eat from the tables piled high with apples, pears, cherries, figs, apricots, plums and peaches arranged in displays of small houses, bells and animals.

At another house, they would find all kinds of vegetables, also in decorative motifs, using beets, gourds, cabbages, onions, lettuce, spinach and asparagus.

At the next house they would find different meats and fish in clever molds and designs to tempt them.

Finally, in the last home they would find tables with oranges, lemons, juices to drink, dates, pomegranates, almonds and filberts.

After this they would drift off in pairs, each one finding whatever solace they asked of each other. This was the free and open custom of the "nights of love" in those years.

On his way home alone, one of the revellers taunted Francis with, "Where is thy queen, King of the Revels?"

"Tucked away safe and sound in her bed, O' slave," he replied. "At least I hope so," he added, with a laugh.

"Is she not your queen for the night?" the other continued.

"My friend, I have a nobler queen," he said, "of far greater worth and charm to last a lifetime." He continued on home.

In one of the Revels, Francis met Captain Gentile, who had been in the war between Perugia and Assisi but somehow had escaped from the prison sentence exacted upon the other boys, after a stay of only a week.

Francis learned that Gentile was visiting Assisi after an absence of about a year. He was invited to join the Bernardone household for dinner. He was recruiting for Walter of Brienne for more troops to fight the army of Frederick II. True, this was a war of Pope Innocent III to enforce some promises which the Emperor had not kept.

"I know you like soldiering," Gentile told Francis. "All your friends are with us."

"Who is already on your list?" inquired Pietro.

"We have about fifty, including Rufino Offreduccio, the Count's nephew, Parao, the Duke's son, Paulus and many of your friends."

"Perhaps this would be a glorious opportunity for you," suggested Pietro, turning to Francis. "Better than your singing and gambling to all hours of night."

"You want me to go fight the Pope's war?" Francis was incredulous.

"Why not," his father replied. "He controls all of Europe and you could advance yourself, without changing your religion."

"It would be an excellent opportunity for advancement," the Captain told the boy. "Most of importance, you could become an officer in a short time. Because most of the boys in Assisi like you and you could lead people. I know this as does my master Walter of Brienne."

"Walter, has heard of me?" Francis asked. "How could he?"

"From many others. Your actions in the prison in Perugia, how you were a peacemaker and a leader," Gentile said.

Pietro suggested that as a gesture of friendship, he would buy a suit of armor not only for his son Francis, but also for Captain Gentile, who had lost all his possessions in the war between Perugia and Assisi.

Several weeks went by and the day for Francis' departure drew near and he sat in the sun outside the house, looking downcast. He and his father walked into the house together.

"You must not feel disconsolate, my boy," Pietro said kindly. "War is a skilled professional. Look at Caesar or Alexander the Great. They were statesmen as well as good military men. They are best remembered for their achievements, not the few battles they lost. Tomorrow, you go off to new fields to win."

"Is killing each other something glorious?" Francis accented the last word. "I'm asking. I don't know."

"Men have not learned to tolerate each other," Pica said, shaking her head slowly. "Their Prince of Peace died 1,200 years ago." Francis noticed that the tiny silver pendants in her hair danced when she shook her head. They caught and held the glistening lights from the braziers hung on the walls.

A smile creased Francis' lips as he looked at his mother. She *does not want* me to go to war. Only *he* does, looking at his father's big head, with its heavy brown curls. Strange how different were these two. Her manner was fine and soft, her voice carried a quality of low strength.

Francis was aware that Pietro dominated them all. His was always the final voice of authority in their home. He saw that Pica was lacing her five fingers together. She did this when she was disturbed, Francis remembered. Tomorrow he was to leave for the new war in Apulia in the south of Italy.

"We in Assisi believed we were fighting in a revolution against the yoke of the German barons, hung around our necks." Francis' voice sounded deep as he bounded out of his lethargy. "God grant that someday we'll get them out of Italy. We thought we were to destroy serfdom forever in Assisi, in the war with Perugia. So each one could be a free man and end this stupid system where one man is bound to another . . . like some cattle."

"You needn't be grieved," Pietro said. "They had too many soldiers. Old water down the Tiber."

"We of Assisi lost the battle with Perugia," Francis was bitter. "But, we now learn that the good burghers of Assisi didn't want us to win. They wanted to keep the serfs. They knew it would be good business to go along with the German barons."

Pietro's face got red. "You talk like one of those radical heretics. Dreamers, dreamers, everywhere I go, even in my own household, I meet dreamers. I went to France, they have the poor Men of Lyons; these fools only want to be poor. I go to Provence, there I meet religious dreamers . . . the Albigenses, the Fiori, and Pors and the Waldensians. All dreamers to change the world. I know that the serf system is not good. But, that was created by the Christian world for its own use. Change the system and we will have the world turn over on its back."

"Perhaps it would be a good idea to have the world turn over a new leaf," suggested Francis, smiling to his father.

"We have no other system to take the place of the serfs. Who would till the fields or clean the streets?" asked Pietro. "There are thousands of jobs which must be done. Who will do them?"

"We might do them ourselves," a tiny smile rode across Francis' lips.

His father's temper rose. "You'd want me to sweep the streets or wash this house?"

"Or me take care of the stable?" added Angelo.

"No, no," Pica soothed them all. "Francis didn't mean that. Do you Francis?"

The boy smiled. He said nothing.

"I don't like your humor," Pietro said, peeved.

"Let's see Francis' new armour," Pica said interestedly.

"We've seen it before," Angelo suggested.

"Let's see it again," Pietro responded. "I paid two hundred marks of silver for that suit. Made by Moroconi, a relation of mine in Venice. He wanted three hundred. I got it for two."

"You are a shrewd man of business," Francis complimented his father. What was the mark of a business man, he thought to himself. Is he shrewd? Is he stingy and hard? Pietro was not always that way. He was generous to the city. He'd paid for the erection of part of the new gate. Didn't he generously spend over three hundred pieces of silver to outfit Captain Gentile, the leader of Francis' troop. Pietro had graciously volunteered to buy the Captain his armour. Strange man, his father. Mean in some small things. Generous in full measure with others.

"Come, let's go into your room," Pietro ordered, leading Angelo and Pica, with Francis last.

"You know I'm glad you're leaving tomorrow," Angelo spoke over his shoulder.

"Why?" queried Francis.

"Now I can have the whole bed to myself. You kick too much, Francis. The devil must be riding you in your sleep."

"Perhaps it's the other way around," laughed Francis. "I may be riding on the devil's tail."

"That's my boy, again," Pietro turned around, reaching over Angelo and Pica and mussing Francis' hair affectionately. "A laugh at last. That's what we missed while you were away, your laughter."

Francis' face tinged slightly with pleasure. It was good to know that he was wanted.

"Don't you agree, Pica?" her husband asked. She nodded her head, smiling.

Pietro, Angelo and Pica had crowded into the small room. Francis could hardly get in, let alone get dressed in the armour. Here again was something he couldn't understand about his father. The two boys slept in the same bedroom with their parents. Pica's pleas for a separating partition fell on deaf ears. Pietro's answer was that some of the noble houses had five or six people sleeping in one bedroom. There shouldn't be any "secrets" from the children. (Francis knew of one rich family which had ten people in one bedroom. In fact, the parents and four children slept in one bed!)

Pica finally convinced Pietro to have the partition erected when Francis was nineteen years old. But this "room" was actually a corner of the father and mother's.

Finally, they gathered in the larger room to watch Francis dress in the shiny, tooled breast plates and leg protectors. It had been polished thoroughly by Vollo, their man servant. Angelo walked over and patted the armour.

"Here you," Pietro stopped him. "Do you want it to rust?" He took out his handkerchief and polished the touched area. "Very fine work this," he pointed to the flowers and arabesques etched and trimmed on the plate. "Well worth the two hundred pieces. How do you like it, my boy?"

"It's beautiful workmanship," Francis marveled, looking down on himself.

"Well, maybe someday you'll be a baron, too," Pietro told him. "I'm only a trader and seller of wool and silk stuffs. Your parents are nothing. But you may be a lord of the land one day. That's why I want you to be a soldier.

There are two ways a man can advance himself. Through the church or soldiering. Yes, the military is the better way to become a baron.

"Ever since I was ten, I wanted to be a soldier. But my father was too poor so he couldn't afford to buy me the things I needed. I hoped that my son would become a big man one day. Soldiering is the best way to get to the top. That's why I want you to become a good one."

The others in the room held their breaths. Pietro did something they hadn't ever seen him do. He daubed at his eyes, which suddenly filled with tears!

Francis was deeply touched. He, too, felt like crying. This was so unlike his father.

"I've always wanted to be a soldier," the elder Bernardone admitted with a catch in his voice. "Now, it will be you who will go in my stead," he looked directly at Francis.

"I'll make you proud of me," Francis vowed. "You'll see, I'll yet be a great Prince."

*   *   *

Taking his mandola with him, the next morning he walked the two streets towards Clara's house. He passed it, looking up at the piazza of the gray stone house. Francis waited a few minutes, a little beyond it on the same street. Clara came out. She had her younger sister, Agnes, with her.

Francis bowed his head gently and ceremoniously kissed the hand of Agnes. She blushed, then curtsied. Clara looked at this ceremony with an older sister's disdain. She was tall, near Francis. She stood like a young willow tree. Her dark blond hair rested gently on her shoulders. An oval face was angled by the dignity of her Roman nose. Her mouth was warm and soft.

They walked a few blocks to the new City Gate. Outside it, they drank in with their eyes the Umbrian plains as they stretched towards the south and east. The Foligno road, its stones trampled a gray-white by the centuries looked foreign and cold in this green landscape. Towards their left, rose the majesty of Mount Subasio with olive and oak trees garlanded across its ample bosom. On their own level, to the left, the small Castle guarded the jutting eastern approach to Assisi.

"Our wet nurse once told us," Clara said, "that all the monsters of the devil's making once lived on these Umbrian plains. Now, they live on the top of Subasio. They hide in the walls of the monasteries." Francis joined Clara's laugh.

"Who drove them up there?" queried Agnes.

Clara laughed. "They say the good Umbrian spirits."

"Are they still here?" the little girl asked her sister, looking at the valley ahead of them.

"I wonder," mused Clara. "What do you think, Francis?"

"I heard my father once say," he replied, "and he's been everywhere— Lyons, Venice, Paris and a few times in the fairs of London. . ."

"I'd like to see London and King Richard," Agnes was enthused.

"Dont interrupt," her older sister admonished.

"But you said you would like to see King Arthur and Gallahad and the others," the little girl persisted.

Francis looked at her. How much alike these two were. Clara with golden hair dressed around her clean white skin. He noticed with pleasure that she wore the gold pin he had given her. Agnes, her younger sister, had a coppery tint in her light hair. Clara had once told him that their inheritance was the blondess from an ancient Persian Lord.

"Whenever my father returns from his travels," Francis continued, "he sighs with relief, saying, 'there are friendly spirits at home in Umbria'. I've heard others say as much. You know Ser Bernard de Quintavalle? Well, he's said the same thing to me many times."

All three looked about them, expecting some movement along the outer walls guarding Assisi.

"They must be here," Clara said, sniffing the air. "I can smell them."

The three of them laughed.

"Let's have some music," Agnes ordered.

"You are presumptious," warned her older sister.

"Everybody likes to hear Francis sing," the little girl smiled. "And I especially like to hear him talk. He has such a friendly voice. You said so yourself, Clara."

The other girl laughed. "Luckily, Francis you have no younger sister to spank."

"We have Angelo . . . . " Francis sighed, as he picked up his mandola. "Well, what shall it be, my ladies?"

The two sisters sat down on a large stone. Francis looked at them and smiled.

Clara caught his smile and read his thoughts. Shaking her head gently, "Agnes wants to do everything I do. If I have red shoes, she must have the same. If I have a new scarlet dress with yellow trimming, so must she."

"But I love the clothes you wear," Agnes told them. "Aren't you my mother too?"

Francis and Clara laughed. "I hardly ever see my mother," the little girl pouted. "Didn't you teach me my letters and reading and how to sew pretty things?"

"At this time," Francis laughed, "I bow to the request of you, my patrons," he bowed to the two girls. "And to you my audience," he bowed to the wide empty plains drifting towards Foligno. There was nothing there except the fields and some trees and the inevitable white stone road.

1. These wild ... spirits so free and wild
2. They scare ... children in their beds
3. So shout ... and cry 'away with it

1. Dance on ... trees-ride on plains
2. As they scatter on the roof
3. Bad spirit find another lair

1. They rustle leaves as would a child
2. Cock rafter shakes and glad its weed
3. Toss some salt and only a bit

1. And sprinkle the earth with rains
2. To stone and brick and solid stuff
3. He'll run and hide for he is scared

"All the spirits, the noble ones?" Clara almost whispered.

"All of them." Francis' voice was hushed. "King Arthur, Sir Lancelot and Galahad and all the good people of the story books. From real life Pons and Fiori and the thousands who died for the right to live like free men and each of those who added a little of his own goodness to make living a little more worthy. They did what was worthwhile. Where else could they come to eternal rest, than on these Umbrian plains?" He spread his arms wide. "Here they are about us."

The two girls looked up at Francis, hushed by the drama in his voice.

He looked down at them and smiled. The spell was broken. He strummed his mandola. "I'm in no mood for this," he thrust the instrument away from him and placed it at the girl's feet. Agnes snuggled her small feet close to its shiny sides.

"This," Francis motioned to it, "has been my good friend. Many times it has been a silent brother to me. Though I pluck his heartstrings with no gentleness."

"All people love you, Francis," Clara said quickly.

"I guess I love people," Francis joshed. He looked full into her eyes. "Do you?"

"Of course," she replied quickly. "Tell me, Francis, where is your troop off to. Tell me some things about this."

A trace of hurt crinkled his face. "You know that Innocent III has ordered the Emperor Frederick to keep some promises. He didn't want to, so soldiers have to be sent against him. Walter of Brienne is a good General so he wants to help. He has sent agents all over Italy to recruit an army to fight for the Pope. Lord Gentile is the Captain from Assisi. We leave this afternoon for Spoletto; tomorrow we meet some other troops in Rome. Then we go to Apulia."

"Is he bad, our Emperor?" queried Agnes.

"No, he's a good man and the people love him," Clara said. "He's a wise and learned man."

"Is the Pope a bad man?" persisted Agnes.

Francis shook his head. "He has many problems. He wants to build the Christian Church stronger. There are many people trying to break it down.'

"My father says that all the small people, the farmers, the serfs and the poor ones, are turning against God," Clara said.

"Perhaps they are disappointed," Francis smiled. "Christians seek God through their priests and I'm afraid they have found little help from them. Have you heard some of the ballads the troubadors sing? 'The priests are squeezed by the Bishops and the priests squeeze the poor.' With all its greed and stupidity the Christian Church is in poor health in this year of 1203."

"Is my cousin Rufino in your troop?" asked Agnes.

"Oh yes," laughed Francis, "I've called him Brother Silence, he seldom talks."

"But you," Clara looked at the boy. "After the battle, what?"

"Who knows," Francis shrugged his shoulders. "A soldier can live a moment, or a lifetime. Whatever is written in heaven," he smiled, "or in hell, by one of Satans' henchmen."

"Don't you want to be a great general?" asked Agnes.

"Few of them have died in bed," Clara added.

"I want to do something with my life." Francis straightened his back slowly. "I'd like to be a good soldier. People listen to me. I can be a Captain. Maybe one day I can be a great Prince."

Then bending closer to Clara he whispered, "My father wants it of me."

"You can be anything you want to be." Clara arose, unbending gracefully. She pointed to the city gate. She led, followed by her sister Agnes and Francis humbly in the rear as they went silently homeward.

The next day Francis joined his troop of soldiers and they rode towards Spoletto on the way to Rome.

Spoletto 1203

The troop of soldiers started their horses across the old wooden bridge over the waters of Clitumnus, on their way to Spoletto, in the heart of Italy. With hollow, trouping clatter the young men-at-arms followed Captain Gentile.

No one of them felt any impending danger of war. They were off to have a tryst with some political enemy. The cause wasn't too important. The adventure of fighting was.

Francis was no less enthusiastic than the others. About him the young lords of the land, each dressed in gleaming armour across chest and thighs, each pair of hands dancing with the tassels of wool dangling from their hands, each thin sword swinging with the rise and fall of the horses' backs.

They were young. They chattered like boys off on a picnic in the hills beyond Assisi. The horses slowed to a walk. Francis looked about him. Then he compared his dress with theirs. Here were the sons of Dukes and Barons and blooded families. He was like them. He was with them. Fighting their battles, he was *One* of them. The taste of life on his lips was sweet. The boy looked down at the fine tooled work on his breast plate. His eyes slid and squinted as the sun beamed against the armour on his thigh. He gently touched the buckle on his arm—a page in the army of Walter of Brienne. He could feel his mandola swinging across his back. The boy drew a tighter grip, then shook the thin lance he carried on his stirrup. The silken pennant on its tip flattened into the gentle wind.

Francis lost his thoughts in the sweet welter of day dreams. Someday he would be a great and gallant soldier. No, an officer and a general. Just like young Alexander, he would lead his troops in a wild charge which would split the enemy army in two. Then he would have all banners dip to him when he arrived somewhere, have all people kneel and pay him homage. He would be the great Francis—why not Francis the Great—leader of millions —a greater soldier than—

His horse, Beersheba, suddenly stumbled. Francis lost his balance and swung over in his saddle towards the river. Because he held the lance so tightly, it swung high, missing Parao, the Duke's son, then made a graceful trajectory as he let it go, into the river. It hardly rippled as it plunged to the bottom of the Clitumnus, the holy river.

This threw the troop into a momentary confusion. Shouts, curses and a clattering sudden quiet. As if an unknown giant had muffled them all with a blanket as large as the horizon.

Not for long. "What's the matter with you?" laughed Rufino Offreduccio. "Have you forgotten how to ride?" He was lean and hard.

"Where did you expect him to learn?" derided Parao, the Duke's son, "riding on a bale of silk in his father's store?" Francis looked at him. Even in prison he always looked well fed. His small round nose matched his face and body.

"And where did you learn the jingle of spurs, in your father's till?" a voice shouted.

"Ho there, young troubador, you ride a mandola better than yonder steed," another voice shouted.

"He must have something on his mind," Parao's voice chided. Francis looked at him indulgently.

"Well, I did have something on my mind," Francis retorted quickly. He offered them bait to change the subject.

"Must have been a woman," countered Parao. "The dear boy," he mimicked, "hasn't even slept with a wench yet. Say, Francis, whom did you rape now—in your dreams, of course?"

The others thought this funny.

Francis' face became flushed under these ribald attacks. Beersheba, his horse, sensed something wrong. She whinnied aloud.

This brought a fresh gale of laughter and abuse on him and his mount.

"See," Parao shouted above the clatter. "A man's best friend is his horse." He leaned over and shouted into the animal's ear. "Come, tell us, who was the pretty maiden Francis was with yesterday?" The horse's ear tickled. So he wiggled it. "Speak up, Sir Horse," the boy commanded. The horse whinnied again.

This brought on more laughter. Francis began to feel very warm. The young men-at-war were in a rare mood and the boy knew he was to be a scapegoat for their horseplay.

"I'm as good a stud horse as any of you," he suddenly shouted, then laughed at Parao. "I need no ducal crown in a ladies' boudoir."

"Ho, Parao," one of the young bloods cried out, "he has you there. "No," he started to laugh, "no ducal crown in a boudoir"—he reeled off in a peal of explosive mirth. The others joined this new sally.

"I'm a better man than you any day, Francis," Parao looked at Francis. "Even if you can sing pretty songs to the ladies. Action, my boy, action is better than a day of plucking on your strings."

"You bray like a horse, Parao," Rufino told him. "You can't pluck those strings like our Francis can."

"Tell you what," interrupted Paulus, "as the only scholar among you—"

"He's read six books all his life and he's a scholar," Rufino broke in.

"As the *only* scholar in this group of illiterates," went on Paulus, "let us emulate that worthy warrior of fame and fancy, King Arthur. Let us have a contest."

"A contest," the word was tossed about on the lance tips. "The long lance," someone shouted. "Not fair," a voice countered. "Francis is half the weight of Parao."

"Hold on," Paulus shouted. Captain Gentile's horse was pushing through the melee. "What goes on here," the Captain said. "You act like a rabble of peasants, not soldiers. We must be in Spoletto tonight. What are you lads up to? Oh, it's you Francis. What new mischief are you up to now?" he asked the boy kindly.

Ser Gentile was the Captain of the troop and well knew the whims and crude horseplay of these young men of the gentry. He knew most of them were spoiled boys whose only gift to life was pleasure. Even war was a dressed-up game for them. As young as they were, most of them, with lots of money and indifferent morals, had already gulped the fleshy wines of night. There was no morality tempered with any logic among them. Gentile knew all this, but he was first a soldier. He had heard that some of these boys had raped their own sisters or the sisters of their friends and boasted about themselves. Yet they fought each other to the death on a question of who wore a more brocaded coat. He shook his head and blessed his stars that he had no sons. These were wild, ruthless years for any youngster to grow up.

"We want a contest," Paulus told the Captain.

"All right, boys, all right," he soothed them.

Just like petting and calming a gamecock. It will gurgle contentedly on your fist. Then kill another bird a half a minute with its sharp claws. These boys with pennants and shiny armour, each one carried a murderous weapon hidden under his baldrick.

"Let's get on to Spoletto," the Captain ordered. "What kind of a contest?" he asked.

"We'll decide on the way to Spoletto," Paulus told him.

The officer shrugged his shoulders in resignation, turned his horse through the crowd, and headed towards the head of the troop. There he paused, raising his arm, pointing forward with his forefinger. As he thrust his arm forward, his horse moved. The other horses began to follow.

The excitement of the last few minutes had given the troop an outlet for their energies. Now they rode in silence. Francis looked about him as they walked their horses down the Flaminion Way.

The deep wide shadows were already spreading on the plains when the troop rode noisily into Spoletto.

Behind them, there was no single ripple where Francis' lance was buried at the bottom of the Clitumnus River.

The young knights were teamed off to billet at the houses of the friends of Captain Gentile. Paulus asked that he, together with Parao, Francis and Rufino, be sent to his uncle, Count Trescia.

As they came clattering into the stone courtyard, they were greeted by the Count and his wife, Lady Trescia. Servants led their horses away and their host brought them into the huge stone house.

"I suppose you lads are hungry after your long ride?" she asked.

"What a question to ask," roared her husband. "Of course these young soldiers are hungry. Aren't soldiers always hungry? They always love good meat." He laughed loudly at his own humor. The boys and Lady Trescia joined in the general laughter.

The Count clapped his hands shouting "Falco, Falco. Where is that thieving dog? He eats my good food, but does nothing. I'll whip the dog, Falco," he roared. The huge stone room caught the word and tossed it around each corner.

A short, thick man with light hair, hurried into the room. He was quickly pushing a fist through the sleeve of his coat.

"Ay, master," he nodded his head.

Francis looked at the man's face and saw tight lips bound together by sullen, hating eyes. "Ay, master." The voice was humble.

"Get some food and victuals," he ordered. "And get them a few bottles of the best. For all of us."

"You and the Lady have had your dinner?" the man started to ask.

"Of course, we've had our dinner, you lout. Can't we eat again?" He picked a small mace which hung on the wall near him, and with one motion threw it at the man. Falco, evidently from long experience, unhurriedly stepped out of its lethal path. The iron mace, struck the floor, flashed a track of sparks and chipped a corner of a stone flagging as it bounded like an angry snake.

"Ay, master," Falco nodded his head. "Right away, as you say."

"He was as deft as a swordsman," Paulus marveled. "That mace had Sister Death on its tail."

"Hurt him," the Count poo-poo'd, "he can dodge a short lance. I wish it were the old times when we could have slaves again." He sighed audibly.

"If I remember, one couldn't kill a slave in the old days." Parao offered.

"We brought him back with us from Germany," Lady Trescia told them. "He was a feudal slave on my father's estate. He used to be my watchdog."

"To keep your lovers away," retorted the Count. "But he didn't keep me away."

"My uncle traveled through the north countries, Germany and Spain for trade," Paulus explained to his friends.

"My father traveled up that way, too," Francis volunteered. "You may know him, Pietro Bernardone."

"That old horse thief—your father? Of course I know him well," the older man replied. "A good hard business man, your father, No nonsense. A shrewd good bargainer. Aren't we all? As a matter of fact, it was he that told me about Hilda—my wife. Yes, come to think of it, I owe him a great favor. So you're Pietro's boy?" He struck the boy a resounding slap on the back. "It's a small world. You may consider everything in this house as yours. To use with discretion." He lowered his voice intimately.

Lady Trescia moved over to Francis and put her arm around his shoulders, drawing him closer. His shoulder probed against her breast.

"Your father is a lusty man," she told Francis. "Have you a sister? No? Very well, you can consider me as your big sister. How is that?" she asked Francis.

He smiled at her—his slow, searching smile.

Paulus kept his voice for Lady Trescia and Francis to hear. "I'm afraid Tante Trescia, he needs something more worldly than a big sister."

Francis flushed. The woman glanced at the boy's face. Her encircling arm drew him closer. It seemed to add an invitation for a promise.

They could hear the clatter and movement of the servants in the adjoining room. A few minutes later, Falco appeared, waiting. The Lady asked kindly, "Is all ready, Falco?"

"We have done well, my lady. All is ready."

"That is good, my Falco," she said. He bowed his head, then disappeared into the stone doorway.

"See what a little discipline can do," the Count decided. "The rabble always need the whip on the back to keep them alive."

"It's good for their eternal souls," Parao agreed. "My father taught me how to use the new cat whip."

"Ay, I've heard of it," the Count said. "I'd like to get one some day."

"You can make one very easily," the Duke's son told him. "It is not one whip. It is five of them. On the end of each one is twined in a bit of fine chain. Then we pad the center."

"Oh, that's why it is called the cat's foot. The soft part for the foot and the five claws," the Count said.

"Doesn't it cut the skin?" Francis asked slowly.

"Cut the skin?" laughed Parao. "Of course. But it doesn't leave blistered welts like a leather whip. We lost a valuable woman on my father's estate once. We used the rawhide whip and her back got blistered and it became all blue and red. She died."

"What did she do?" asked Paulus.

"Do? She accused my father of being the father of the whelp she was carrying in her stomach," Parao countered indignantly. "Of course, he was." Parao replied. "But she had no right to tell it to the Duke's face. We could have handled the matter more discreetly."

"How?" Francis asked innocently.

"Why, by marrying her off to one of the farm peasants. They could have lived at peace for the rest of their lives like two happy satisfied animals. These people *are* animals, aren't they?" He turned to his listeners expecting confirmation.

"What did the bitch threaten?" Paulus asked.

"She wanted to go to the Bishop with her story. Because she didn't want her bastard to be born unbaptized and nameless. Can you stomach such nerve?" Parao asked.

"Bishop Guido is a kindly old man," Francis suggested. "And only the Bishop can baptize a fatherless child."

"A kindly old dodo, you mean," Parao replied. "He wouldn't dare lift one jeweled finger against anyone—least of all my father. He loves to nurse his fat belly and his fine wines too much to risk it for some peasant woman."

"He gets his job from Rome," Paulus said slowly. "Men like your father rule Rome."

"Now, now boys, let's not have any excitement before a meal," Count

Trescia said as he led Parao towards the dining hall. "Bad for your liver and makes a lot of gas. Bad for your liver and, of course, worse for your neighbor," he laughed loudly, clapping Parao on the back. "Come boys, let's fall to and eat a hearty supper. Like good hungry knights engaged in God's work."

Francis looked at the man. As always his eyes searched a face for small details which told him the content of the man. He saw the red, tufted beard in a round flat face. Thin lips stretched across a wide mouth. Eyes which held as much warmth as agate grey balls. There was no kindness there, only brutal cruelty. He was a ruler in the land. Those not his equal were his slaves.

They trooped into the dining room. Francis moved to lay aside his mandola.

Lady Trescia put her hand on his shoulder. "Take it with you. Won't you sing for us later?"

"Very glad to, my lady," Francis replied.

"He doesn't have to be coaxed," Parao enjoined.

"Singing songs is wine for his blood," Paulus said fondly. "He kept us amused for a whole year while we rotted away in Perugia's best prison."

"It was unlucky for the four of you to get captured in that battle between Assisi and Perugia," the Count said.

"Parao was wounded," Paulus went on, "so Francis had to go looking for him. And I had to find Francis. He owed me fifty pieces of silver—he'll never learn to gamble. Hasn't the instinct. I found him all right. Trying to carry Parao. Look at the size of him."

They were strolling into the dining hall and seating themselves on one side of a long oak table piled high with enough food for twenty people.

"Parao is just about twice the size of Francis," the Count Trescia said eyeing the boys.

"Then they found me," Rufino volunteered. "With a banged-in skull."

Francis sat near Lady Trescia. As he sat down, her broad palm very gently caressed his thigh. "So the four of you spent a year in Perugia?" The servants very quickly brought in the steaming broth, which all the diners sipped noisily. Warmed mutton, cold roasted chickens and small birds were piled high on silver platters. Fruits, grapes, pomegranates, figs and sweetmeats were in abundance on the table.

Each one used his own jeweled knife; plucked from the scabbard at his hip, to spear each chunk of meat or a whole bird. One would hold a chicken's leg in the teeth and tear the rest away or use the knife to file the excess.

Everyone ate noisily, talking to each other.

Suddenly Count Trescia stood up. "A little gas," he laughed, as there was a long fluttering report.

"No, uncle," replied Paulus, "you've laced your boot too tightly."

"What, what?" the older man spluttered, then reeled off in laughter. They all joined. A little later, "This is the life," he said philosophically. "Good friends, hearty laughter and fine wine." He lifted his cup of fine tooled silver made by a moslem craftsman.

"I drink to you, good knights, who go out and fight for God and the Holy Church." He raised the cup quickly. Some of the red wine cascaded down his beard and on to the table. "Not the drinker I used to be," he grunted. He looked at his wife. "Guess I'm getting too old for drinking and loving." He belched loudly. "My wife knows that. Probably got herself a lover somewhere."

Francis saw Lady Trescia smile knowingly. "My German mother had four lovers. Yet, she was a good woman and a fine wife for my father."

"Fine lady, your revered mother, fine lady," the Count agreed nodding his head. "I could tell a story or two about her and Pietro Bernardone. Oh, yes," he nodded wisely.

"My father?" queried Francis.

"Your father was no gilded olive, my boy. He knew his way about in a lady's boudoir. Maybe no better or worse than the rest of us. Why should you be vexed?" the older man asked.

"Francis is a romantic," Paulus said. "He lives in his own world of images. You should listen to his songs. They spin their own web of fantasy."

"I still say," Parao countered, "he's yet to have a woman."

"How do you know?" Rufino asked suddenly.

"Ah, the silent one has spoken," Parao countered. "This is Rufino, Francis has christened the Silent One. Says nothing, sees all. He can only see the good in his friend Francis Bernardone."

"How many friends can *you* number?" Rufino asked quietly.

"What do you men think of the chance for success for the next Crusade," Lady Trescia asked the table.

"This makes the fifth one," Paulus said. "Our Christian armies have done little good, except for trade. Four times we've beaten the Saracens' walls and four times we've left the bones of our nobility and Christian soldiers to rot in the desert sands.

"That's what Coeur de Lion and a dozen kings have said," Paulus added. "For almost two hunded years we've stormed Acre and Jerusalem and been beaten. Perhaps we are not in the right."

"This is a foul statement," Parao shouted, standing up. "We fight for our Holy Church and the birthplace of our Saviour. Isn't that enough to die a thousand fold?" He banged the heavy table with his dagger butt. "I would fight to the last drop of my blood against those Saracen dogs of the Soldan."

"Are you accusing me of being a bad Christian?" Paulus stood up from his chair, pounding the table with his fist.

"If you are against the Crusade, you are for the Saracens," accused Parao.

Each started to move towards the other, with daggers in their fists. Rufino caught Parao about the shoulders as Trescia held Paulus in a powerful grip.

"Sit down, you hot-headed fools," the older man shouted at them. "Sit down," he commanded Parao. "Let's get on with our meal. There's no purpose in killing each other. There are better enemies to kill."

The table was silent as they continued eating and each one was trapped with his own thoughts. Count Trescia was drinking deeply and his cup was filled constantly by the servant near him. Finally, he threw his half filled cup on the table, the wine dancing between the plates. He reached for the flagon of wine. The servant bent over to set the cup. With a powerful arm he flung the man backwards. "Get out of here," he grumbled. He was off balance and sat down on the floor. "He's drunk." The Count pointed to the servant.

He picked up the flagon of wine and drank from it, spilling most of it on himself. Reaching, he then set it away from himself on the table, with a loud thump.

"Listen here, you young whelps," the Count's voice was thick. "We sent preachers through all the lands to talk about a holy war. The war for Jesus, Our Lord. We gotta fight these unbaptised Saracens. Save them from the unholy fires of Hell. Birthplace of Jesus belongs to us. The heathens can reach Him—but we can't. Must fight them—must fight." He stood up. His chair walloped the floor. "I'm a little bit drunk."

One of the boys rose to help him. "Salright," he assured him. "Stay here and keep the Countess entertained." He winked knowingly, screwing his lips into a drunken leer. "You are nice boys. Take care of the lady. You know, knights of old . . . and so bold . . . help a lady in distress." He winked again, as his servant walked by his side. He threw his arms around the man's neck. They moved out of the room with uneven steps like a four-footed monster, with two heads.

"How about some songs," Lady Trescia smiled to Francis.

"Does Uncle Trescia go through this all the time, with company around?" asked Paulus.

"Often enough," she replied. "I'm used to it now. He did get angry because I had a little girl."

"Not his child?" Parao offered.

"Of course not," she added. "I'm fertile as the rich earth. Any seed will find life. The Count was perturbed because the man was one of our farmers, not someone of the blood. My husband is a great believer in the nobility of the race."

Francis looked at the woman. She was talking about her morals as if she were discussing a new brooch for her hair. He was not amazed nor shamed by such disclosures. He'd heard of many such incidents. There was little moral pride among women of the "blood." Everyone clothed their indiscretions in a cloak of justification.

She was a deep-chested, broad-hipped woman, with a heavy mass of honey-blond hair, roped high on her big head Her eyes were wide set between two flat cheekbones. Lady Trescia was a big woman, among many short ones in Italy. Her eyes rested softly on Francis' fingers as he limbered the strings of his mandola.

His voice began to hum a lilting melody which was remote and sad. The others were quiet, ready to listen.

He got up from his seat and strolled around to the front of the table, facing her and his three friends. He didn't look at them, his eyes were lost in the haze of composition and a search for words.

Francis had a good voice and used it. It was a voice which was at once tender and soothing. His friends and Lady Trescia listened carefully, each one held by the quality of charm in the boy. Some of the servants in far-off corners of the house were held quietly by the songs.

Lady Trescia looked at Francis and was surprised how young his face was, with the flat cheekbones and the golden hair. The eyes were set wide across a broad forehead. The mouth and chin to a slow point. It surprised her, as many others, that such a voice, with such fullness and quality could pour from this boy.

Then Francis sang this song, looking directly at the Lady Trescia:

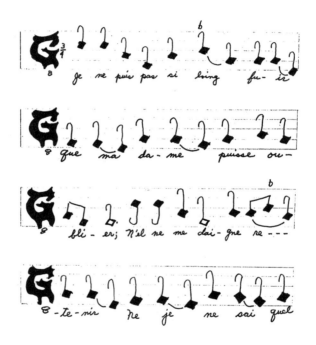

("I cannot flee so far that I can forget my lady. She will not deign to keep me and I do not know where to go . . .")

("... My heart and my desire and misfortunes and loving too much and what I cannot conceal from her have killed me, so that I can suffer no more.")

There was a compelling and clutching force in the voice which said to all people, "Listen to me," and people stopped what they were doing and listened. Each one found an unexpected peace in the lilting words; the worldly one, the wise, and the unbeliever.

Francis stopped singing. The halls caught the end fragments of his song and gently tossed them across the stone walls, cherishing each tiny breath. Then there was complete silence. Each one was lost in the bounty of his own thoughts. Through each mind paraded a score of tiny events long lost in the woods of daily living. Tiny events which are fondly stored away. Only on rare occasions are they brought forth like jewels, to be seen, then stored away again.

This quality of restoration, of giving light to memories, hidden deeply in the mind, this was the substance in his voice.

"Paulus," Francis called softly. "Paulus," he repeated. The other was spun from the threads of his reverie.

"Yes Francis," he answered.

"Have you forgotten? What about the contest?"

"Oh yes, the contest," was the reply. "Don't mind now. Some other time. Some other day."

"What contest," Lady Trescia asked with interest.

"Maybe you can suggest something, Tante Trescia," Paulus explained suddenly. He repeated some of the details of that afternoon on the wooden bridge near the Clitumnus. He repeated with some relish, "Francis doesn't need a ducal crown in a lady's boudoir."

She laughed aloud. "I didn't know Francis had *that* kind of humor. Excellent."

She looked at Francis. Her eyes slid over his body and rested on his fingers across the strings of the mandola which slept in his arms. "One can never tell," she mused softly.

"And you Parao, you are a Duke's son, and I presume, fear no challenge."

"No, my lady," Parao stood up and inclined his head courteously. "What is your favor?"

"You can be assured dear Tante," Paulus told her, "we are gentlemen of discretion."

"Very well," she smiled to the boys. "I will be both monitor and the tester. How can we find out who is the better lover . . . except by finding out?" She stood up smiling. "By now my husband is asleep in his quarters. Give me some time to prepare for bed." She chucked Parao under the chin with her fist. "Which will be the first to reach the altar?"

"We'll toss a coin," Paulus told her. "Would you mind an audience . . . shall we say observers . . . dear Tante?"

"Of course I'd mind," she retorted.

"But as judges, we'd have to see for ourselves," he argued smiling. "It's our Divine Right."

"Very well, the judges may remain hidden from sight behind the silken wall covering of my boudoir." She started to walk away from them, then turned. "I shall see you soon," she looked full into Francis' eyes.

After she left, Rufino remarked succinctly, "What ungoverned heathens we are. It reminds me of the Roman soldiers gambling for the clothing of Jesus."

"Don't be sacrilegious," Paulus warned. "This is a contest between two gentlemen. Don't warp in the Holy Church at a time like this." He shuddered as he made the sign of the cross.

"Look who has become holy," Parao snickered. "Do I have to remind you about those two servant wenches in Spello?"

Rufino was silent. "What say you, Francis?" Parao asked. "Is it a coin?" The other nodded his head silently.

Francis dug one from his pocket. "What is your pleasure, Parao?" as he tossed the coin above the table.

"Tails," the Duke's son cried.

Rufino glanced over at Francis and saw that he was not happy. A gloomy suspicion tipped his mind. Preposterous. Francis had lived the wild and carefree life of all boys in the hill cities. He must have known the taste of flesh . . . the others had long ago. Was it possible that Francis had not?

Despite his boasting, his singing and the fine poetry of his songs, Rufino wondered if it could be possible that Francis at twenty-two had never had a woman! He suddenly pitied him. With the same thought, regarded Francis in wonderful luck. That his first journey to woman's flesh would be with an experienced one like Lady Trescia.

The coin bounded on the table, slid on end a short distance and rested wearily against a silver wine cup. In later years, Francis remembered this incident clearly. The sight of this coin waiting to turn. This is something he told no one, but kept it hidden in his own mind. That coin fell and led to a series of events which altered his plans, and his life. It came up heads!

Francis nodded his head and reached for his mandola. Rufino walked over to him and took it from him.

"I think the lady does not have need for this," he told him kindly, smiling to his friend. Rufino saw in his face something he had never seen before. A fear—perhaps? As if he were afraid of disillusion fringed with the glassiness in his eyes telling of a boy's passion. He patted Francis on the shoulder, as they walked away together.

"Just take your time," he whispered to Francis. "You have lots of time."

Rufino walked back to the others. Francis stepped into Lady Trescia's bedroom. He stood a moment in the room, hesitating. The room was large and filled with long gloomy shadows. Near the bed hung a pitch fire ball, dipped with incense, hung in a brazier. It flung its glow of light across the woman's white naked body.

"Come here, I'm over here," she spoke from the huge bed. He came closer. "Oh, it's you Francis," she smiled. "Come here, sit by my side. I'm glad it was you . . . the first one." She smiled again. "Take your things off over there," she pointed to the couch which stood near the bed.

As Francis moved away he saw the rustle of the wall covering near the bed. He knew Rufino, Paulus, and Parao stood there. He could hear the gentle tear of the knife slitting an opening in the silk. He could feel his heart beat and trip itself merrily. Once or twice before had he felt like this. Once when the hour approached the battle between Assisi and Perugia. Another time when he plunged down the snowy slope of Assisi. Not fear, but apprehensive waiting for the next event.

Count Trescia had awakened and stood behind the silk curtain watching them. "Hey," he suddenly exclaimed to the boys, "I want no 'jewboy' laying with my wife." He made a half motion towards the curtain.

"It's a contest," Paulus soothed his uncle. "It's a contest, to see who is the best lover."

The older man half asleep, half in a drunken stupor, was content to watch through the slit in the curtain.

"Lie down here alongside me, you dear boy," Countess Trescia said softly. He did as he was told. She kissed him full on the lips, the tip of her tongue darting quickly inside his mouth. She held him in her arms. He pulled his head away suddenly. She laughed.

"A Saracen Emir taught me that," she told him. "Don't you like it?"

Francis could smell the rich scents around her hair and face. These were rare perfumes from oriental lands.

"The devil's brother," Paulus exclaimed behind the curtain, "What the hell is he doing?"

The three boys crowded to the slit opening, shouldering aside Count Trescia.

Francis had sprung from the bed and ran to the open window. There he retched in horrible spasms. Lady Trescia rose from the bed and walked over to the boy. She tried to soothe him. The night air chilled her so she returned to the bed. She waited.

With a sudden gasping cry, Francis ran over to the couch, crumbled his clothing into his arms, without a backward glance, ran from the room.

For a minute the three boys became entangled in the wall curtain. They emerged hurriedly.

"I'll go after him," Rufino said, "I'll get him back."

"If you do, I'll bash his brains in," cried out Paulus. "The shame of my family honor. That low . . . boasting fool. Imagine leaving my Tante Trescia's bed like this . . ."

"You stay here and cool off," Rufino said slowly. "Family shame or not. You know Francis. Something must have happened."

"You go take care of my Tante," Paulus told Parao. "It isn't decent to leave her like this. You prove yourself a worthy knight of Assisi."

The young hopeful, thus encouraged, hastened to obey.

"If I ever see Francis again," vowed Paulus, "I'll kill him."

"Cool off," warned Rufino as he left the room.

"I always said he was a phonus pollutus," said Parao loud enough for everyone to hear.

Rufino found Francis sitting in a niche on the lower floor. He was partially dressed. There was such dejection about him as if all his energy was drained. Once again he was stung with pity for his friend. At last he had an opportunity to repay his kindness in the prison of Perugia. It was there when he, Rufino was depressed, friendless and his spirits had reached low ebb. Then Francis was the good Samaritan, soothing, healing, and joking.

Now Rufino could, in truth, repay that debt. He put his arm across the shoulders of Francis.

"What is it, my friend," he asked kindly. "Tell me, I'm your friend."

"The shame," Francis cried out bitterly. "My manhood is shamed forever. What will the men of the troop think. How they'll laugh at me. Parao will see to that."

"What happened," persisted Rufino. "You were doing very well. Did you have a sick stomach? That's it. We'll go back and say that."

"No, no," Francis shook his head slowly.

"That was your first," Rufino told him quietly.

Francis nodded his head. "I've always hated dark, fishy odors. They make me sick."

"Oh, so that was it," Rufino replied. "She will use the most costly perfumes about her head." He looked around him with a trace of astonishment on his face. "Look you, these women are surrounded by all the wealth of the Indies, yet forget or hate to wash their privy parts."

"You can see why I cannot return," Francis said slowly. "A soldier in the army of knights, tell a woman *that?*"

Rufino told him, "There is no purgatory worse than a stinking woman's flesh. Paulus won't listen. He'll kill you. I think he's given you time to get away."

He waited until Francis got into his clothes and spoke while he dressed. "Look around you, this castle once belonged to a rich baron, who said quite frankly and openly that he did not believe in the Holy Wafer as being the Body of Jesus. You know what Count Trescia did? He got the Inquisition to interrogate the baron and make him confess to his religious beliefs. When a man is on the rack he will say anything and it will be used against him. So now, the Count owns this castle."

"And the same Count," Francis' voice was wry with distaste, "who was willing to watch his own wife be had by some young . . . lout, like myself."

Rufino helped his friend get mounted on his horse. He waved farewell to him as Francis slowly walked his horse towards the road back towards Assisi. Francis suddenly remembered that he had left his fine suit of armor near the bedroom. He wondered what his father would say about the loss of this expensive suit.

Rufino called to him, "Wait a minute," and ran into the house and returned with Francis' mandola. He made a two-hand toss to Francis who caught it gingerly, hugged it a moment and draped it around his neck.

When Francis left Rufino, the reins hung loosely from his hands. Beersheba walked daintily and gingerly over the heavy cobbled streets. He let the animal have its own head because he cared little where he went. The boy was indifferent to his surroundings. He felt as if a purple blanket was draped over his spirit and, like a blotter, draining its pith. He again remembered that he had left his armor at the house. There would be little need for them now.

Then he was relieved to find his mandola riding across his shoulders. Turning his arm he saw that the page boy buckle of Walter of Brienne's army was still there. He stifled a desire to tear it off. His fingers touched the sheathed dagger at his side, from habit. People did not venture alone into the streets after dark unarmed. There were too many footpads anxious to relieve one so foolhardy of purse or clothing.

The dark curving streets of Spoletto were dank from their deep narrowness with houses closely packed like rookeries. Suddenly he felt a hand clutching at his stirrup.

"Food, master," a voice pleaded. "A coin to buy some food." Beersheba got dancing feet in her sudden fright. Francis looked down and saw a bony face in the poorly lit street. The rest of the person was lost.

"Get away from that stirrup," the boy ordered. The man held on.

"Please, master, a coin for the poor. I haven't eaten for two days." It was dark and Francis was suddenly afraid. He pulled his foot out of the stirrup and promptly pushed it into the man's face. The man and the face disappeared into the night. Beersheba continued on her stiff-legged way, unconcerned with the problems of men.[9]

The mare walked slowly, the steady yet irregular chopping of her hoofs filled the night with unwanted sound. In the darkness the houses above him seemed to converge over the boy and his horse. Francis felt as if he were being choked.

To find some measure of relief, he looked towards the sky above the Umbrian plains. The moon was hiding behind a gentle fluff and the sky was sprinkled with lights. Francis knew it was common knowledge that

[9]This act plagued him for the rest of his days. It was his first thoughtless and no less vicious bit of violence. He never forgot it.

those lights were holes in the heavens. He remembered that he with many others had laughed at a man in Assisi who thought those lights were separate worlds. That people like themselves could be living there. The man was so derided that he had to leave Assisi. The Bishop called him a fool and a heretic!

Francis was brought back quickly; he heard the sound of voices. As Beersheba turned a bend of the street, they came to an open square fronting on a large, well-lit house.

Each window hung like a patch breaking the dark night. He could hear the moving sound of revelry; laughter of women sprinkled with some music. He was curious, so he drew his horse closer to the compound wall to look inside the windows. The rooms were filled with people. Some girls were dancing in the middle of the floor with sinuous movements.

Beersheba whinnied.

A few minutes later two young couples spilled out of the doorway. They spied the horse and the rider. The mandola caught their interest.

"A troubador," one of the girls shouted. "Hail the troubador," the others chorused this. They bowed in mock courtesy repeating, "Hail the troubador," and surrounded his horse demanding a song. Francis was in no mood to sing.

"Come ahead," one of the boys coaxed him. "A knight of chivalry can't refuse a lady's request."

Francis smiled. "Very well, what shall it be? Something gay or something sad?"

"There is enough gaiety," one of the boys pointed with this thumb to the house. "Out here under the sky—the night *is* sad."

Francis ran his fingers over the strings, humming to himself. Then in a low, sweet voice he sang to them. They felt this was personal, for them alone.

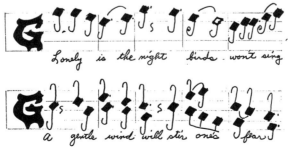

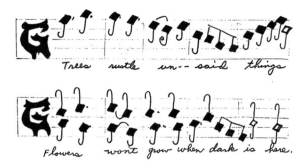

He kept on humming a tune without any words. The four young people were held, silently, about the horse. The boys plucked at Francis' legs.

"Come inside, good troubador. Come with us inside our house. There are many friends."

Francis started to refuse. One of the boys opened the front door and started to lead the horse and the rider in the house.

Francis laughingly consented, got off the horse and was himself led inside.

The first sight which caught Francis' eye was that of three girls, completely nude, dancing with suggestive gyrations in the middle of the floor. He observed that their young breasts shook like mounds of soft white jelly as they moved. With a wry smile he noticed how large and deep their navels holed into their flat stomachs.

All about him on the floor, the tables, the sofas were men and women. Some were eating, drinking wine and spirits. Others performing acts which belonged in a bedroom, in total disregard of their company. Hardly anyone was paying attention to the three dancing girls. All but one. A man seated in a heavy carved oak chair with a small canopy above it.

"Who is that man?" Francis asked one of the boys, pointing with his free elbow.

"That is our host," replied the other. "He is a very great man. Generous, too. Gives lots of parties."

"What is his name? Who is he?" persisted Francis.

"That's the Baron. Tomorrow he will go to Rome and there become a Cardinal. Pope Innocent the Third has summoned him to his side. The giver of the Bulls needs help."

"He will become a Cardinal?" queried Francis. He looked at the man whose head was cupped in the palm of his right hand, his gaze was fixed on the movements of the three nude girls.

"Why not," one of the boys volunteered. "It cost him 10,000 pieces of silver. Of course, the Baron will assure you it is a contribution against the Saracens."

"My brother will also inform you," the other boy said, "that the money is going back in the same direction from which it came."

"How do you know so much about this man?" asked Francis.

The boys laughed, their girl companions joined them. "They are that man's twins," one of the girls said, pointing to the future cardinal. Francis nodded.

"That money is loot from the Fourth crusade. My father's father came home with a shipload of gold and precious stones."

"Very profitable crusade, I'd say, indeed," said one of the twins.

"My name is Francis Bernardone," he introduced himself with a bow. "Late of Assisi," was added solemnly.

"This is Jacque," one boy said, "and I am Toreo. Welcome to our brave home, Ser Bernardone. It is a bit upset now, but it will be cleared by cock crow."

The three boys bowed to each other ceremoniously.

"Won't you come over here and meet the Cardinal?" said Toreo. "Ever meet one before?" Francis shook his head. "He's a good fellow despite his faults," the other added.

The twins led Francis across the middle of the floor, paying little heed to the dancers. As they walked by, Jacque slapped one of the girls on her bare rump. "That's for yesterday," he hissed at her. The girl smiled and continued her dancing.

When Francis approached the Baron, he saw he was a heavy man with thick blond hair. He wore puffed sleeves and the cloth was woven with gold and purple threads. There were several jeweled rings on his fingers. He wore a small well-trimmed beard which curled in sleepy, curled ringlets.

When one of the boys introduced Francis, the older man rose from his chair and approached him. He felt his fingers crushed in a powerful handshake. Yet, Francis was surprised by the gentle culture in the man's voice.

"Are you finding pleasure, Francis the Troubador?" the man asked. "Food? Drink? Perhaps a girl or two? Ah, I see you wear the insignia of Walter of Brienne. Fine thing you young knights are doing. Fine thing. Ah, I wish I were young and supple again. Remember the way of Jesus" he said sententiously, "He was a happy man. Remember how He turned water into wine. Miracles are the spice of life." He laughed, then sat down. The interview was at an end. As he walked away, Francis saw that the man had again fixed a pleasurable gaze upon the nude dancing girls.

As they walked across the floor, one of the twins, Francis wasn't sure which one, pinched the breast of one of the girls. She squealed in mock terror.

The two girls whom Francis had met outside the house came over.

"Get him some food," Toreo told one of them. "By the way, do you know our sisters, Genia and Balda?" The two girls curtsied.

"What is your pleasure?" Genia, who was the older one asked.

"I'll leave it entirely up to you, dear lady," Francis smiled at her. She turned to the huge table which still groaned under its weight of food.

Toreo bent over and whispered into Francis' ear, "Genia likes you. Sing her a song or two and you can go upstairs with her—and you can be alone," he confided.

Francis shook his head.

"Oh, don't fear," the twin told him. "My father told me stories about the harem women of the Saracen lords. You know," he whispered carefully, "my father spent a month as the guest of one of them. He had the free use of a dozen Oriental girls. Imagine."

Francis stared about him. His eye for details in people's faces again searched those near him. The saliva dribbling from the mouth of a drunken sleeper, a woman near him in a drunken stupor trying to replace one of her breasts into her bodice, the glazed eyes of a young boy whose face was deep on the naked breasts of a much older woman. He saw enough food laying wasted on the floor to feed many families.

Suddenly, he felt restless and disturbed. This life, these parties he had seen before. They were nothing new in his experience. He had accepted them as normal. Now, he wasn't sure.

The twins moved towards some other guests. In a quick decision Francis decided to leave. He arose and hurried to the door. Outside, he mounted his horse.

"Come back here, Francis, the Troubador," he heard Genia's voice. He turned in the saddle and saw her in the doorway with a plate of food in her hand.

Francis waved to her and continued riding.

"You dirty lout," her voice rose. "How dare you leave this way!" She continued shouting, but Francis continued on his way. He was no longer concerned with her or her family.

He looked up at the skies, to help him guide his course back to Assisi.

Francis wasn't sure where he would spend the night. It would certainly not be at the home of the Cardinal-to-be. He headed Beersheba towards the next large city, Trevi.

Far off ahead in the moonlit night, he could see the dark peak of Montefalco, butting shadows into the sky. Farther on to the right he could see Mont Subasio and his mighty brothers guarding the approaches to Assisi.

He had been riding a short while, his eyes vainly searching for a light or a house where he could ask for lodging. His eyes felt raw and pained him. It had been a long and eventful day and he was drowsy.

Off to the left of his trail, he detected a faint light in the distance. He jogged Beersheba into a faster walk. Upon approaching, he saw there was a light in the barn. Someone was milking a cow there. Francis judged it was nearly midnight.

"Who rides there?" a voice alive with vigor demanded. "For a friend, peace. For a foe, I have a stout cudgel. Speak up."

"I desire a night's lodging," Francis replied. "I am neither foe nor perhaps, friend."

"Well spoken, who ever you are. Come in. The door is on this side."

Inside Francis saw a cow being milked industriously. The barn was lit by some pitch beginning to smolder in an earthenware bowl. It cast an acrid odor into the sweet hay smell of the barn. The cow blocked his vision of the man. He approached closer to the cow.

"I can see you are no thief," the man said.

"How do you know?" asked Francis. "You haven't seen my face."

"Well, I can see your hose and your shoes," laughed the man. "That little sense I have. Anyway it is good thinking to praise a man who may want to rob you. It puts him in a better humor and he may decide you are a good fellow. I'll be finished in a moment. Whew! I was never cut out to be a farmer." The milking ceased and the man stood up.

Francis could not hide the look of surprise on his face.

The man laughed, "I always surprise people . . . the first time." Francis saw a huge man. He towered over the boy. His shoulders were huge. The man wore the clothes of an ordinary peasant farmer. But his head was shaved neatly, leaving a belt of hair around his head.

"Surprised?" the man smiled.

"Yes," replied Francis. "The shaved head?"

"I am a priest, that is my first occupation. The second is that of a farmer. I must earn my sustenance. Where do you come from? Where do you journey? Such nosy questions. You asked for a night's lodging. Enough! I am called Father Bellas."

"I was looking for someplace. I am tired from a long day. I saw your light."

"Good, good," the man answered. "I said that I was a farmer second—didn't I? Truth to tell, I forgot about Anta here. It seems that I was lost in less worldly things than milking a cow. This good animal bellowed lustily to be relieved of her provender. So here I am in the middle of the night."

"Lucky for me," said Francis.

"Come, come, less talk and more doing. I'll show you to a bed." He led the boy across the farmyard talking as they walked.

"Confidentially," his voice dropped, "I named Anta for our Pope's latest mistress." Raising his voice slightly, "May his days be long and his nights fruitful." Dropping his voice again, "I heard he has four bastards floating around someplace in the countryside."

Francis didn't remember any of the details, except that he slid off his shoes and lay down with his clothes. He awoke the next morning with the sun shining brightly into his eyes.

Francis sat up on the rough cot, easing his bones and muscles to their normal places. He looked about him and saw the usual poor man's cottage of a room or two. This place was clean. The brass pots near the fireplace were dull bright. Something was cooking slowly in a small pot over the fire. Then he saw something Francis didn't expect. A few shelves with several books and rolled up parchments! In this house?

He walked over and examined some of them. Many were in Latin, some in French. Curious, he tried to lift one of the ponderous volumes from the shelf. It was too heavy, so he let it drop with a careless thud. He lifted a smaller volume, broke it open and saw it had the letters of a language he recognized. Trying to remember, he focused his eyes on the strange curly letters.

"It is Hebrew, my son," a vigorous voice said. Francis turned, there was the priest-farmer. The man came into the room, behind him came a stocky woman carrying a little girl in her arms.

"May I introduce myself?" Francis asked them. "I am Francis Bernardone of Assisi."

"This is Jacopa—late of Provence, who is my wife," the man told him. "And this is her daughter, Gloria." The woman bowed her head, the child looked at her mother, then at Francis. She smiled, her round face lighting with mischievousness.

"How old is she?" asked Francis, reaching out and folding her tiny hand in his.

"Gloria is a few months less than two years," the woman said.

Francis looked at her and saw a woman of about twenty-five. Her face was pear-shaped and melted to a tiny mouth and firm small chin. Her eyes were dark and luminous, which was framed by walnut red hair, draping down to her shoulders. Francis' eye was held by her tiny bow mouth as he watched her talk.

"My little girl has seen few men except Father Bellas in the past six months," she told Francis.

"Ooh, ooh," the little girl strained from her mother towards the boy.

"She wants to go to you," Francis hesitated. "Don't be afraid. Here, hold one arm like this. The other you hold behind her back. See, how easy it is?"

The child was held in awkward arms. "See, Gloria has an eye for a young man," Father Bellas said. He sighed. "All she can see these days is me, a poor old bag of bones."

Francis thought wryly, "this poor old man could carry my horse, on those bones."

"Well, let us break our fast," said Father Bellas. "We will have a bite of food together."

From several cupboards, the woman and the man drew some food and earthen platters. He drew some hot liquid from the pot, simmering in the fireplace. In a few minutes there was a simple and frugal meal on the table. They sat down in their chairs. The child, Gloria, refused to leave Francis, so he had to manage eating with the little girl on his lap. Her light, bronze-gold hair nestled gently against his neck and shoulder. He hadn't ever held a child in his arms before, yet he felt as if this was an old knack.

Father Bellas started to intone the Latin prayer over the bread, then caught himself and intoned slowly in French. "Dear Lord God, we thank thee for this bit of bread to commence the day. We trust that all who seek a haven of refuge here will not be disturbed. Amen."

Francis' eyes bounded over the simple fare on the table. He rememberd the waste he had seen at the Count Trescia's table and at the Cardinal-to-be.

They were soon finished, there wasn't too much to eat. As Francis arose, the child struggled to be released. She slid down his legs to the floor, at the same time grasping his forefinger in her small fist. She pointed to the door.

"Go ahead, Francis," her mother smiled to them. The little child led him through the door. He walked, his shoulders bent slightly to ease Gloria's tensed small arms.

"Hoo, hoo," she pointed to the cow, Anta, which stopped her cud-chewing to look at them with big, wet eyes. Francis looked about him, breathing in deeply. He could see the small house where the child and her mother lived, the small, neat rows of the garden, the wheat field strung with long stalks dignified by their gentleness. The sun was warming the earth.

There was a strange feeling of peace about him, which started around his view and ended in the child attached to his finger. He didn't feel detached, he felt part of the scene about him.

He heard the steps of Father Bellas. Francis turned and saw that Jacopa stood with him. A smile played across both their lips, for the little girl was trying to put both her feet on each big toe of Francis.

"You can find peace here, my son," the man told him. "You may stay here and share our food for as long as you want."

"You ask me, a total stranger, to share the little you have?" asked Francis.

"Why not?" the man replied. "Giving is of far greater nobility than taking. So you see it is a bit selfish of me."

"I don't understand," the boy wondered. "Some great philosopher said, 'if you have one loaf of bread give it away for you will obtain two in return.' "

Father Bellas laughed, his voice danced across the fields. "Wise undertaking, a return of two for each one we put in. Very wise." His face was serious. "You are welcome to stay here, young Francis."

"How did you know I had considered this? Perhaps I have a family somewhere, or I have killed someone . . . "

Father Bellas laughed again. "You see the simple life allows one to laugh and find happiness in laughing. If I were the Pope, I would have him add one more to his thousand Bulls. To wit: every person in Christendom—all of it—must laugh heartily at least three times daily. That would cure everyone in all ills, including the Holy Father in Rome. Lord, have mercy on my blasphemy." He made the sign of the cross, touching his head and shoulders quickly.

"You are welcome here," Jacopa said quietly. "For I, too, am an unlawful, yet perchance, a guest."

"Let me show you around," Father Bellas encircled a friendly arm around the boy's shoulders. The child remained with her mother as the boy strolled around the small place with the older man.

"You may work or you may not work." the Father told him. "Methinks, looking at those fine hands and well-kept nails, that you've done little manual labor in your life. Look you, go into the house, take off your coat

and shirt, come out here and let the sun drench its warmth into your skin.
Go ahead," he struck the boy a resounding slap on the back, "leave your
things and come out here."

Francis did as he was bidden. His bare chest and back cooled to the
sudden exposure to the sun and air.

"Learn to let the good sun be a kind brother to you and cast his mantle
of goodness over you. Why drive him from you by your clothes? Eh, my
boy?"

Father Bellas had slipped off his own shirt, took some farm tools and
started to do some weeding in the garden.

"Could I help you?" Francis asked.

Father Bellas gave the boy something to do, guiding his awkwardness
with tact and praise.

Later, Francis told the man, "I'd like to stay here a few days." The other
nodded his head silently.

It was three days later, one afternoon, that Francis asked him, "I would
like to stay a few days more, Father Bellas."

The other nodded his head agreeably. "Stay as long as you wish. But
moving away or staying from your home will not solve your problem.

"How did you know? I said nothing to you."

"I am not as simple as my cow, Anta. You come to my barn in the middle
of the night. You have a fine horse, good clothing which fits you. Evidently,
then not procured by theft. You are not anxious to leave. Ergo—you are
afraid to go someplace, Touché?"

"Touché" responded Francis with a smile. "No one can solve a man's
own problems. Only he alone."

"Well spoken," replied Father Bellas. "Go and face it. Whatever the
consequence. Be true to your own heart and trust in the Lord. What have
you got to fear?"

"Perhaps only myself," Francis dropped his voice.

"Jesus carried that heavy wooden cross up the hill to Calvary, with pride
through the jibes and the mocking ones. Can any of us ever carry a greater
burden and feel it is weightier than that beam"? the older man asked
steadily.

A little later Francis asked him why he was here alone, except for Jacopa
and the child Gloria. The man told him that he had gone to Provence in
Southern France several years ago, with the permission of the local Bishop
of course. He had gone with the Dominicans to probe the heresy of the
Cathari or the Waldensians.

"I had gone to probe and find the devil in heresy. Sometimes," the man smiled reminiscently, "the probe goes too deep and finds the truth. Then he himself becomes free. That is what the truth does to a person. It frees him from the chains of his superstitions, and the small things he never realized chained his soul and did not let his Eternal Spirit grow."

"Is that what the Waldensians taught you?" Francis asked "My father once told me about them."

"The Order was founded by a good Christian, a man of some property who sold all he had for this cause. His name was Pierre Waldo."

"He went to Rome, didn't he?" asked Francis.

"He and some of his followers went to the Pope and asked permission to preach and translate the Bible into the vulgar language . . . ha, they call French the vulgar tongue. Let be." He sighed audibly. "They did that by papal dispensation. A few years later the Council of Verona ordered Pierre Waldo to be excommunicated from the Church. This meant death by fire."

"What did he do?" asked Francis.

"Do?", retorted the Father. "He tried to save the Church. Look yonder in those hills, on Subasio, Montefalco . . . rich abbeys of stone. They are rich and still collect more from the poor and the priests. And they still want more.

"That is what Waldo and his followers criticized. They wanted Christians to follow the simple precepts of Jesus."

"Is that all?" interrupted Francis.

"No, not all. The Waldensians said that the sacraments must not be given by unholy hands. Alas, those who follow to do God's work have indeed corrupted His purpose and made rotten their souls. The clergy of the land care little for the poor, who need goodness and good graces to live better lives. They saw all these things. They spoke and Rome had to silence them."

"How?" asked Francis.

"By fire and sword, and more wealth. Yet, this same wealth will so corrupt it that the Church will one day die by the weight of its own silver or gold."

"You speak as a man perplexed," said Francis.

"Ay, that I do. But I have seen the torch and the swords drenched with blood. Holy Mother of God, when will man cease to kill with the Prince of Peace—on their lips?"

Francis asked that he sleep in the storeroom. He was told that the roof leaked. If that happened he was to come into the house at once.

On the third night it rained heavily. The wind and the rain tore at the old roof of the store room. Francis was drenched in a short time. He lay on the soaked cot shivering, numb with knowledge that morning was far off.

He heard Father Bellas call him, large and grotesque across the walls caught by the shadows of the light from the small lantern he carried.

"Come boy, come," the older man ordered him. "Come to the house, you'll catch your death of cold. He drew a small horse blanket around the boy, as they rushed across the open way to the warmth of the house.

Jacopa was standing near the open fire and called to him, "Come in Francis. Stand by the fire for a while, and take the chill out of your bones." He did as she bid him. Feeling the deep glow of the flames, he sat on the small bench, his head drooping.

He missed the exchange of looks between the man and his wife. She had nodded her head and smiled at her husband in assent.

"You best get into this bed," Father Bellas told Francis "But, first get out of those wet clothes."

"This is the only bed in this room," pointed the boy. "I could sleep on the floor near the fire."

"No," Jacopa said, "It's cold and hard and you could get the rheumatics. It's all right, you can sleep right here on this side."

Francis was too sleepy to argue. He stood in the dim lit corner and removed his clothing, leaving on his underclothes. Again he started to protest about sleeping in their bed.

She put her small hand over his mouth and led him to the side of the bed. He was under the heavy blanket quickly. "Now give me the rest of your clothes," she held out her hands.

He reached under the blankets and obeyed her. Father Bellas took and hung them near the fire. The man then handed Francis a cup of warmed wine, which he drank quickly, feeling its warmth and tanginess drench into his chest.

He watched the flames dance across the wall. A feeling of happy contentment bathed him into drowsiness. His mind and body burrowed into the depths of sleep. This was home at last.

A little later, it seemed to him, he felt the warm, soft body near him. Much later, he felt her small hand caressing his body, sliding over his abdomen and across his thighs. He made a motion to raise his head.

"Stay," he heard Jacopa whisper into his ear on the pillow near him.

He could feel the night movements of Father Bellas on the other side of the bed, as he turned his back towards Francis.

"Feel warmer now?" the man's voice came to him in the darkness of the room. "Fear nothing," the man's tone was gentle. "We let you share our home and our food. It is also fitting that you may share the goodness of Jacopa too."

He turned his back fully away from them.

Jacopa turned and with a quick motion had her body on top of Francis. She began to rub her softness over him, murmuring small sounds, holding his head in the fullness of her soft arms. He could smell the sweet woman delight of her two breasts.

Over him went coursing an eagerness he had never encountered. All his life it seemed to him he was waiting for this one moment. The gnawing tide across his stomach wanted something, not knowing what it was. And in one silent, warming moment it was here.

"Put your arms around me," her voice demanded softly. She reached under them, helping him, guiding him. Suddenly, everything seemed to explode in his body. She laughed, a tiny chuckle near his ear.

"Am I the first one?" He nodded assent, touching her forehead to his. She rested for a minute over him then said, "I'll come back to you later. I'm glad I'm the first," her voice was kind.

He fell asleep and an hour later she was on him, this time demanding fulfillment from his youth and vigor. As the sun dimly lit the room, he could barely see the contours of her body.

She caught at his hands guiding them over her breasts, making small animal sounds in the half darkness, bathed with the soft tendrils of light reaching into the room.

Father Bellas turned and smiled at them for a minute, then left the room, first glancing over to the crib, where Gloria was fast asleep.

Suddenly, Francis felt ashamed for this kind man. With it was mingled the nobility of a generous gift, humbly received.

Francis continued to work in the fields and make himself useful around the house, repairing walls and fences, milking the cow and gathering firewood.

About two days later Father Bellas, spoke quietly to Francis. "You cannot solve your problems by staying here. Whatever it is, you must face it manfully."

"Do you want me to leave?" asked the boy.

"You are welcome to return any time you want," was the reply. "For your own well being, I suggest you go home. Think on it and you will observe that I am right."

Francis decided to go home and face his father Pietro Bernardone.

Assisi 1204

The next day Francis didn't turn until he had walked his horse for a few minutes. Then he did. And saw that Jacopa, with Gloria in her arms was watching him go away. Father Bellas was busied with something on the ground. Beersheba kept walking, limberly, away from them.

A sudden thought caught at his memory. He would soon have to face his father in Assisi! In the expanse of the wide fields, the boy felt alone, weighted by a pall of loneliness. Why couldn't his father understand and help him? Why were they always pounding at each other? His father loved Angelo, Francis' younger brother, because the youngster liked the trading business. Francis did not.

The only one who really understands me, Francis thought, is Pica, my mother. Ever since he was small, she had known how to talk with him.

They would go for long walks together. She would talk about her girlhood in Provence. He always could find peace, just by being with her. It was always different with his father. He insisted things be done *his* way and only by his direction. No one could do anything right but Pietro Bernardone.

His mother, Pica, in one of their long walks together explained things to him.

"You must forgive your father. He is a strong-willed man." She sighed as if her breath were bruised across her white teeth. "My little Frenchman."

These were his scrambling thoughts as Beersheba, continued walking, when Francis drew the check rein. He turned around to see if Jacopa were still there. He could not see her at this distance. Who was she? Where did she come from? Many other questions riffled through his mind like falling cards, each one with another face. One day, he decided, he would return this way again.

He soon reached the old Flaminian Way. The mare reached and touched each cobbled stone daintily as she walked towards Bovara. Francis looked down on the roadway passing beneath him. He could see how carefully and accurately each stone was bedded. He noted how clean each joint was angled and set. The Romans certainly knew how to build roads. This one was built many years before the birth of—Jesus of Nazareth. He had heard that every foot was paved with the blood of the overseer's whip and the blows from the short Roman sword. The irony of this story, Francis learned, was that this road, built with great care by the Romans was used by the Goths and Visigoths to sack and destroy Rome! There is a moral hidden somewhere, Francis thought.

He looked up ahead and he could hear the clatter of some horse soldiers approaching him. Beersheba moved daintly off the road.

The leader of the troop, noting Francis' apparel, raised his hand in the ancient salute. Francis was proud to return it, with palm faced towards the officer.

One soldier shouted at him, "The fighting is in the South. You are heading the wrong way."

Another, "Maybe he is Innocent's letter carrier with a fresh message."

Beersheba, unconcerned, dipped her head searching for some tender grass. Francis leaned forward and his mandola swung around in front of him.

One soldier shouted, "He's no soldier, he is a troubador. They sing pretty songs to the ladies. They can't fight," he spat out. He ended with a raucous laugh in which the others joined.

All the pride Francis had felt a minute ago slid away from him. He drooped his head as his eyes watched the horses' hooves move away from him. Only last week, it seemed a year ago, he, too, had ridden down this road. He was a proud soldier then, and happy with his friends. He had been proud of his fine armor. Pica and Angelo and his father had gathered around him and admired the fine fit.

They had all been so excited about his going off with the troop to fight a glorious war for Assisi. Now all was lost| All the hopes, all the dreams and ambitions, lost like the faint outlines of these soldiers who had passed and were blending into the horizon.

With a sigh he turned Beersheba in the opposite direction, heading towords Bovara.

A short time later he came to the Clitumnus and the bridge where he had lost his lance a week ago. Dismounting, he let Beersheba dip her snout into the water. Then she did a strange thing. The mare walked into the water up to her shanks. Francis kneeled down and sipped its sweet coolness into his mouth. Still on his knees he looked about him. It was still early and he was hidden near a few willows. Why not?

In a few minutes he was out of his clothing. Those infernal long hose needed a servant to draw them from his limbs. Hurriedly, he plunged into the water. His body was spangled with the sudden spat of cold water. A few moments later his body was warm again. Like a young pup frisking, he plunged under the water. He opened his eyes meanwhile paddling along, his body sliding over the green life on the bed of the river. He could see everything about him in a crystal clear yet foreign world.

A thought waded through his mind. Why not stay here? In the sweetest of all Nature's children. Water had no lust, no war and no ambition. Remaining here, there would be no Pietro Bernardone to face, no soldiers to jibe at him. He could find eternal peace. He closed his eyes, letting his body float gently.

Memories of past events strung through his mind like bright links to an endless chain. When he was seven he had asked his mother to tell him a story. His father who was standing nearby laughed and said, "He always wants someone to tell him a story. I'm afraid that Francis has such a thick head he will never learn how to read for himself." Francis smiled wryly; he had never cared for reading or writing.

But his mother, Pica! She had once told him about this very river. How poets like Virgil and Propertius had written great songs about the Clitumnus. That many people had come from all over the empire to see and write about this river.

Now, he, Francis, was ready to breathe all its holiness into his body. Thus he, too, would become a part of it. And people would come here and say, "Here died that great soldier Francis Bernardone of Assisi, the Lord rest his soul." Would they?

His body suddenly convulsed like a coiled spring and his head bounded out of the water. He panted for breath in deep sucking gasps, as if he had never breathed before. No, people would say, "Here died that half-man called Francis. He quit his troop in time of war because of a lustful woman. What manner of knight is he? Coward, dullard and fool."

Somehow, the laughter of the soldiers echoed across his memory. For a moment, he thought he heard their voices swirling through the poplars, the bent willow trees and the grassy rushes of the small islands near him.

He shook the water from him as he lifted each leg gingerly over the tiny stones on the river bed.

It was then he heard the man speak. He was startled. "I wondered if my voice would reach you," the stranger said.

Francis look at him. He was above medium height and had a long white beard. His clothes were poor yet clean.

"Did you think . . . ?" Francis started to ask.

"I wasn't sure," the man replied. "You were down quite some time. I remember you," he suddenly recalled. "You are Bernardone's son from up Assisi way."

"Yes," replied Francis, rubbing his skin quickly to make it dry. Then he started to draw on his clothes over his damp body.

"I suppose you don't remember me? "the man asked solicitously. Francis shook his head.

"Do you remember sometime ago, you helped a beggar at your father's house. A man asked you for a coin. Remember now?"

"Yes," Francis remembered. "I am afraid there aren't too many beggars who have come into my life," the boy smiled slowly.

"That coin saved my life that day," the old man told him. "I am called Old Isaac. I am a Jew. Once, in happier days there was a young Isaac."

"I remember now," Francis cried out. "You asked me for a coin in the name of God. That is what caught me."

"Otherwise, you would have given me nothing?" the man asked slowly.

"You would have gotten nothing if my father were around," Francis laughed. "I remember now. My father had just paid a gambling debt of forty-two silver coins to Parao, the Duke's son, which I had so gallantly lost the night before."

"Strange," Old Isaac said quietly. "A small ransom for a gambling debt and not a copper for a hungry mouth."

"We could be beggared in a week if we answered every plea for help," Francis told him.

"Yet there are so many who need help. Often not in coin alone. Most people who dwell about Assisi are not in poverty. A crop failure, disease or misfortune break upon them like the plague." The old man spoke slowly. He spoke French with a curiously familiar accent to Francis.

"What could people do?" asked Francis.

"A smile, a friendly shake of the hand," Old Isaac answered quickly. "These are things from the heart, not the purse. Mark it well, my young friend."

"There is no justice," Francis was solemn as he rendered this decision. "Else why do the ancients say justice is blind. Tell me, you are a Jew. There aren't many of your people in the Umbrian hills." A perverse thought entered his mind, not to tell the man they were of one people.

The man bowed his head as if he were addressing a king. He drew up his head proudly and smiled. "You see, we have no horns or the tail of the Devil."

"I don't understand. I heard all Jews are rich and don't need to beg," Francis suggested.

"Some of us are more fortunate than others," the old man said. "Where I come from I was a man of some substance. Not perhaps in money, but more worthy things. Like the arts, fine scholarship and good music. These are the more lasting assets of mankind. Money is good, yes. But it can only buy certain things from life. Believe me, one finds with the years that money alone without the others is not important. Money can only buy other things which have a value as money. So in reality one only buys more money. Am I boring you with my philosophy, my young friend?"

"No, no," Francis repeated. "I guess I have been troubled in spirit of late. To tell you the truth perhaps in some manner I have been trying to tell my father all you have said to me," the boy spoke with a tone of reminiscence in his voice. "But I gave you a coin," he brightened, "and you say that it saved your life. Well," argued Francis, "that coin brought you here." He turned and pointed his finger toward the river, Clitumnous.

"A point," the man said, "and well put. But, I needed food, that is the difference."

"You said that you came from another land," Francis remembered.

"Yes, I come from a small city, Bezier, in Provence in the south of France."

"Ah, so *that* is the accent," Francis said. "The Provencal one, my mother was born in Provence."

He shook hands with the boy.

"Where do you go now?" Francis asked him.

"Somewhere in one of these towns is the wife of my son, Shmuel. I must find her for we are the last of our family. Farewell, my son. One day we will meet in happier circumstances." He bowed again. Then picking up his long staff from the ground, he trudged away from the silent and wondering boy.

Later that day, Francis rode in to the busy town of Foligno on his way north to Assisi. It was the middle of the morning and the small square was crowded with people, vendors calling their wares, buyers removing their purchases on asses and carts. Everywhere there were the beggars in their shambled rags, pleading their eternal plea, "a coin, messer, a coin."

Francis suddenly remembered that Jacopa had come from Provence. He shook his head in self-mockery. He always remembered something unsaid or undone long afterwards.

This was a familiar town. He had been here many times alone and with his father selling their woolens. There were shouted greetings to the boy. People liked him and businessmen wanted to transact business with him. He was fair and didn't try to drive a sharp bargain. He waved, smiling, to some familiar faces. An open carriage stood near one of the large houses. As he drew closer a man got into the vehicle. The man recognized the boy. "Ho there, Francis, How are things faring with you?"

Francis recognized the speaker. It was Bernard de Quintavalle. He drew Beersheba closer, bending towards the man. "Not too well, Messer Bernard," he told him contritely.

The man smiled knowingly. He was slim and looked like an aristocrat. His short round, black beard was neatly trimmed. "I have heard a tale or two. Are you riding for home?" he asked kindly.

"Should I," Francis countered, a smile of mischief on his face.

"That is a small mountain you will have to overcome first." Both of them laughed as if it were a long-standing joke. Assisi was a mountain with houses clinging in winding paths around its side. The top was crowned with the ancient castle like a decoration on top of a cake.

"I take it that Messer Pietro Bernardone is displeased with my actions?" Francis asked slyly.

"You had best have a valid reason for this, you young scamp," the older man warned, smiling.

Francis started his horse alongside the carriage.

"Come in here with me," the man said. "Tie Beersheba behind us."

In a moment Francis sat alongside the other.

They left Foligno behind them and drew into the open fields leading to Spello and north to Assisi. They passed some serf farmers working the fields a short distance from town.

As they looked towards them, Bernard said, "It is strange that in this year of our Lord 1204 we cannot stop robbers from attacking anyone beyond the city gates. These fields are good and the land is fertile. They can't be tilled because no one dares work out there alone. These Umbrian lands are good lands. The good Lord wants them to bear their fruit and the harvest from its bosom. Ah well," he sighed. "Perhaps a day will come when there will be peace again in all of Italy."

"I suppose you want to know what happened," Francis asked.

"I have asked you nothing," Bernard replied. "That is for your father to ask. Not I."

"Yet in many ways you have been closer to me than my own father,"

Francis said quietly. "From the night I was born you have been a source of help to me and Pica."

"Well, that night you were born—your mother, Pica, was alone in the house. As your neighbor, it was the only Christian thing to do."

The horse in front quickened his pace and Beersheba obediently clattered behind. The boy and the man were silent. Each one was weighted into silence by his own thoughts.

"If you weren't like a father," Francis said quietly, "then you have always been like a good, older brother to me. You warned me about my gambling. I didn't heed your advice."

"Gambling for money stakes is stupid and often leads you a merry chase around a wheel. If you must gamble, stake your brain in matching wits with another. Gamble for freedom, for tolerance in all men's hearts. Gamble for the love of your fellow man. *There* is something worthwhile to do with a man's life."

"You are always reaching inside me to make me think," Francis said.

"No. I have learned this from a man named Jesus of Nazareth. He taught us many things. But essentially he wanted all of us to be dignified human beings. It is only when a man has dignity within himself that he can find true respect for his fellow man. It is not new with me. Jesus said that, much better, without doubt, many years ago."

"In many ways you talk like Pica," Francis smiled.

"Madame Pica is a fine, gentle woman." Bernard answered quietly. "You are fortunate to have such a mother."

"I know it is common these days." He hesitated. "Do you love my mother, Ser Bernard?" the boy asked the man, quietly.

The other was silent for almost a full minute. The steady clop-clop of the horses' hooves punctured the peaceful landscape.

"I have always respected your mother," he replied. "The way one dear friend respects another, as intelligent and understanding people do. Does that answer you?"

Francis nodded his head. He said nothing until they left Spello behind them. They came to the road which swung off towards the old Roman amphitheater.

"Would you like to scramble over the stones again?" Bernard asked him.

Francis' face lit up in boyish anticipation of something pleasant to be repeated. They approached the broken walled theater set high into a hill. Bernard tethered his horse to the branch of a tree. Everywhere about them the wild brush crept around the old columns and stones.

"Do you remember we found a lanista buried under some stones," Francis reminded him.

"Yes," laughed Bernard. "Perhaps some thief buried his find."

"Let's sit here and talk," Francis suggested.

"We can for awhile," Bernard answered. He looked up at the sky. "It grows late. The sun will dip below the edge of Subacio soon. We still can't be alone in the night. I would hate to be deprived of my purse. But I can assure you I have no desire to arrive in Assisi without any clothing."

They both laughed. Robbers were not loathe to take everything a man or a woman, wore or owned.

"I want to tell you about Spoletto," Francis said soberly.

"If you don't want to talk . . ." the older man paused.

"But I do," Francis replied quickly. "Here, let's sit here, on this stone."

Below them serried downward like a huge saucer was the old playground of the Romans. There stood the stone archways where hundreds of spectators had entered. Over there, partially crumbled, with a small tree finding life in the ground at the jamb, was the entrance of the gladiators or the animals.

Bernard followed Francis' gaze.

"The Romans were wily politicians. They understood that all people want to see death in all its gore. That's why we have so many wars. The Romans knew that to keep the people in peace instead of at each other, they must satisfy that hunger in men to see death."

"Go ahead. I was just thinking aloud. What do you wish to tell me?"

Francis told him about the "contest" and his actions at Lady Trescia's boudoir.

"Oh, so that was it," he said under his breath. "The lusty witch." Aloud, "Don't let it worry you. Why should you waste the good substance of *your* body upon some dung hill. God gave us a mightly seed to cherish with love and dispense its godliness with humble respect and charity. Don't you see, Francis. It isn't ours to waste. Do we fling the seeds of the fruit trees to the four winds? No, we care for them. Does this answer you?"

Francis nodded. "You always make me find the road, I *want* to travel. It *is* good to have a friend like you. I wish I could call you my brother, Bernard."

The man laughed. "Who knows, you may yet," he said. "Aren't we brothers under the skin?" He looked up at the sky again.

"We had best be on our way—brother," he added humbly. They climbed down towards their carriage. An hour later they were riding through the arched wall of Passagio d'Assisi. The entrance to a city spread across a mountainside.

They wound through the narrow, dark streets and stopped when they saw a crowd of people ahead of them. Francis jumped out of the carriage to go ahead on foot. A few minutes later he returned.

"What is it, Francis?" Bernard asked him.

"A funeral," was the simple answer.

"Elaborate, no doubt," Bernard's voice was succinct. "They will place themselves in debt for life to make a show for the neighbors."

"It is the custom," Francis replied. "Anyway, people find pleasure in sending the departed off with festivity. We welcome the birth of a child. Why not, by the same token, give ourselves some happiness by celebrating the last day of a grown person?"

"You speak like an ancient Roman philosopher," the older man said. A quizzical expression caught his face into a look of inquiry. "You surprise me, young Francis. You surprise me with these flashes of wisdom which belie your years."

Francis smiled, his lips and eyes crinkling under the sudden praise of his friend.

They both watched silently as the cortege wound its way ahead. Their religious banners had to be dipped now and then because of the large over-hanging second stories over the streets. Two large boys with sticks had to lead the funeral in order to drive away stray pigs, chickens or an occasional ox out of the streets. The boys would go ahead, shouting lustily, "A funeral comes, good citizens. Hold everything." They wanted no accidental dumping of garbage, filth or dirty water into the street or on the heads of the mourners.

The deceased was carried on an open pallet, fully dressed in her best clothing. Her arms were folded and jeweled rings spun their own light on her fingers. Everyone could see the wealth being sent to Heaven. Across the bier was strewn several fine blankets covered with satiny brocades and fine embroidery.

"Who is the dead one?" asked Bernard.

"Some woman named Larniero or Larnera," said Francis. "Must be a very rich family. Did you see that brocade? It is worth about thirty-two pieces of silver. She was dressed as if she had just come from a wedding."

"Larnera, did you say?" queried the other. "Where *did* I hear that name. Oh, yes, Delia Larnera. There was some scandal about her. She was the mistress of Father Lurgia; he was the abbot of a monastery near Spello. Some say they were married."

"I had heard of these things," Francis' voice carried a trace of irony. "These false idolaters—with the right hand they hold the sacred cloth and sacraments, with the left they dip into false sin."

Bernard laugher. "I have never heard *you* become vehement about the customs of the day. If you speak against the Church and the clergy, you will be declared a heretic. You know what has been happening to heretics?" he warned, smilingly.

Francis nodded his head. They heard the voices of two men above them on a second story piazza. Their voices were low, but they could be heard by Francis and Bernard seated in their carriage. The older man put a restraining hand on Francis' arm. He slid a warning finger on his lips. This is what they heard:

"I want all her possessions. That is the only way," said an unctious voice.

"You are a fool, Guldo," an incisive voice replied.

"You are well aware that she cannot be buried in sacred and hallowed soil," the unctious voice, said. "I control all burials in the area about Assisi. You wouldn't want to go to Bishop Guido with your plaint, would you?" There was a trace of bitter laughter.

"You have me there," the incisive one replied slowly. "You know damn well I won't go to the Bishop. All right, How much?"

"That's better," replied the smooth, oily voice. "Since we are both members of the clergy, and since we are all vicars in the service of Our Lord, ahem," his voice stumbled, "and since the sadly departed, the Lord rest her soul in Paradise, was your mistress—"

"My good friend," interrupted the short, incisive voice. Lowering his voice slightly, "A good friend, shall we say?"

"Yes, I understand," the other replied, condescension in every tone. "Even an abbot must have—shall we say—a release of the internal emotions. Well and done. I'll take half of all her possessions."

"A quarter," the other suggested.

"I'll be fair with you," the smooth one said. "A third and not a copper less."

"Done," was the chopped reply. Their voices dropped lower.

Francis attempted to stand up and reach over to the top of the piazza. He wanted to see who the two priests were. Bernard drew him down gently, shaking his head.

"This is nothing new, my young friend," he whispered to him. Francis shook his head in slow anger. Bernard made a move to start the horse, when again they heard the smooth voice saying something.

"Of course, I don't expect to go to Heaven or Paradise. What will I find there? Broken down old cripples who wear tattered clothing. Old men and women who creep like silent bats from church altar to burial crypt. We can only find lepers and the very good, sanctified people.

"When I die, I want to go to Hell. There I will find scholars and men of refinement or culture. No doubt I will find many of my brethren from the clergy." The older man coughed, suddenly. "And, of course, *we* will find the better dressed ladies of noble blood and humor. No, my friend, I would rather go to Hell."

Their voices continued, receding into the house.

Francis jumped from the carriage and walked up to the horses' bridle. He led the animal forward, because it was dark and the street wound upward. The houses were strung so closely as if they resented the little strip of opening called the street.

They walked this way for a few minutes, until they reached a small open square. Francis stopped the horse and returned to the carriage. Without mounting he spoke to the older man.

"I'll leave you here," Bernard glanced about him at the houses of that street.

"Clara, the daughter of Offreduccio lives here, doesn't she?" he inquired kindly, a tiny smile breaking his lips. "What is with you and that child. You have known each other all your lives."

"Her father, the Count, says I'm too old for her," Francis replied.

"Poo and again poo," the older man spat out. "A few years between you? There must be some other reason."

"Could there be?" Francis asked sadly.

"My mother has never denied being a Jewess," Francis said speaking slowly. "Yet, I know she suffers. She, whose dear heart is akin to a saint must find anguish while those—" he pointed in the direction they had just left. "Those—jackals in the robes of the Church can flout their infamy openly. It is men like these who corrupt all life."

Bernard watched the boy's face. He could see that Francis was moved, his wide-set eyes alive with anger. The timbre of his voice rode it across the small square searching all the dark, silent corners.

"We talk among ourselves, among my friends about the priests," said Francis. "I have never heard one of them, *one* of them, ever say something good. Do you know what the little children in the streets say if they won't do something? 'I'd rather be a priest than do that.' What a low estate have come these spokesmen for God."

Francis' voice had carried resonantly, as it usually did when he was disturbed. Some of the sleepy neighbors protested. One looked down at them.

"It's young Francis again. Why don't you marry that Clara so we can all sleep in peace forever after? The next time it will be a kettle of dirty water, remember?"

Francis nodded his head, waving his hand. *That* neighbor had done that one night when Francis had serenaded Clara with his lute.

Bernard smiled at the boy. "He evidently does not appreciate you," he whispered. "I'll be off. Come to see me soon, Francis. I live but a stone's throw from you. You used to visit me more often. Goodbye." He clucked to the horse and it clattered away into the night.

Francis heard a loud whisper above him saying his name. He looked up towards one of the larger houses facing the small square. It was Clara, looking down from the piazza. She signalled with her hand.

He tied Beersheba to a rail, then from long experience his supple wiry body bent as he jumped for a masonry overhang. Grasping this, his body twisted until he swung his legs over. In another moment he was alongside the girl. He could have used the stone stairs.

"I hadn't meant to awaken you," Francis started to say.

"Yes, you did," she began, then laughed. Her voice crinkled like tiny bells to the boy. She liked to laugh for Francis. She knew he liked to hear her.

He held her small palm in between his two fists and looked at her. She was tall for a girl of eleven, her round, sweet face was caught inside the rambling dark blond hair floating past her shoulders. Beneath the flowing robe she had tossed over her nightgown he could see the gentle curves of her awakening breasts.

They looked into each other's eyes. Then she drew him to her closely. Her small, strong arms drawing him, holding his with fierce fingers.

"I love you Francis," she whispered fiercely. "I love you despite anything you have done."

"I love you dearly, Clara," he bent as he whispered into her ear. "You know I come to you whenever I am in trouble. You and Pica are my two women. But your father, the Count, doesn't like me—not too much."

"But he does," she responded. "He admires you."

"But he won't let me marry you," Francis replied.

"He wants me to be practical," the girl pouted. "He's arranged my marriage with a Pedro Casalon of Madrid when I was born."

"But you have never seen the man," Francis replied quickly. "How can you marry someone you have never seen?"

"You talk like a child," her voice mothered him. "Haven't all my friends been married the same way? Estelle de Lamont, Canthia Werrell and the rest. And we forget Berenice; she was married at twelve. You see, my troubador, it is the custom of the land."

"Custom of the land," he kept his voice low, almost exploding. "Such customs make women no better than cattle. Are you better off than any of the serfs who live about? They can be sold with the land, like a house or—or—a pig."

"My, my how you orate," the girl chided him. "Something has disturbed you, Francis. What is it?"

"I don't know, Clara," the boy shook his head. "I see so much around us that is bad. I know you will say everyone does it. This does not make it right."

"What can we do?" the girl shrugged her shoulders. "Do you think you are Atlas and carry the world on your shoulders? The evils of this generation can't be cured with talk alone. Neither can they be cured by edicts from Rome. My father showed me one that Innocent III had issued sometime ago. It said that the Pope knew all about his clergy. That he knew some of them sold indulgences for heavy fees, that they taxed heavily, that some of them were vulgar and perhaps heretics. Do you know what the Pope suggested? That the only means of curing these evils is with fire and the sword."

"But that is no answer," Francis responded. "A heretic isn't cured when he is burned to a crisp at the stake. The only ones who may get satisfaction are the people who gather to watch the exhibition. People must be led through their hearts, not with fire."

"Aren't we the silly ones," the girl suddenly laughed. "You have come here to talk with me. And we concern ourselves with all humanity. I don't think we can do anything."

"I guess not," Francis replied slowly. "But somewhere there must be an answer for me. Perhaps one day I'll find it."

"Perhaps one day you will find what?" a man's voice asked quickly.

Francis and Clara turned to face her father who had come behind them in slippered feet out on the piazza.

"I don't know sir," was the boy's courteous response.

him, his stocky body, his stocking covered head bobbing. He looked small

"Well, sir," the man said, drawing his satiny dressing gown closer about

and effeminate in his night clothes. "You have a confounded nerve coming up here and waking people, young Francis. What did you mean about finding something? What does a young rascal like you hope to find, the philosopher's stone?" he laughed.

"We were talking about the world's ills," Francis said quietly.

"The world's ills—" The man exploded in restrained laughter. "The world's ills! You come out here with a young woman in her nightgown, a pretty young thing even if she is my daughter—and the best you can do is talk about the world's ills." He laughed again. "I don't know if you are a fool or if you're playing some devious hand, young Francis. Here you, young miss, get into the house before your morals get corrupted." He whacked her on the rump as she passed by.

Clara and Francis looked at each other. A message of understanding passed between them.

The girl walked into the house. As she turned in the doorway she saw her father move closer to Francis.

"Don't you think it would be best for you to leave Clara alone. Firstly, she is too young for you and, secondly, she has already been spoken for."

Francis nodded his head. "But she has never met the other man."

"I know the boy's parents well. It takes good breeding to make fine children."

"She doesn't love him or even know him."

"That will come with time, my boy," the older man put a friendly arm around the boy's shoulder. "You know, I like you, Francis. I have two daughters and would like to have you for a son. It just won't work out. I know your father, Pietro Bernardone, a fine man. Your mother, the Madonna Pica, is a gentle lady, but—" he stopped and shrugged his shoulders.

"Are you too, afraid of the Jews?" Francis asked the older man. "What have you to fear?" he said. "You are Count Offreduccio."

"Listen, my boy, we are an old family," was the reply. "We too have a position to keep up. There has never been any mark on the Sciffi or the Offreduccio family arms."

"And I would be that mark?" the boy asked.

"There has never been a Jew in the family," he said. "Would you like to become a Catholic?" he asked suddenly. "No, I guess not. It is bad enough being an open-minded Catholic these days . . . but being a Jew is far worse."

With his arm still around the boy's shoulders, he started walking with him towards the stair leading off the piazza.

"Now be smart, young Francis," the man spoke confidentially. "And be civilized. After Clara is married and she wishes to have a lover, that is her affair. Of course you must be discreet. Let us act like intelligent and civilized people in this matter. On her fourteenth birthday, Clara will be married to Pedro Casalan of Madrid." His voice carried a note of finality. He patted the boy affectionately on the shoulder.

"Give my kind regards to Pietro," he said to Francis who was walking down the stairs. "And of course to your dear mother," he added.

Francis nodded his head. "Thank you," he replied. He found Beersheba and holding her by the bridle, walked slowly, his mind drenched with his thoughts. In a few minutes he stood before the Bernardone residence.

He opened the door into the lower floor, at the street level and was held by the dank, shut-in smell of the room. He detected the faint pungent odor of camphor. This room was used often to stack an overflow of bales from the warehouse, at the other end of Assisi.

He was held for a minute in the darkness. He felt clammy and alone. (Francis could not have possibly known that one day he would sleep forever in that wall and the Church of San Francesco would be built over this room. That millions upon millions of people would have stood in this same spot trying to capture an elusive quality of the boy who had once been born and lived in this house.)

Rather than wake the house, he lay down on one of the bales and fell asleep.

Because Francis had fallen asleep in a corner of the basement no one knew he was there, so he slept far into the morning.

When he walked into the living quarters and greeted Pietro and Pica eating their lunch, their surprise was not casual.

Somehow, Francis had forgotten to make up a believable story which would be understood. He certainly could not tell them about the degrading "contest."

He told his family that he had a bad coughing spell of his lung fever and Captain Gentile had told him to go home and rest. If he felt better, Francis could meet them later in the month.

His parents seemed satisfied with this answer. Pietro suddenly noticed that Francis was not wearing his silver armor. When he learned that the boy had left it in Spoletto, he became angry.

"That armor cost me two hundred pieces of silver." He barked at the boy. "Do you think that kind of money grows on trees? It is bad enough I had to buy off that Captain Gentile with a new suit of armor so you could join the Brienne troop. Now this."

"Father, I'm sorry," the boy said. "Rufino will care for it until I reach them."

"Now, there is a fine lad," his father told him. "He will make a gentleman one day, just like his father and his Uncle, the Count. Still I'm sure that he does not waste money the way you do. To leave a suit of armor worth two hundred pieces . . ."

"Money, money, you are always talking about money," Francis said quickly.

"Well," his father asked him slowly. "Can you find a better way to get it than to work for it?"

"A man could beg it," Francis replied. His eyes looked at his father innocently.

"Beg it!" Pietro's voice sprang at him. "Beg it, you say. You young scoundrel. I am not going to take any more of this nonsense from you." His voice slowed as he tried to control himself. "I have gone along wth you—I have given you time. Your mother has pleaded your case. You have fever, you have headaches, you are thin. I must be calm. I am always calm with you." His voice began to rise in pitch. "Calm—I should have taken a birch rod to you when you were seven years old."

Francis stood quietly before the wrath of his father. A tiny smile kept tugging and playing with his thin lips. His round wide-set eyes outholding his father's in a gentle grasp.

"I'd rather beg in the streets than take anything of yours." Francis knew that he was igniting new fires.

"Beg, you say," Pietro barked at him. "Pica," he shouted in a different key. "Pica, come here." A moment later, Francis' mother appeared. A harried look drifted across her face as she took in with a glance this tableau. Once again the father was facing his son in anger.

"Francis, have you been aggravating your father again?" She looked Francis full in the eyes. They brought him a message of pleading.

"Do you know what this—this—I brought up. He threatens me, Pietro Bernardone who is known across Europe as far as England. I have given him every opportunity to do something for himself. *He* tells me to my face that he would rather beg than take any of my money."

"That is unkind, Francis," his mother reproached him.

"I'm sorry," the boy murmured. He often wondered why he blurted out words without thinking. Then he would regret them after some thought. She is the dearest mother a fellow ever had, yet I always manage to hurt her. But Pietro always rubbed him the wrong way, making him say things he did not want said.

"This—bag of bones can talk this way to his father. I ask you, my dear Pica, would *you* talk this way to your father? Would *I*?"

"No, I am sure you wouldn't," Pica agreed. "You must forgive Francis. He is so impetuous. If we lived in Provence he would be a great mimic or a fine actor. You know how he makes people laugh."

"Do you think so?" Pietro asked suddenly, slightly mollified. "He is not much good in the business. Maybe he is good for something. What kind of pay do you think good actors earn?"

"They do fairly well," Pica replied. "Many of them are well received in the homes of the nobles."

"Well, anyway, he shouldn't talk this way to me," Pietro almost pleaded with Pica. "I have worked hard to give you and my children the best in life. How many women in Assisi—or anywhere in Umbria—have the clothes you or the boys have?"

"A beggar is not one because that is what he wants." Francis knew he was putting his thoughts together lamely. "He has no choice."

"I don't know what you are talking about," Pietro responded.

"He means, perhaps in another way," Pica joined in, "that there are too few rich ones and far too many poor ones. Is that it, Francis?" She looked at him.

He nodded his head.

"I think you must have a touch of a crazy person," Pietro's voice started to rise. "I am talking about working hard for my wife and children and this darn fool talks about beggars."

"They have nothing to eat and they have no way to get it," Francis again realized these were not the words he wanted to frame his thoughts.

"We help those who need," his mother replied quietly.

"Didn't we help that Lionetti women, or whatever her name is, last week?" his father suggested.

Francis shook his head.

"You didn't know that, did you?" Pietro asked. "If you are so interested in the beggars why don't you become one, eh?" He started to laugh without mirth. "Imagine him," he pointed at the silent boy, "the dandy of Assisi, the Lord of Love in beggars' clothes." His voice changed to steadied calm. "There's the door, my fine—clothed dandy. Go into the streets of Assisi and try being a beggar."

Francis remained where he stood. Again that tiny smile pulling his lips. "You haven't the guts," his father added.

Francis looked at his mother and again realized that, too, was more pain for her. Every wrangle he had with Pietro was followed by several days of nagging, sanding her nerves with blame. Blaming her for the poor job of upbringing she had done with her eldest son.

Francis had heard several of these harangues. He remembered how quietly Pica stood up against them. Bitterly, Francis pictured her as if she were Beersheba and tied to a stone with a torrent of rain pouring over her. He knew it was disrespectful to concoct such a mental picture—but it rang true.

He tried a dozen methods of avoiding any arguments with Pietro. Yet, somehow, like lodestones, they were drawn against each other. Some trifle would set them off. The original source long lost in the morass of their stubborn wills.

Francis retained one bit of knowledge which he saved from long experience. That was to remain silent when Pietro was angry. The mere fact that the boy stood humble and silent added fuel to his father's wrath. The angrier he was, the more tight-lipped Francis became.

"Well, there is the door," Pietro said finally. "Go ahead and try begging for a few coins and see how you like it."

Francis looked at his mother. He always found a tingle of pleasure from looking at her face. How clean was her skin and fine was her nose and chin. Her skin was taut against her cheekbones, her brown hair shone from constant brushing. She was so proud of her lustrous, live hair. He looked at her, his heart speaking lipless words. He was sorry. Words wouldn't form his lips.

He walked out of the door without glancing back. Francis shut the door slowly until he heard the latch click. Then, he turned and walked towards the stable in the rear of the house. He started to saddle Beersheba.

"Off for a joy ride again?" he heard Angelo's voice from the end of the stable. His brother stood up, shaking stiff threads of hay from his clothing.

Francis detected in the partial gloom of the stable that a pair of small shoes, pointed upward were suddenly drawn backward. A smile of understanding creased his face.

"I see where you are selling a customer a roll of satin," he said.

"I don't admire your sense of humor," his brother retorted. "Anyway, can you do as much?"

"Touché," Francis thought. "It will take me a long time to live down the Countess Trescia."

"You know Mama has always objected to anything like this in the house," Francis warned.

"Well, I am sure you will be quiet," Angelo seemed sure of something.

"You needn't fear," Francis assured him. "Yet I always thought you were such a stickler for business—in the daytime."

His brother didn't reply. Turning quickly, he murmured something which was lost in the gloom of the stable. As Francis mounted his horse, from the block, he heard the bedraggled crackling of the hay.

Francis tied down his lute to the saddle. He rode out into the narrow street. For a moment he hesitated; which way? The reins hung limply from Beersheba. The horse turned her head, questioning. He bent over and patted her between the ears. The horse shut her eyes in delight at his touch.

"Honestly, I don't know," he admitted. "Right or left?" he asked. Impulsively, Francis swung the reins walking the horse slowly. Then he remembered Father Bellas. Perhaps he could help him find some answers.

No, it was too soon to go there again. Pietro found some errands for Francis in Perugia and some nearby cities, so it was almost a month before he was free.

Then, one day he decided to return to the home of Father Bellas and find a peace he could not seem to find in his own home.

Rome 1204

As he rode steadily towards Spello, he kept thinking of his father's words. There were a lot of beggars in the world and it was no fault of the Bernardone family. It was true that Pietro was a little pompous, but he was a good father. Better than most. He, at least, lived at home with his wife and children! His father was a practical man who had to work for every copper. He had no wealthy father, to pay his debts or help him with money and fine clothes. No, Pietro had done these things himself. Building a business and a name which was known from Rome to Flanders to the great fairs in England. Such a reputation was not earned by moping in the fields or sitting in caves or talking about beggars. He agreed that Pietro was a better man than he, Francis.

Anyway, what concern was it of his, Francis, if there were so many beggars? Let the world carry its own worries. Very well, he would do his share by helping the next one he came close to. But they smelled so awfully. Their stinking rags and bodies were almost fetid with the horror of their odors. Didn't these people ever wash? Or rinse out their clothes, even if they were tattered?

This was a world of practical people. Why should he be any different? He remembered what happened to a priest at the school of San Giorgio. The priest had told a group of students that it was possible for the earth to move around the sun! This was unthinkable! But for intervention of a few powerful friends, he would have been excommunicated. Nevertheless, this "crazy priest" was transferred to a solitary monastery for such apostasy.

This is what people got for wanting to be different. The easiest thing in life was to be like the others.

Yet, Francis knew that some of those things, accepted as commonplace, reviled him. Just the way bad odors and filth did, or urinating into the street. There was something wrong about all this. Francis could not fathom the reason why he felt this way.

Later that day, he drew up to the small storeroom of Father Bellas. He looked around the fields where all was quiet. Opening the door without knocking, he strode into the room. The man was fast asleep on the cot. His stomach rising and falling gently, a slow wheeze slipping out of his teeth. Francis paused, wondering if he should go further. He turned to leave.

"Hold there, friend," a voice rose from the reclining man. Francis stopped. The priest sat up with a grunt, his sleepy eyes sought for awakening.

"Oh, it is you?" he said yawning. "Just took a nap. Been up half the night with Jacopa's child. You remember, Gloria?" Francis nodded his head.

He yawned again stretching lustily. "How are you, young Francis?"

"I'm well, thank you. I have come to see you."

"We thought you had forgotten us." His voice was harsh yet kindly modulated.

"You told me to come back," Francis sugggested.

"I did. You are welcome here." The priest's voice was stating the fact. He got off the bed and started busying himself with some pots near the stove. From the corner of his eye, the priest saw that Francis was ill at ease and apparently uncomfortable.

"Sit down, my boy, sit down," he pointed to the rude bench near the heavy table. Francis walked the few steps to the seat and did as he was bidden.

"Well, how did you fare at home?" Father Bellas asked him. "I presume not too well. Get disowned?"

"Almost," Francis smiled impishly. "This much away from it," he lifted his thumb and forefinger to indicate a thin space.

The priest exploded in a hearty laugh. "Well done," he said, "very well done." Soberly he added, "want to spend some time here?" he asked the boy. Francis nodded his head.

"Do I have to work for a living?" An imp grinned out of the boy's eyes. The priest turned towards him. There was silence in the room.

"As you wish," the priest replied. Francis got up and slid out of his coat and tossed it on the bench.

"Why don't you go outside and breathe in some fresh Umbrian air? Do you good." He walked over to the bench still talking, picked up Francis' coat and hung it on a peg. "Fresh air in the lungs is like elixir for your liver—makes you think better."

Francis watched the priest hang the coat, then walked out the door. The dusk was leading the night over the fields like a sentinel hushing an intruder near a sleeping child.

He looked towards the cottage and he could see a light breaking the shadows on the walls. Francis walked over and tapped the door gently.

"Come in" he heard Jacopa say.

The door creaked as it swung open. At that moment Gloria started to cry. It was full of pain.

"Did I waken her?" Francis asked sympathetically. From the corner of his eye he saw an old man seated on the other side of the room. Francis didn't turn. He kept looking at Jacopa, admiring the trimness of her body, the compactness of her face and hair. She had bunched her walnut-red hair into a large knot behind her head. He remembered the soft woman touch of her body with his.

The child continued to whimper.

"She's teething," Jacopa told him. "It is rather late for her so her gums are hard. I think she is making about two or three at a time. We don't have any soothing syrup for her. The poor child must suffer this alone."

"I know what she needs," Francis said quickly. "It never fails." He went out of the door, then returned a minute later with his lute.

Jacopa smiled when she saw what Francis held in his arms. Gloria kept whimpering.

"Most of her older sisters love my friend here," he patted the round glossy side of the yellow wood. "Let me try," he begged her. She nodded her head.

Francis' fingers were gentle as he grazed the strings. He touched them delicately as if he were riffling fine velvet. His voice was low and sweet as he hummed softly to the child. He sang an old Provencal lullaby he had heard Pica sing to him. ". . . and guardian angels near the child, sweeten the breath of night air, with garlands fresh and mild."

His voice stroked and soothed the child's nerves. Her muscles relaxed and she stopped whimpering. When she looked at him, Francis lay aside the lute and took her small hand into his. He bent down over the bed. The child rubbed her shoulders, twisting them in delight. Her eyes closed. Francis withdrew his hand gently, believing her asleep. She moved quickly and grasped his forefinger in her fist. Holding it, she fell asleep with a faint sigh. The room was quiet except for the sound of the child's breathing.

Gently and slowly he pried her small fingers away. Then, holding her wrist, he allowed her hand to rest on the pillow. He was able to straighten up now. Looking at Jacopa's eyes he caught the look of tenderness in her eyes.

Francis turned when he heard someone behind him stand up. He recognized Old Isaac!

"We meet once more, my young friend," the old man said. "This time it is my grandchild."

"You were looking for your son?"

"No, you remember I told you he was . . . lost in Provence, the so-called crusade against the French. This was his wife. This is their child." He pointed to the bed. "I am fortunate indeed to have found them alive. The God Of Israel still watches over His children."

Francis stood there, listening quietly. His lute lay on the floor beside him.

"Here it is 1204 and they are killing Jews. Twelve hundred years ago the Romans killed one on a cross. Now Christians kill his brothers and sisters ten thousand times over," the man said bitterly.

"Please Father," Jacopa's voice pleaded with the old man.

"Of what avail is all our philosophy, all our wit and wisdom when the sword and the torch still rules the world," he argued solemnly.

"They are not all bad," Francis suggested.

"Of course not," the old man responded warmly. "This isn't a world of monsters. They fought each other until they destroyed themselves. We are human and we have brains to think. Is the regeneration of man to find no haven of peace?"

"Father, Francis is our guest," Jacopa broke in.

The old man walked over to Francis and put his arm around his bony shoulders.

"I am not speaking to the Francis' of the world. You have fine qualities of manhood in you which few men possess. Save them well like rare treasures which we nurture carefully."

"What could I do?" Francis asked. There was an interruption as the door opened and Father Bellas came in. He glanced at the corner where the sleeping child lay.

"Welcome my good friend," Old Isaac said.

"How do the Jews say it?" the priest asked smiling. "Shalom, shalom."

"We say Shalom Aleichem," the old man told him. "Peace unto you." The response should be 'Aleichem Shalom.' Unto you I offer peace. The greatest gift one can offer to another."

"A noble saying," Father Bellas replied heartily. "Unfortunately not too well prescribed by many of my fellow Christians."

"This young man wanted to know what he could or should do to make this a better world," Old Isaac informed the priest gravely.

Gloria stirred. "Hush you men," Jacopa smiled to them. The three of them walked outdoors.

Father Bellas spoke first. "What can be done? Speak up and be heard. Call each infamy by name."

"Do you want to see me burned at the stake," Francis asked impishly. "I am too young for that."

"The Church is like a big wholesome mother. She has good sons and bad ones. It falls upon the good ones to chastise the others. Because there are bad and spoiled children—one does not condemn the mother."

"One should call her to account for her bad ones as well as the good ones," Old Isaac added.

"True, many of us who are devout Catholics realize that there is rottenness which must be rooted out. But how, Lord God of the Heavens, how?" the priest asked. "I've been caught myself."

"Protest," the older man spoke, enunciating the two syllables.

"But it means the club and often the fire," Father Bellas told them.

"There are in every age men of courage who will fight and die for their ideals. There is yet a small portion of God in all of us," Old Isaac told them.

"A small portion of God," Father Bellas mused on his tongue. "Very well put."

Francis' nimble mind caught this phrase, too. "There is yet a small portion of God in all of us." He stored it away. For this thought would help him many a time in later years when he would search for help.

"Look at us," Old Isaac told them. "Aren't we, the Jews, a sign of protest. As long as the world vexes its childish yet murderous wrath against us is there yet room for Christians to learn Christianity?"

Francis caught at this too, storing its succinct philosophy away for future use.

"You have gone about the land begging," Francis asked of the old man. "How does a person feel—I mean, doesn't he feel ashamed . . . oh, I can't find the right words."

"One day you will find yourself," Old Isaac told him. "That day you will find the words too. Don't despair. How does it feel to be a beggar? Let me see if I can find the words."

"Let us relax and therefore learn something of use," Father Bellas beckoned to several stones nearby. They sat down. Old Isaac remained standing. The moon hung bright above them in the sky, the night filled with soft light and a tiny breeze slipped across the Umbrian fields. The moon's light danced in the tiny white ringlets of the man's beard. Francis noticed for the first time that the man wore a small embroidered skullcap on the back of his head. The man stroked his soft beard, then he spoke to the boy and the priest seated near the ground.

"There is a philosophy of religion in the world, and this is not of the Hebrew, that there are only two spirits, Good and Bad. That people are good or they are bad. If we do good then that spirit is with us; if not, then the other. I would go a step further and say this, that the messengers of God and the Devil are all about us. We cannot see them because they are like the wind. They can see us, and penetrate and fathom our veriest thoughts. Does that sound incomprehensible to you?"

"The basic idea of the Holy Ghost," Father Bellas offered.

"You mean, I may be having the devil on my shoulder?" Francis smiled. "In that event, begging your pardon, get thee behind me, thou satan."

The priest and the old man laughed aloud. Francis, at first unsure of its reception, joined them.

"This is a wise one," Father Bellas said, wiping a tear from the corner of his eye with his sleeve. "Francis has a keen wit."

"A laugh is sometimes worth a thousand words," the old man said. "Yes, there is probably a messenger of God there too, near the other one."

"We choose either one?" Francis asked. "Do we have a choice?"

"We most certainly do," Father Bellas said. "But go on, Isaac, what about your begging."

"Don't you see at that moment when a beggar asks you for something, you must make a choice—the good or the bad?" Old Isaac smiled to them.

"If I give, then I have chosen the good spirit?" Francis wondered aloud.

"That is about it," the priest said.

"The beggar gives a person the opportunity to make a clear choice without any frills or soul searching. For a few breaths of time, he has let the spirit of goodness within his heart."

"You see, my son," Old Isaac spoke to Francis, "there is no shame in being a beggar. You are giving people an opportunity to become human."

"But I don't want to be a beggar," Francis told them.

The two men laughed. "No one said you should," the priest said. "We are not talking about you. When two old duffers like Isaac and myself talk, we philosophize about the world. You don't need it, but it certainly wouldn't do you any harm to try and beg. Try it sometime. It is good for any cockiness you may have. It will certainly teach you humility."

The next four days, Francis learned how to work in the fields, milk and feed Anta the cow, wash clothing, lime the barn and make himself generally useful. Up at dawn, he worked all day except for meals and then into bed, tired and pleased with himself. He spoke little with Father Bellas or Old Isaac. Yet he found some time for little Gloria. The little girl would call him 'Fants' and always came close to his side when he was near. It was a source of gentle amusement for the three adults to watch this young female wile her charms at the boy. She would grunt and point with her fingers to the open fields. He somehow understood her and would lead the child out.

Walking together she would chatter her glib, senseless sounds, thinking she was saying something to him. Francis would listen gravely and encourage her to say more.

Sometimes he would talk aloud to her as if she really understood him. Once a flock of birds flew overhead. They both craned their necks watching them wheel about them in the sky.

Francis lifted the child in his arms, she watched his face intently as he spoke. "These are birds . . . birds . . ." he formed the word for the little girl. "They are God's chosen creatures. They have the full sky for their playground. They do not work and earn nothing. Yet the Good Lord provides his bounty for them. They must indeed be God's chosen ones."

He spoke to her of nature and the beauty of the flowers and the trees about them. Once he lifted up a fistful of cool soil into his fist.

"See, here is the rich earth. The earth gives us all our things to eat like a good brother shares with his own. See here, we plant a few tiny seeds which are useless by themselves. But, in the soil, God nurtures and warms it into life. And thus we have food."

He bent on his knees as if in a moment of worship, lifting up a few handsful of cool earth and dropped them down again. The girl imitated him and she, too, bent and clasped two small clumps in her fists.

"Dood, dood," she repeated.

"The earth is good, little girl," Francis smiled down at her. He felt grateful to this child for in a few days, she had given him more confidence in himself. In loving her, he loved all children. By this token, he felt stronger.

It was on the night of the fourth day that he spoke with the priest.

"I don't know where to turn. There is something alive inside me which wants the light of day. I don't know what it is which wants life. I can't probe or touch its heart. But somehow it has made me hate scholarly learning, to dislike my father's business. It has made me nauseous of dirt, of filth and becomes reviled at the fleshy gluttony of women. All these things it has done. To all these things it has said *no*. To what will it say *yes?*"

The priest nodded his heavy head, sympathetically. Again, Francis could sense the tremendous physical power of this man.

"I know what that could be. I felt something kin to that just before I took my final vows. There is a period of searching within your own heart."

"Didn't you ask for any help at all?" asked Francis.

"I most assuredly did," was the answer. "I prayed most earnestly. Yet I felt that God in his wisdom decided to leave me alone. This one decision must come from within and with no compulsion. I had to decide freely, honestly, and of my own volition."

"That and no more?" asked the boy.

"I could suggest something," the priest replied. "An old priest and a good friend, Lord rest his soul, told me to go somewhere."

"Where?" queried Francis.

"Go to St. Peters in Rome," Father Bellas said. He answered the surprised look on the boy's face. "Somehow at the tomb of this most volatile of the Apostle Saints, people from everywhere find respect, dignity, and often the answers for themselves. Think of it, a poor fisherman who found a great ideal in his friend Jesus. Remember he was a Jew too. Then, after the death, go off into the far reaches of the world, selling that ideal to people."

"I suppose that requires better selling ability than having them buy some rolls of silk," Francis smiled.

"You can see a roll of silk stuff, touch it and know its value," the priest pointed out. "But Peter sold them and made them cherish only an idea."

"Do you think I may find something there?" asked Francis.

"Even in death, the spirit of St. Peter lives. Every year thousands of people from all parts of the world go there. They somehow find peace and a road to happiness."

"I may find what I want," Francis said very slowly. Then shrugging his shoulders, "then again, perhaps not."

Early the next morning, Francis, after a frugal breakfast, left for Rome. Once again he found his road down the Flaminian Way. Briefly, he encountered his daydreams of becoming a great soldier. He felt no bitterness or regret at their passing, *then* he knew *where* he was going and why. His life had direction and purpose. What had it now? Wasn't he searching for some firefly which flashed life then was lost. All these and many other questions sped through his mind.

His head suddenly perked up. His nose detected that most horrible of all human odors, the lazar house. He kicked Beersheba into a canter, meanwhile holding a perfumed kerchief to his nose. Every time he came near one of these leper hospitals, he felt like separating from his last meal. Not until he had left odors and building far behind did he remove his nose covering. Even then his stomach began to throb.

When he reached Spoletto, he kept to the outskirts of the town to avoid any chance meeting with the Trescias.

He slept overnight in a house outside of Rieti. The next morning he pressed on to Rome. He found his way towards St. Peters. Francis noticed that pilgrims left their horses and wagons close to the Basilica, some of them trodding over the gardens and walks. As a mark of respect, he tethered his horse at the end of the garden. For safety, he hired a street urchin to guard Beersheba until he returned. He was in no mood to walk back to Assisi.

Walking down the flat-stoned path leading to the marble stairs, he remembered the story Pica had told him about Charlemagne. As Francis approached them, he felt as if he, too, were standing here back in the year 774 and watched this King of Kings mount these same stairs on his knees, kissing each step. Then, at the top, he was received by Pope Hadrian I. In his mind, Francis could see the young king towering over the paladins around him, his glossy blond hair catching the gold from the sun, as a jeweled crown was placed upon his head. There, and the boy's eyes tried to locate the exact spot, was crowned the Emperor of the World.

Francis looked down at himself. He saw his bony legs. Then he slid the palm of his hand over his face, feeling the flat cheekbones, the small round chin and his lips. Against the memory of that—he thought to himself—who am I?

He felt the impulse to turn away and go home, because there had stood a great king and a greater soldier. What could Francis bring with him up these steps but a few empty daydreams?

Looking about him, he saw the beggars. There were dozens of them, each pleading for special dispensation from a passerby.

"A copper for the flesh on my face, eaten by leprosy."

"A few coppers for an arm cut by a bastard of a magistrate."

Francis saw others with noses and ears hideously slit (probably punished for their crimes, he thought). There were more beggars near St. Peters than there were flies which swarmed around each one of them.

A curious twist of his lips portrayed Francis' smile at the memory of his conversation with Old Isaac and Father Bellas. An individual would indeed have to be of sturdy character to approach one of these stinking bits of flotsam up here, let alone give it a coin.

Maybe his father was right. Why should *he*, Francis, worry about scum like this?

A beggar near him pleaded and kept intoning, "A copper for this armless one."

Francis tossed him a coin which the man caught adroitly in his remaining fist. His long brown shaggy hair strung to his shoulders. It gave the boy a feeling of superiority that he could *give* and the other had to *take*.

The armless one did a curious thing. Francis expected the usual profuse thanks. The man said nothing. Holding the coin in his fist, he waved his forefinger in a greeting to Francis. Boy and beggar looked at each other, held by their eyes. Somehow, one was evaluating the other. They were not to forget.

The boy's eyes moved towards the people moving up the huge marble steps. He was no longer afraid. Mounting, he counted them methodically.

At the top, he moved with some other people across the atrium into the marbled courtyard, framed by arched stone cloisters. With a trace of amusement, his eyes were held by the bronze cone above the Pilgrims' Fountain. For a moment, he thought the artisan had designed a huge man's organ, then thought the better of his humor. Francis with an eye for the dramatic, thought this unknown sculptor would label his handiwork, "There, man, stands thy King."

He strolled about the yard, drinking in its sedate and cloistered beauty. There was nothing like this anywhere he had been. Some of the visitors moved past the solid silver door into the huge cathedral. Entering from bright sunlight into the sudden half darkness of this huge chamber, all mundane thoughts were driven out of his head.

It was as though a powerful soundless voice had instructed, "come unto me with an open heart. Observe the might of my handiwork." Francis' eyes traveled down the long, columned expanse leading towards the altar and the apse.

He asked an attendant where the Apostles' tomb was. Francis learned it was near the altar. Once again, he felt small in this huge edifice. But he didn't feel lost, because there was an inviting yet cool warmth here which bade him go on. He walked down.

He approached the altar and saw the canopy resting on the four marble pillars. Francis drew himself against the wall, watching the others kneel close to the grating through which one could look into the chapel holding the tomb.

He moved closer to see the kind of people who were kneeling at the tomb. There were many strangers from far-off lands. Wealthy ones he could determine by the quality of their clothing, the fine veils of the women shot with gold thread, the satiny brocaded dresses. He saw a few pilgrims in dress of the clergy. People came to the grating and made their prayers on bended knees, left some money and then went away. There was a continual stream of people coming, staying and going. There was something strange here which Francis couldn't fathom. He wasn't sure what it was.

He was curious as he looked at the three men dressed with white turbans spangled with jewels who had servants put small cushions on the floor for their knees. He noticed how fervently a few young priests prayed. Several women came there for personal problems, and without shame pleaded their cases aloud.

There was a curious sameness of pattern in the supplicants. Each of them wanted something for which they were willing to pay adequately. It was as if they had come to a powerful prince to ask his intervention with a King, in exchange for a price. To some this price was negation, to most of them it was money. If the King wanted to sell they would buy.

Then he saw the Countess Trescia! Francis hadn't recognized her, because she wore a veil around her thick, blond hair which partially covered her face. Once again she wore a long, simple dress. She had no jewels. How unlike she was in dress from all the other women who had been coming here. Some wore dresses, cut low and deep under their breasts. Hers was tight to her neck. He glanced at her face and a trace of pity flashed in his mind. She was no longer the rich lustful countess. Here was a woman child-like in some personal hurt.

She was kneeling close to the grating. Francis was curious. He also kneeled down, slightly behind her. Her low voice carried very clearly.

"This vile thing a man has planted in my body, Dear St. Peter, help me rid myself of this affliction. If you intercede for me, I will give 100 pieces of silver to your church."

Her voiced dipped lower as a few other people came near her. Francis watched the Countess extract a piece of silver and drop it into the holder near the grating. She rose hurriedly, shielding her face and moved away quickly. Francis didn't turn around to watch her go.

At this moment he pitied these supplicants who came to ask favors and contribute a little money to the upkeep of this cathedral.

No, he would ask no favors of St. Peter. What could he ask? He didn't know for what.

He would show them! Dipping into the purse which hung inside his belt, Francis extracted six silver coins. They sang among themselves as he dropped them into the holder. Several of the people, caught by the sound, paused to look at him. He knew they were looking. He straightened his back and felt proud. So he *could* attract attention, Francis thought to himself. Walking up the long expanse of the huge chamber, without thinking, he counted the marble pillars.

Stepping past the huge silver door from the semi-darkness inside the church he stepped into the bright sunlit courtyard. He got the impression of being pushed out of the darkness into the light. That was a strange feeling, indeed.

Walking slowly and a little perturbed he moved towards the Pilgrim's Fountain. He looked at the bronze cone again; this time he could find no humor in its shape. He stared at it, his eyes held by the glint of the sun's rays. Somewhere, he could hear the fast trickle of water, sounds building on themselves. He knew people moved near him. Some of them looked at him, wondering at his fascination of the bronze cone. They looked, too. Seeing nothing, they moved on.

Francis was held there; he had no power to move. Everything around him was blurred and non-existent. The only thing in his life was the sight of that point on top of the fountain. The only sound he heard was that of the trickling, dancing water. There was nothing else.

Then he imagined someone speaking to him. He remembered the words but had little recollection of the voice which spoke them.

"You will find the sign. Go where it leads you," the voice repeated, "go where it leads you."

Suddenly, Francis became aware of the movement around him, the details of faces, people and things. An involuntary shudder raised gooseflesh on his arms and back. He felt as if he had just shaken loose from a deep sleep.

He continued walking outward towards the huge porch above the marble stair. He could look down and survey the gardens, the stone walks, the tradesmen selling their wares, the movement of horses, wagons, and people. Then he saw the one-armed beggar still in the place where he had left him. His eyes slid across all the movement below him and he could spot the beggars in various positions. Some were seated on the ground. Others stood up, hunching their shoulders.

It was then he remembered something which had haunted his thoughts when he was inside St. Peter's. Now, he remembered what was missing! He didn't see *one* poor person come into the church. All the supplicants who had been there were rich ones or priests! St. Peter, the poor fisherman, who himself disliked the rich ones, was prayed to by them alone! What cruel irony, Francis thought.

Caught up in his own perturbed thoughts, he slowly walked down the stairs.

"Ho, there, my young friend," he heard a voice speak near him. Francis, startled out of his vagary, turned. There stood the beggar he'd met before.

"Well," the man asked heartily. "Feel better now?"

Beggar and rich man's son looked at each other like equals. The man straightened up and he was taller and broader than the boy.

"Should I?" Francis asked.

"Makes all people feel good, having a cry with good old Pete up there," the beggar said. Francis could hear a note of mockery in the man's voice and see disdain in his eyes.

The boy started to move away.

"Don't go," the man's voice ordered. "Afraid to hear more?"

"No, I'm not afraid to listen," the boy faced the man. He could see the tinge of red-gold was spun by the sun in the man's shaggy hair.

"If people would listen to us, the beggars, this would be a better world."

"I'm listening," the boy said, humbly.

"We beggars have hit the bottom of life itself. A body can't go any lower in the scale. Can you think of anything lower?" the man asked.

"No," Francis shook his head gravely.

"Maybe except a priest," the man laughed, "but they don't count. Just a minute," he had turned towards a man who was passing them. "A copper for this armless one. A copper, please," the beggar pleaded. The man moved on without turning to look.

Francis hadn't seen the man's face but something about his back strung at his memory. He *had* seen that man before. Where? Then he remembered it was Peter Cattaneo. He was the canon of a big church near Assisi. This Peter could have well afforded a few coppers for the beggar. Francis shrugged his shoulders.

"Well, let's get back to our conversation," the beggar said heartily. There was a glint of amusement in his eyes as he probed the boy's thoughts.

"It doesn't bother us," the man added. "More pass us by than stop."

"He could have given you a few coins," Francis said.

"Look at us." The man's arm took in all the beggars near the huge church. "You see in us the truest philosophers in the world. What value are all the scholars, all our art, all our great religious teachings if we, people like myself, must exist? What price does our civilization have to pay for such fine quality?" he asked.

"You speak like a scholar yourself," Francis said.

"What is a scholar? Only one who knows where to find the right book or where it reposes. Oh, I have read a book or two. But reading is the simplest of all occupations. The harder one is to think and feel right here," the man placed his hand over his heart. "Scholars can be awfully stupid people, because they know what is inside the four corners of a book. They don't know anything else outside it. I know, believe me."

"I wonder how it would feel to be a beggar," Francis mused aloud.

"You could learn something about human nature. Want to try it?" the armless beggar asked him.

Francis thought a moment, then agreed.

They walked behind the cathedral toward a small atrium on the side. As they approached they saw a small crowd of people crowded in a corner. Francis hesitated.

"Don't mind them," the beggar told him. "It is only a dice game."

"Here in St. Peter's?" Francis wondered.

"Why not?" the man responded. "It's quiet here. They can have some fun. What will they do upstairs? Pray to old Pete? There is no room up there for them."

Francis remained silent. He remembered his own recent thoughts.

They pushed their way through the crowd of men to a corner. It was semi-dark. There Francis took off his clothes; his brocaded jacket, his finely woven long hose and trousers. The beggar lifted off his long tattered robe. With a feeling of distaste and slight nausea, Francis smelt the dried sweat as he pulled the sacky robe over his head.

The beggar dressed in Francis' clothes. Being taller, the jacket was short at the wrists and the hose considerably shorter at the calves.

They surveyed each other critically.

"Nice material," the man commented, fingering the cloth.

Francis imitated the beggar, grasping the coarse robe. "Nice material for a sand-bag," he laughed. The other joined him heartily. He struck Francis a resounding wallop on the back.

"You're a good boy," he laughed. "You are all right."

Francis noticed that none of the dice players had turned to look at them. They were too intent on their game.

"Let's get outside," Francis said.

Once again they pushed their way out into the sunlight.

"Where do I go to beg?" asked the boy.

"That's the spirit," the man replied. "You can go in one spot and only one. That's the one I had."

"Why only there?" was the query.

"Because if we didn't, we would be fighting each other every minute," was the answer. "This way we have agreed among ourselves and we have peace."

"As simple as that." Francis' voice was succinct.

"That's right. Some of us were even thinking of pooling all our collections, then sharing them at the end of the day."

"You could form a beggars' guild," Francis suggested, an impish gleam in his eyes.

"Don't think we haven't thought of that," the beggar told him. "We have."

He led him to the spot where Francis had first met him.

"How long have you begged here?" the boy asked him.

"Two years," was the laconic response.

Francis looked across the square and pointed to one of the beggars. "Those strange marks on his cheeks. They look like two neat crosses."

"They are," the man replied; he pressed his lips together as if he were angry.

"Why that?" Francis asked, innocently.

"Haven't you seen those before? That's old Armenio. Spent two years in the clink and got those on his cheeks. So he won't forget. Helped himself to a piece of pottery up at a monastery somewhere in Calabria. Worked a week there as a mason. They tried to gyp him out of his money. So he took an old pot."

"For that, he's marked for life?" Francis asked.

"Yes. He won't forget now. He can steal anyplace else, but never from a holy building."

"Would I offend you if I asked you about that?" Francis pointed to the armless side of the beggar.

The man inclined his head towards his right side. "This?" he queried. "Sign of the times. We are returning to the old Bible days. An eye for an eye—and, you know what I mean. . . ."

"What was your crime?" Francis asked, "which paid for that?"

"I come from up north, little town called Sienna. Friend of mine, name of Arno, bought a bone from sombody. Said it belonged to one of the Saints. If a man fasted ten days and made a wish, holding this bone in his mouth, he could have anything he wanted."

"Another stupid superstition," Francis bit out.

The man laughed, disdainfully. "I said the same thing. I guess Arno didn't like to be told that he'd been fooled. We had words and Arno lost two teeth. So I got myself in the clink."

"But the arm?" Francis queried. His voice was low.

"Oh, I forgot to tell you. Arno's brother-in-law was the magistrate of the district. So I lost the arm to pay for two teeth."

Francis shuddered. "How much do you collect in a day?" he asked. "The best day."

The man looked at Francis carefully. "About twenty coppers," he replied. "Depends on the day . . . happy day, everybody gives. On a weepy day no one gives anything. They have their own troubles."

"I won't deprive you," the boy said quickly. "Here," he reached under his belt and drew out two gold coins. "Take this."

The man and the boy looked at each other, waiting.

"I can't refuse this," the beggar said. "Two gold coins. I could live like a king for half a year with these." He shook his head as he started to walk away. "A fellow could believe in God with miracles like this."

For half an hour he pleaded with people passing by to give him a coin. No success. He sat on the ground. Still no coppers. Still determined, he hid one arm under his robe and across his chest. "Alms for the armless one," he pleaded.

A woman dropped a coin in his open palm.

"Thank you dear lady," Francis said. "God will thank you, too."

The woman stopped, dipped into her purse and returned. She gave Francis two more coins. Then she walked away.

He still had little success after a full hour. On impulse, he strode away towards his horse. He moved to take the lute off Beersheba's saddle. The street urchin didn't recognize Francis.

"Hey, you can't take that," he shouted. "I'll call my friends."

"This is my horse and my lute," Francis told him, staring at the little boy. The urchin looked at the other carefully, memory carried its wings across the boy's face.

"Did someone steal your clothing?" he asked incredibly.

Francis laughed. "No," he shook his head. "I didn't lose them. I . . . well . . . I'm playing a game of mimes with some friends."

The urchin was satisfied with this answer.

"Now, mind you," Francis warned. "Take care of my good friend. There is another coin for you when I come back."

Francis walked back with his lute. Several small boys gathered together and strung after his heels like small dirty puppies.

Returning to his begging place, he started to work his strings, playing a catchy tune which had been recently introduced by Pierre Vidal from Provence. In a few minutes, a large crowd had circled him. Some from curiosity, most to hear a free show.

"How about a song, troubador," a fat, paunchy man shouted from the edge of the crowd. Francis nodded his head. One of the urchins who had followed him took off his worn, old hat and approached the man. The fat one glanced at Francis, who nodded his head, smiling.

They could hear the clink of silver and copper coins in the hat. Francis waved his free hand for the man's generosity.

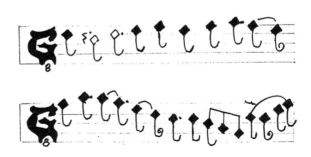

"Give a coin to save your Soul,
  Give a coin to save your Soul,
    To save your Soul, so give a coin."

Francis sang in his clear voice, using the music of an old childhood ditty he had heard. As he started to sing, the crowd about him was hushed into a sudden silence. He glanced at some of the urchins.

Francis looked about him as he sang, reaching them with his voice. Jibing at them with his just concocted words to an old melody, popular with many troubadors.

His gaze was fixed on the cathedral above them.

The street urchins passed among the crowd collecting coins in a hat. In the pause Francis looked at the crowd which surrounded him. He was curious about them. His mind paused and surveyed each face. Each one was so different!

—That heavy matron, with the heavy chest and good rich clothing, caught his eyes. Her face was sensual, pudgy and yet her eyes were soft and searching for things they could not see.

—The young dandy, in pretty, foppish clothes, with a swaggering feather in his hat, looking at Francis with a smile tinged with the sight of seeing all follies and now met something he could not fathom.

—That man leaning on a cane, the scars of war on his face and the beaten wrinkles of open fields, were silent watchdogs of a scene to be stored with other memories of other places.

Then he saw Bernard de Quintavalle, with his head slightly cocked, an amused look on his face. Francis smiled knowingly at him, embracing his friend by opening his arms in a gesture of including him in this nonsense.

Later, as he and Bernard walked away from St. Peter's Cathedral, they heard loud noises. Coming closer, they learned that, this being carnival time, there would be a foot race held on the Corso, as one of the dressed up dandies told them "to make sport for the people."

That year for the first time, eight Jews of varying ages and sizes had been ordered by the authorities to appear before the "judges" in the Corso on the Bourse. This was demanded of the Jewish community.

Carnival time drew people from all Italy to enjoy the parties and the fun. This also drew many hooligans, pickpockets, and thieves who flourished on their innocent victims.

As Francis and Bernard walked along the street, two crowded lanes of people formed on two sides, waiting for the race to begin. They could see them preparing sticks, stones, old vegetables, eggs, and bags of human offal.

Several people noticed the lute on the boy's back and asked for a song. Two young girls made as if to take the instrument away from Francis. He avoided them with a smile.

They heard a commotion and loud shouts near the starting place. Coming closer they learned from the bystanders that one of the Jews refused to race, claiming he was sick. In fact, he had vomited a few minutes earlier in the street. They could see an emaciated man with a thin face and thinner body, racked by illness.

"If you are sick," one of the officials pompously shouted at him, "why did you volunteer for the race?"

"Sometimes, it is better to die in the sunlight than some stinking hovel of a room," the man replied, speaking slowly. "Even one like me is worth ten like those those." The man pointed his thin hand at the mobs lining the race course.

The eight men were then forced to remove all their clothing, hose and shoes, except for their loin cloths and line up at the start. The thin man had his clothing torn off his body and pushed into the line. The starter had a big brass pan in his arms, which he started to beat with vengeance. The people behind the racers pushed them forward into the open area between the two lines of people. Someone pushed the thin man viciously. He sprawled into the street, sliding on the cobbled stones. He lay there a moment and started to rise.

Francis moved forward and started to pick him up. Beside him was Bernard. One of the officials came over to Francis and the sick man.

"Only one Jew would help another," the dandified official shouted at Francis. Francis rose angrily to confront the older man.

"Francis, don't," Bernard warned the boy, knowing that the temper of a crowd would turn on them in a few minutes.

Some had short spears and many had leather whips at their sides. They all had one thing in common. They were waiting for the hapless Jews to come racing near them, so they could vent their rages at them.

Walking closer and craning his head, Francis could see where the eight hapless Jews stood. These were no athletes. These were men with the soft paunches of middle age.

There was not a single racer who was under forty. "These men can't race a mile," Bernard told him. "That is why they are selected for this. So they will fall, faint or be so slow that they will be beaten easily by this mob of crazy ones."

"Can't anything be done about this," Francis asked the older man. "Why do they have to take it?"

"Customs and habits of many years cannot be easily broken," he was told. "The mobs, like the old Roman festivals in the Coliseum, always needed victims and the blood of the dead appeased the crowds. That is human nature. It doesn't change. We have only changed our language from Latin to French and German. People need goats to appease their hungers. Eight hundred years ago the Romans made the Christians the scapegoats. Today, these same Christians use the Jews for this purpose."

"Are people so weak that they must turn on the Jews to satisfy their desires for pleasure?" Francis asked.

"Many Jewish families have lived in Rome from the time of the early Roman Empire, yet the newcomers to Rome think of them as foreigners and Christ killers," Bernard told him.

"Who encourages this kind of treatment?" the boy asked.

Bernard pointed his hands towards the residence of the Popes. "If they didn't want this, it would not be. They encourage this to make the Jew into a creature of pity and low estate. If you spit on him and drive him like a mangy dog, you destroy a man's respect not only for himself, but among his neighbors. This race is another example of bringing a people into the dust."

"I'll take his place," Francis told the official, tearing off his beggar clothes and tossing them into the street. The other runners were already a distance away. Francis raced after them knowing the faster he would run, the less the roughnecks in the two lines would be able to strike at him.

As he caught up to the racing men, he could feel the mushy crush of decaying vegetables and eggs strike his body. He hated these people for striking at his clean body and making him so dirty. Someone tossed a thin bag of human offal at him, striking his legs. He shuddered in anger and shame.

He wavered for a few moments coming to a narrow line of the mob. One of them, reaching out with a short spear, aimed it at his manhood. He turned slightly and received the thrust on his thighs. He could feel the burn of the cut across his flesh. He grabbed the spear from the hands of the man and turning, thrust the handle into the man's face. The face was gone, as Francis ran on, holding on to the short spear.

Francis moved on towards the runners, feeling repulsed and shamed by the dirt and filth on his body. One man reached out from the mob and struck at Francis with a cat-o-nine tails. The boy felt the sting on his bare back. He turned and caught the whip in his hands.

The man held on to the whip. It drew him closer to the boy. He spat full into Francis face. The boy heard a shout near him, "Go on. This mob will kill you. Run on boy, run on." He could sense the mob trying to choke him into a single place to surround and buffet him.

He started to run again. The stones under his bare feet felt cold and slippery from centuries of use. He was behind the other runners. Pausing for a moment, he wondered if he should run ahead or behind them. If he were ahead of them, he would receive the brunt of the blows and the rage of the two mobs would be vented on him. He dropped the short spear he had held just behind him. Like fish bait, the mob fought itself to possess the weapon.

He pushed through the panting, sweating men. Their naked bodies, white marble like, contrast with the dark skins of their assailants. Francis glanced at these strangers, Jews like himself, strangers in an alien world of Christians. He wondered who they were and what they did. The panting breaths of the runners came heavier and sodden with gasps of pain.

One of the older men stumbled and he was ready to fall. Francis held him under the shoulders. He could feel rather than see the sullen mob around him, beating his bare body with stones, fists, and whips. And all this in this year of peace, 1204. A thought raced through the boy's mind. "Is that what Jesus died for? What these ruffians are doing to His own people?"

Someone shouted in his ear. "Run boy, run . . . this mob will kill you. Leave the old man and save yourself."

Francis held on to the older man, stumbling along and running with his arms under the man's shoulders. He could feel his own breath coming in long, deep gasps searching for more air.

His body was beginning to feel numb with the blows and the added ones were no longer felt. His shoulders were bleeding from the whip lashes.

The sweat and tears of shame were mixed with the salty taste of blood on his lips as he moved along with the man.

At last he heard a shout as if from a great distance and knew that he could run no more. The two lines of the mobs had ended. One day of degradation for the Jews in the Rome of 1204 had just ended.

He felt the man under his arms go limp as he slid to the ground. There was a rattle in the man's throat, rasping and drawing for air. Then the man was quiet and Francis knew he was dead.

One of the officials, evidently a doctor, bent over and listened at the dead man's chest. He arose shrugging his shoulders, "Too much for his heart. These Jews are soft." Francis looked up at the doctor and his hands wanted to strangle him. He felt a restraining arm and heard Bernard whisper into his ear. "No Francis, no boy. We'll go home now." His voice was kind and soothed the numb anger the boy felt and the cuts and bruises on his body.

Two men with a cart took away the body of the dead Jew. Francis walked away from the spot with Bernard, who took off his cloak and covered the sweaty and bruised body of the boy.

The two walked close to one of the Roman fountains spouting water. The older man helped the boy wash the slime and dirt off his clear white skin. The man knew that the boy was revolted and shamed by the outrage upon his body, for he knew that Francis was meticulous about keeping his body clean. Bernard knew that the bruises would soon be healed, but the memory of this day would live with Francis to his last days.[11]

"Why, why?" asked the boy. "We don't have anything like this in Assisi. Are the people better than those who are here?"

"At carnival time, this is before Lent, and all the criminal elements come into Rome. The authorities made this up for the 'sport of the public.' The Jews are the easiest targets."

"Why can't they fight back?" the boy wanted to know.

"For a simple and obvious reason. The Jews are outnumbered a hundred to one. Who will you fight? It would be like striking the waves in the ocean."

"All this must start someplace, Bernard," Francis said and his voice shook. "There are probably some fine people in that mob. A few leaders make a mob and there it is becoming like a wild animal."

[11]This practice of racing Jews on the Corso in Rome became an annual fixture by order of Pope Paul II (1464-71). There is no proof that this race *did not occur* in 1204. The degradation of the Jews in Europe had already begun with the elevation of Pope Innocent III in 1198. Worse events were to come.

"Where does it all start?" Bernard asked. "It all starts in the churches. It started when the churches were taken over by the Romans and the Greeks about 800 years ago, about the year 400. For 800 years, children coming into the churches hear that the Jews crucified Christ and that he was killed by wicked men. These children are told that Jesus cursed this people and punished them for all time. Some of them grow up to be good and most others have some Christianity. But all of them grow up hating the Jews, the Christ killers."

"But, this is not true," Francis replied.

"I know it," Bernard said "I am only saying what children are taught and have been taught for about 800 years. The priests twisted around the true words of St. Matthew and St. Paul."

"I talked with my friend Benjamin, you remember my friend Benjamin?" the boy asked. "He showed me that Luke, Matthew, and Mark took special care to say that the Jewish people, they too were Jews, did not kill Jesus. Because Jesus was one of their people and they only wanted a leader to free them from the Roman yoke. The Jews believed that he would help them do this. I am sure if Jesus were alive today he would not like to see something like we had today." Francis pointed to the Corso.

"If Jesus were alive today," Bernard said quietly, "the Popes would probably burn him at the stake for being a Catharist. All he wanted to do was to bring some new life into Judaism. He *never* intended to found a new religion bent on destroying His own brethren."

San Damiani 1204

When Francis returned to his house, he found that Pietro had also returned from one of his long trips across Europe. It was summer, so Pietro asked Francis to go to the Foligno Fair, below Assisi. He took a wagon load of goods, drawn by one of their pack horses, with Vollo behind the reins. Francis took his own horse, Beersheba.

At the Fair, as he rode through the streets, he was greeted with familiar shouts of "Hey Francis," by many of the merchants, who had their stalls along the streets. He had often been there with his father and the boy had entertained the men at the inn, during their midday meal, singing troubador songs to amuse them.

Francis was able to sell the entire load of woolens and silks easily to the merchants who came to the Fair to buy and sell from many miles around. The boy liked to wander alone in the streets, touching with his fingers the many brass and metal pots and pans, the fine lace work, to jiggle the hanging sausages and bolognas and long cheeses—to stop the swaying of a few with a shout of "Hola."

More than this, he liked people and enjoyed being near them. He would be jostled by the moving pedestrians in the crowded streets, whacked on the back by someone who wanted to be remembered to his father. For all these he had a friendly smile and some quip which brought a smile to their faces.

Vollo told him that they would have to return soon, because he was not feeling too well, so they started back to Assisi. The heat of the late afternoon became oppressive and they stopped near an old church called San Damiani, where Francis wanted to get some drinking water and wash his face and hands.

The afternoon heat beat down on them. Vollo sat down under a large tree to rest and take a nap. Francis wandered into the dark, cavernous church to get out of the heat. He was alone and his nostrils could detect the ancient woods inside the building aging with each year. There was a heavy dank odor, which weighed on him like a dark contrast with the bright clean air outside.

He suddenly felt enveloped by this strange place and was about to leave, when his eyes caught a dim light from the door, which bathed a wooden crucifix, standing at the end of the little church.

Francis became curious about the face on the carving. It was a young face, full of kindness, standing easily, surrounded by figures which must have been his eleven Apostles. The hair was reddish light in color framed by a round, bearded face.

Francis came nearer and a thought struck him that this face looked like himself! This face was closer to being *his own brother* than Angelo was! He studied that face and saw that the artist had carved eyes which seemed to talk with him.

He stared at the eyes and then heard a voice tell him in Provencal French, "Sauva nostro gleiso, es tombado en ruino." ("Save my church, which has fallen into disrepair.")

Francis' practical mind made him turn around to see if anyone was playing some kind of joke. But he was alone in the tiny church. He was sure that *he had heard* the voice. Outside, he saw that Vollo was still asleep in the afternoon shade and the old priest was seated on a bench under another tree, his head drooping in half slumber.

Francis returned to the inside of the little church to look again at the carving of Jesus. Then he sat down on a bench and stared at the wooden figure.

Impulsively, he went outside and awoke Vollo, who was startled and incoherent for a few minutes, grunting and clearing his throat.

"Did you hear that . . . Jesus talked to me?" he asked him.
Vollo's heavy bullish face was in a twisted, contortion drawn from a sound sleep into reality by the question. He shook his head.

"No, how could you, dear old Vollo. You were fast asleep and perhaps I was dreaming too?" the boy said.

"Whatsa' matter?" the man questioned. "Who said what?"

"Never mind," the boy replied. "I don't know whatsa' matter." He smiled at the older man. 'I think we better get back home."

They went over to the horses to get them ready for the journey. The little old priest awoke and came over to them.

Francis drew the pouch with the coins from his sales at the Foligno Fair and handed it to the priest.

The sudden exclamation of "No, Francis, what are you doing?" from

Vollo, stopped the hand of the priest in mid air. "Your father will clout you good for this."

"Take it," the boy told the little old priest who shook his head.

"I don't want to start trouble," he repeated several times. "If this is stolen, I'll lose my job here."

"It's not stolen," the boy assured him. The priest still refused to take the pouch. Vollo had saddled the horses and tied one to the cart and was ready to leave for home.

"I'm not going back with you," Francis told him. "You take the horses and I'll walk home in a few days."

Vollo almost exploded in sudden consternation at what he would face from Pietro's anger when he got back.

"Well, I heard this voice of Jesus tell me to save his church," the boy explained slowly. "Tell this to my father. On second thought, knowing my father, Pietro Bernardone, you better not. He won't believe you. In fact, I hardly believe this myself."

"What will you do here?" Vollo asked him.

"I don't know. Perhaps fix these walls of this church," was the reply.

"You're no mason," the older man told him. "How can you fix any walls." They argued back and forth for several minutes until, finally, Vollo left with Francis' horse tied on the back of the wagon.

Francis stayed at the church for two weeks. He sold his clothes and wore old working ones he found in one of the cupboards of the church. During this time, he bought stones and materials to repair the walls. His work was crude and lacked the finish of a skilled worker. His hands became hard and calloused.

Then he went home. As he walked down the streets in Assisi leading to his house, some youngsters who knew him called him "Pazo, pazo" crazy. Some of the older people stared at him as if he were mad and laughed at him, thinking he was miming. They knew Francis and his tricks!

Some of the youngsters were less kind. They threw some clods of dirt at him and a few tossed stones, hitting him as he approached his home. There stood Pietro in front of their house watching all this. The boy could see that his father was writhing in anger and shame. He caught hold of his son and drew him quickly into the house and slammed the door behind him.

Assisi 1204

"Why do you shame me this way?" Pietro's voice cried out. "All our lives we have dressed well, we have conducted our lives with dignity and respect. Now, the people in the streets call you a crazy man."

"Does that hurt you so much," Francis asked, "or the fact that your own hurt is deeper than my own?"

"What is your hurt?" demanded Pietro. "You have lived the life of wealth and plenty, this house, your friends, what is your complaint?"

"There is more to life and living than this wealth and plenty."

"Listen to the philosopher of this generation, the twenty-two-year-old telling off his parents," Pietro added.

"What is it you want of life?" asked Pica. "It can't be as simple as you think. You must work and reach for it. We Jews are alone in a sea of people who neither want us here nor tolerate our living.

"By chance I walked into the Church in San Damiani to get a drink of water. I've hardly ever gone into a church and it was cool from the heat of the bright sun. I looked around this tiny old church and I felt rested."

"Weren't there better places to rest than a church," Pietro demanded.

"It was just curiosity," Francis' voice was patient. "My own religious training has been so little." He paused for a moment. "Then I saw this wooden carved head of Jesus."

"They have a thousand of them in Assisi and Rome," Pica suggested.

"But this one, Mother, was different," Francis insisted. "Somehow the sculptor, whoever he was, caught something of the young Jewish carpenter, the strong face, the small beard, the high forehead." Then he paused, searching for words . . . "then those eyes." . . . his parents waited in thoughtful silence for this next words. "Those eyes were searching heaven itself for something."

"Oh, Francis," his mother was chiding him. "You and your imagination, you see in every animal and every bird, another person who lives."

172

"How in the name of a piece of wood," Pietro's voice tried to be patient, "could you see someone searching for heaven in . . . No one could do this."

"But father! Whoever made this head, was trying to find something probably, something he himself knew nothing about." Francis replied.

"Let the boy tell his story," Pica asked her husband gently Pietro nodded to his son.

Francis went on. "Somehow, call it my imagination or something else, but I saw that statue cry with real tears and say to me, in Provencal French, 'Sauva nostro gleiso, es tombado en rouino.' (Save my church, it is fallen into disrepair.)

Pica moved closer to Pietro and held her arms around the man.

"Just a voice in this small church?" Pietro repeated, "telling you to save the church?"

"Just that," his son replied.

"Let us not be wise, but understanding," Pietro suggested.

Pica then asked, "You heard a voice, could it not have been that of the priest looking for a donation? That is a reasonable thought. Don't you agree?"

"Yes," Francis nodded his head. "That is a possibility. But the old priest does not speak Provencal French. And then he refused the money bag, I first offered him. So I left it on the window sill. He thought the money was stolen and would not take it."

"What money?" demanded his father. "Not the money from the sale of the goods in Foligno?"

Francis nodded his head in full humility. Then he felt the pain carried across to him by their faces. He knew that he had struck a blow at them which could never be recalled.

Angelo walked into the room, with an account ledger under his arm. "That was some spectacle you made, older brother. Walking through the streets of Assisi like a common beggar. Oh, Francis, how could you?"

Pietro reached under his son's arm and drew out the ledger. He looked at one of the pages, then turned to Francis. "You had about 60 pieces of silver in that bag . . . . . You mean to tell me that you gave that money to a . . . . . church?"

Pietro drew up his arm as if to strike his oldest son in anger, then withdrew it, looking at his hand, wondering if it was his own.

"Then the people in the streets must be right," Pietro surmised shouting in anger. "You are crazy. Giving our money, my money, to some broken down church . . . . Francis how could you . . . have you lost your mind?"

He looked into the pleading eyes of Francis and there was the Old Testament wrath in his face at the witless son.

"You let me spend money on fancy clothing, rich jeweled swords, and pay my gambling debts. You pay them gladly, with a laugh. Why do you stand in anger now?" Francis demanded.

"Ours is a heritage of pain," Pica's voice was calm. "The Christian Church has always hated all of us. If they did not try to convert us into their church and beliefs, they burned our people and our sacred writings." Her voice reached back into her memory, "and they burned my home . . and the night my father and Angela died . . . this we cannot forget . . . . "

"Mother, I did not want to hurt you and father, believe me, with all my heart," he pleaded.

"Yet, you strike at us, doing this . . . thing . . ." Pica replied the hurt in her voice. "Why to a church?"

"I cannot give you an answer," Francis replied sadly. "I had to do this."

"This was the act and the answer of a madman," shouted Pietro. "I can see using money for your enjoyment, your pleasures. But to help this hated church!"

"Then tie me up like they tie up mad people," Francis told his father.

This barb seemed to anger Pietro more than anything said and done until now.

"Very well," his voice was angry. "Then I will." He turned behind him and found some light chain used to tie heavy bundles in the rear of the storeroom. He grasped Francis about the arms and chest and drew the chain around him and binding his son to a pillar.

"What are you doing?" cried out Pica. The tears began to fill her eyes.

Angelo moved closer to his mother, holding her arm, his face a study in incredibility.

"He wants to be treated like a crazy man," Pietro told her quickly. "Then I will satisfy his wishes."

"No, no, Pietro," she tried to hold his arms. He shrugged her off. "Not this way. Try it with kindness. Perhaps we don't understand him."

"Understand him," he cried out. "I don't understand him. All our lives we have talked to our boys about our people. What the Roman Church has done to them for a hundred years. Now, he wants to help a church from falling apart. Fall apart . . . . let the whole forsaken Church fall apart . . . ."

"But tying him up like this won't help us one bit," she told him.

"No, it won't," he admitted. "Let me out of here," he started to walk away. "When I'm gone, untie him," he told his wife. "Or by God Almighty

I will lose my mind if I stand here another drop of sand is lost in the hour glass." He started walking up the stairs slowly, as if he had a bale of wool on his shoulders.

"Why?, Why?" Francis kept asking.

Angelo helped his mother untie Francis from the pillar. When he was free, Francis slid down on the pillar onto the hard stone floor. He held his arms around his head, the tears rolling down his cheeks.

As Pica walked up the stairs to the house above them, she saw her husband standing in the corner of their living room facing the corner of the room. She came close to him as the racking sobs in this man of hers shuddered within him.

She had never seen a man cry before . . . not like this. For in that moment she realized that Pietro was burying her son.

This was the ancient cry of a father who had lost hope for carrying on the tradition of his people. This was the cry of one who had indeed lost a precious hope for the future. This was truly death.

Pica started to lace her fingers into one another, almost in desperation, at seeing her last stronghold for her own strength, standing in the corner crying.

She approached him, putting her arms around him, sharing their mutual pain. Then she too repeated, her eldest son's question "Why? Why?"

The next morning father and son met at breakfast. The man's only comment to him was, "Francis, please think of what you are doing. Give it careful thought. Will you at least do this for me . . . for all of us? It is a matter of high principle to me. I have talked this over with your mother. We want that money back. You will go to that priest and get the money back. Give him a silver coin for his trouble. Tell him the money belongs to me."

Francis nodded his head in agreement.

Later that day he did go to the old priest and was told that he no longer had it. He had turned it all in to the Bishop of Assisi. All donations must be given to the Bishop and he, the priest, gets his expenses and salary in return.

Francis knew it was useless to go home and tell this to his father. Instead, he went to see Bernard de Quintavalle, his friend and godfather. Since they needed advice and counsel from a lawyer they then went to see Peter Cattaneo, a neighbor in Assisi. He was also an expert in canon law.

Here they learned that the only way to get this money back was a direct appeal to the Bishop. When they got to the palace, the old man blithely told them that Pietro must make a personal appearance before his court and demand the return of the money. He must swear aloud that the money was his and not Francis' to give away.

Pietro became very angry when he received this message. The boy asked his father not to make the appearance in the Bishop's court. That he would work hard and return this sum to him.

Pietro again repeated that it was a matter of high principle and that he would indeed appear before the Bishop. He asked Peter Cattaneo to act as his lawyer in this plea.

At the hearing before the Bishop's Court, it seemed as if there was a sudden division of the people of Assisi on one side and the Bishop and the church on the other side.

There stood the Bishop, in the full regalia of his office, with mitred hat and staff of his power as the shepherd of his flock. Behind him stood several priests.

As he looked around him, Pietro suddenly realized that this had become a fiasco over a small sum of coins. To his practical mind, his anger had gone and he was about ready to withdraw from the court.

Behind him was his friend and partner Count de Offreduccio, his wife Ortolana and their daughters Clara and Agnes. There was his friend Bernard de Quintavalle and Peter Cattaneo, his lawyer. Holding his arm was Pica and near them stood his sons Angelo and Francis. There were also a few other townspeople, who knew them and brought them sympathy in a *cause against the church.*

Once again Francis whispered to his father to drop the whole matter and "let us go home in peace."

Pietro stared hard at the face of one of the heavy priests near the Bishop and recognized Fra Baccionne, the priest who had raped Volla in a drunken assault at the inn at Arras in France, many years ago. Pietro shook his head and, without thinking, brushed Francis aside in sudden anger and memory of past wrongs of other priests.

Pietro had made up his mind. No money of his would support the likes of this drunken fat slob. In a loud voice he declared that the money had been his and not Francis' and demanded its return.

The Bishop tried to reason with him that a gift of money to the Holy Church even from a non-Catholic was greatly appreciated and acceptable. That it would be in his, Pietro's, favor to merit a good standing with the hierarchy of the church in Assisi.

Pietro had set his mind and was not turning. He again demanded the return of the money. The Bishop nodded his head and one of the priests be-

Giotto   ST. FRANCIS RENOUNCES HIS INHERITANCE
(*Alinari-Art Reference Bureau*)

hind him tossed the bag of coins at Pietro's feet, who let it lie there, as he looked down at it, like a strange hateful thing.

Francis became angry at his father's and his family's shame in the open court of Assisi. He felt very small and humiliated not for himself, but the hurt he saw in the eyes of his mother Pica, and the sudden glee he saw in the faces of several of the townspeople at this sight.

Without thinking, Francis drew off his cloak and tossed it on top of the bag of coins. He drew away from his father and then took off his other clothes and shoes and hose and tossed them on the pile at his father's feet. His father shook his head as if he was ready to laugh at this new spectacle of Francis' play acting.

In total disbelief, he looked down at the pile of clothes and Francis who stood only in a loin cloth before all of Assisi to see. All his life, Francis had heard the repeated declaration from his father from the Talmud. "Better to wear good clothing than feed your stomach." With this gesture he was defying everything his father had told him. In anger, Francis realized that he had shamed his father more.

Pietro looked at his tall blond son and admired the strong muscled lines of the chest and arms of the young athlete. He admired the proud stance of his head and smiled at the position of defiance. He bent down and picked up the clothing and the bag of coins.

Francis stepped back and the kindly Bishop Guido, embarrassed by this unexpected turn of events in his courtroom, drew his own cloak around the boy to cover his nakedness. He then asked the boy to return to his own quarters in the palace. Francis turned without looking at his family. Feeling like a prisoner entering the dock of criminals, he entered the door, held close by the Bishop's cloak.

The others waited in the courtroom until the closed door had become mute. Then they slowly turned away and walked slowly to their homes.

(None of them could know that history had suddenly been made! A decision giving birth to an idea, which would sweep across Europe and the known world. Before them was enacted the scene of a 22-year-old boy deciding that a few possessions were a vanity. By challenging his father, he separated himself and was alone with his own pattern for living.)

Inside, the Bishop told one of the priests to give Francis some clothing, which to the boy's skin was rough and dirty. He looked down at himself and grimaced at the exchange of his fine clothing for these poor sacks. With a smile on his clear face he remembered an often used expression of his father about "making his bed . . . "

Outside the palace, as he came out the back door, stood Clara. A short distance away hovered Volla, an anxious frown on her round face.

"I asked Mama," Clara told him, "Oh, Francis, I am so sorry for your hurt." She was almost in tears.

"I saw you in the court," the boy towered over her lithe body, topped with its reddish blond hair. She wore a long yellow striped dress with a matching apron hung low to her toes, which made her sturdy shoulders seem almost boyish in strength.

Volla ran over to Francis and hugged him closely, whispering small sounds into his ears. She moved away from him hiding her face.

"Let us walk together," Francis told Clara, holding her small hand in his larger one. She walked quickly along his striding legs.

"I told Mama I would wait only a little while to see you," she told him.

"Dear little Clara," Francis' voice was somber and low. "You are the only one who wanted to see me, after that business in there." He pointed behind him to the palace. He bent down and kissed her forehead. She walked back to Volla.

Whenever Francis felt troubled he often returned to the small cave in the hills above Assisi. He needed this moment of isolation today. His mind wanted to be alone to think in the stillness of this cave.

The sun was warm and high in the sky, the cave itself felt gloomy and weighed with black, after the brightness outside. His thoughts went back to the events of the past few weeks, the church at Damiani, its total and complete quiet as the voice told him to "Save my church." His work in the courtyard, the trip through the streets of Assisi and then the events in the cellar of the Bernardone home.

He remembered his promise to his father to think over the entire course of his plans. Then his father's words. "This Jesus was only another Jew, who lived as one and died only as a Jew. He died for Peace and the Jews have been murdered and kicked about ever since, all in this man's name."

Francis had looked at the face of that statue in the church and had seen his own brother in that face. Not Angelo of course, but a blood brother with whom he had kinship of thought and affection.

Yet why did Jesus have to die when the Jews in ancient Palestine needed a leader against the Romans? The Jews hated to be under any kind of tyranny and Rome was just another enemy. Most of all the populace mourned and the "people wept" as Jesus walked to Calvary carrying his huge cross. The old Roman practice of "divide and rule" had again won.

By killing off this new revolt against Rome, in the person of this young red-haired Jew, they would crush this possible uprising at the start. Francis remembered that the revolt would be against Rome, not the people of Palestine.

Francis sat down on the floor of the cave as a wave of cool air bathed his body, warm from the climb up the hill. In his mind, he began to see and feel the last minutes of his Brother Jesus.

He could feel how easily the large wooden beam and its crossbar was carried on the strong young shoulders. Then the quickening of his breath, in short close gasps as the Roman soldiers held him down on the beam on the ground.

A man could only die once and he would die with courage. Then he shut his eyes as his arms were outspread on the crossbar and he heard the soldiers muttering some words to their fellows about this "Hebe" who was taking it like a Roman soldier. He heard the word "Hebe" repeated several times close to his ears. Suddenly Francis felt the sharp stab of the rusty nail through his open palm. The agony of the pain racing across his arm and into his neck. There was a stabbing pain in his other hand.

His heart was beating and pounding at the cage of his breast, pounding and pounding with greater speed. Then he opened his eyes to look at the soldiers near him.

As if from a great distance he could hear the rumbling of the large crowd kept away by the short Roman swords and spears. There was a wave of sadness like an unseen, muted being in deep agony.

This was reaching into the bowels of the earth with no surcease. The Jews were losing one of *their kinsmen* to the might of Rome. Most all of them were also dying with him. They were losing one of *their own* sons. The ache was mounting and surging over all of them.

Francis' heart was pounding in his chest, enclosing him and drowning the pain in waves of noise as if from a distant throbbing ocean.

Francis opened his eyes and could see the faces of the heavy Roman soldiers holding his body, as two men were clasping his feet together.

In the faces of these soldiers were neither joy, nor sadness, nor pleasure. Only the stony hardness of men looking at hot sand and rocky lands, which was the last place for the scum and the incorrigibles of the Roman army. The worst criminals within the Empire were sent here as final punishment. These faces saw no people, only objects which got in their way and must be moved. Crucifixion was *an old Roman custom* and these men were experts in the craft.

Francis could feel the cool arms of one of the men holding his legs together and the sudden numbing sensation of the spike driven into his two feet. For a moment the pain was like a single sharp wallop. Then it muted all feeling across his legs and up into his thighs, clamping on his groin like a vise.

Francis lay on the cold, damp floor of the cave, each trace of memory a searing knife across his brain, reaching, reaching into his bowels, twisting in the agony of endless pain.

His arms were numb and his legs were dead. His strong body was resisting death as his mind drifted away into ancient memories.

He remembered, like wisps of spun silk weaving across his mind, the love in the eyes of the Jews who would come and listen to him talk. How his voice would gentle them, for most had little of the spirit of God in their lives. They were so close to the dry earth of poverty. They were so poor!

These people had so little to live for and he was bringing them closer to God. He had told them that God was always about them and each one could reach God by himself without the long standing rituals in the Temple or through any of the animal sacrifices.

Standing on a hill he had shouted to them, his voice dancing across the valley, "Open your arms and bring heaven close to your heart."

Francis could begin to feel the numbness of death entering his arms and legs with the sudden pain in his jaws and face, tightening and locking the muscles forever.

Then, with all the force of his mind compelling the last words from his locking jaws, his voice cried out in final desperation, reaching across the clouds and the sky beyond . . . in Aramaic . . .

"Lama Zava' thanni . . . lama zava' thanni?"

The rumble of this cry echoed and bound from the walls of the cave as Francis beat out the words, from his pain racked mouth.

With a rush, he dashed out of the cave into the warm sunlit air. He was stunned, as if he was struck by a torch of bright sunlight. Then his voice shouted across the Umbrian hills, into the valley below him and lost across the plains.

"God, why hast' Thou forsaken me?"

The valleys picked up the cry, tossing it into the nooks and crannies of the rocks, the hills and the lonely trees.

The warm sun bathed his golden head, warming his cool body like a blanket of soft tendrils. Francis extended his arms wide, sweeping into them close to his heart, the far reaches of the clouds, the distant hills. His mind touched the edges of the sun and danced across the blue skies.

Francis knew, then what the answer to his father would be. He would follow his blood brother Jesus, perhaps do in this life what the other could not do alone—to finish the tasks that were left to only a few men.

No, Francis would find a way to do and complete the job started over a thousand years ago and left undone. The job of one man looking to another as his brother. If you strike at one and drive him into poverty and want, you do this to *all* men. Push a man into the drift and mire of slavery and you must go into the mud *with* him. Men would only become the children of God when they *believed* in God and *loved him* as their Father.

This was the job which Francis must start.

Later that day, Francis returned to the house of his parents. He walked into the living room and found Pica talking with Pietro and Bernard. They both became silent waiting for their eldest son to speak.

"Would you kind people want me to leave?" asked Bernard.

"No, dear friend," Pietro replied. "Please stay."

"How tall and straight and strong is this son of mine," thought the father, looking at his wife. They both saw how his hair glinted in the rays of the sun through the window. They could see his strong chin was fixed, his eyes alight with some inner fire, warm, soft, knowing.

For a curious moment, Pica's mind raced back to the day in Lucca, when Francis was thirteen. "Strange," she said quietly, "that I should now remember, when you stood up to make your speech in Lucca. So many, many years ago we thought our young son, would ever remain thus. But, sons grow up as they should."

"I truly remember, Mother," Francis answered quickly. "Perhaps, I remembered all the things which Rabbi Jehudah Halevi told us that day. That each of us can reach out to God the Master of the Universe, with his own heart and soul. I remember that he told us that the ancient order of the Priests died with the animal sacrifices and the Temple in Jerusalem."

"You did not forget all these years," Pica asked.

"No mother, there is nothing that happened that day that I would ever forget," the boy replied.

"Knowing and remembering . . . " his father began, "yet you still want to be one of *them*." He snapped the last word.

"Even, Rabbi Jehudah Halevi went over Europe preaching the word of God. This was his own mission in life. Can't I find something in that?" asked Francis of his parents.

"But, *for what* and *to whom*?" persisted his father.

Francis told them of his experience in the cave earlier, that day, and how he had felt all the agonies of another Jew, named Jesus. He repeated the call of the quiet voice in the church of San Damiani "to save my church."

"Do you still believe that he meant *you* to go around the countryside repairing church walls like a common laborer?" his father wanted to know.

"Father, father,—mother, I love you both, dearer than life, but, please try to understand me . . . " the boy begged. His eyes turned to Bernard pleading.

"But, Francis," his mother asked him, "do you know what you want to do?"

"Honestly, mother, I do not," was the reply. "Somewhere, out there," he turned his head, "somewhere out there, I will find the answer. Until then, love me Mama . . . and papa."

"If this is your wish for your life, then so be it," his father said, his voice weary with resignation. He opened his arms wide as if to embrace his son in a farewell. "Let me read a portion of Isaiah to you." He reached for an old heavy book. "Ah yes, chapter fifty-three . . ." he thumbed quickly through the ornate pages, "here it is . . . " He showed the page to Francis. "This is the portion you were to read at your Bar Mitzvah, which you started to read in French . . . then that . . . that priest interrupted you . . . unfortunately you never learned Hebrew . . . "
"Thus sayeth the Lord . . . .
I have called to thee in righteousness
and have taken hold of your hand
And kept thee for a covenant for the people
For the light of the nations."

* * * * * * * *

Pietro stopped reading, all of them caught and trapped in the silence from the cadence of his voice.

"Each of us, each Jew in this world has a mission to improve this world through the word of God Ruler of the Universe. Each one of us is one of His witnesses. If this is the kind of mission you truly want, then do it you must. But *do it well.* Do it with style and a full understanding of what you want. But there is only one favor I must ask of you, even this I cannot compel you to do . . . "

Francis looked into the pain of his father's eyes, keeping silent yet nodding his head, accepting and granting in the motion of his head.

"You are never to become one *of them* . . . never to become a priest," his father's voice faltered, searching for better words.

"I will never become a priest or join their church, this I promise," Francis replied accenting each word carefully. (This promise Francis kept faithfully.)

That night he stayed at the little church of San Damiani.

he Letters of San Damiani 1204 to 1209

Francis was now 22 years old and during these next five years he had to find out what he was to do with his life. Since he was no scholar, he had read few books and these letters are a means for us to know of his doubts and the crucible of his thoughts and trials.

In this period he was learning to think and to form the soaring thoughts which led him to a state of mind . . . . leading him to Sainthood.

Saints are not made in heaven. Their feet must touch the earth first and their own thoughts must reach into the souls of their fellows.

How is a Saint made? How is a Saint taught?

These next chapters are the beginning.

A letter from Francis to Rabbi Jehudah Halevi

November 5, 1204

My dear Rabbi,

As you no doubt heard in your travels, there is a crazy man about near Assisi who has a good strong body and the skills with the mandola and does not use these talents for any good.

It seems that this crazy man goes around begging for stones and mortar to fix old church walls. I still do not know what my life is to be and what useful things I can do. Sometimes as I sit in my poor, tiny hovel of a room, writing to you by the flicker of the candle light, I can so easily reach out and snuff it with a flick of my fingers.

Is this all my life is to be? To end in one day, one moment, like this tiny candle, to flicker a while and die, unknown, unloved and soon forgotten?

Is this my destiny for this world and the world to come? I ask these questions of myself as the years flow by quickly. Should I have done this work, say for some synagogues instead of a church. For my own people instead of the Gentiles?

Up to a while ago, the name of church and synagogue meant the same thing. One of my learned friends Peter Cattaneo and I discussed this matter.

The synagogue means a "meeting place" and is a Greek word. Pope Innocent III in one of his Bulls refers to the "Priests in their synagogues." Many churches sell wine and food and use their buildings for sleeping places. People have to pay a price, small enough, but pay they must.

I have written this letter to you in Regensburg in the hope that somewhere some kind people will send it along to you.

Your old friend,
Francis Bernardone

Letter of Benjamin Kolonymus to Francis

December 19, 1204
Fostat, Egypt

Dear Francis,

Yesterday, Moses Maimonides my great teacher, friend and physician passed away. To me, in my personal life, he was the father I never saw. For you remember my father was killed in Provence in the riots against the Jews. His loss will be mourned by all the world for his many contributions of new kinds of herbs and drugs to help all people everywhere. The benefits of his research into these materials for medicine will help mankind for the next thousand years. Moses Maimonides was also a great writer and philosopher, who in these uncertain times of wars, corruption and greed offers all people a plan for living. His book the *Guide for the Perplexed* gives both Jews and Christians a scientific approach to the belief in the One God. His book *Moneh* was translated into Latin and used by such scholars as Albertus Magnus, Duns Scotus and Alexander of Hales. For centuries the Jews wanted someone to enunciate their personal relations to God. Maimonides gave us that.

Perhaps Francis, I now find the reason *why* I became a physician. In this way, I, too, have acquired some semblance of holiness and can come closer to God by helping His children.

Many a time I have seen Maimonides so fatigued from his duties, that he will counsel his patients from his own bed, rather than let them go in pain or suffer from some malady.

I wish in my own small way to follow this great man's path of science and righteousness, please God. Why haven't you written to me?

Your friend in mourning,
Benjamin Kolonymus

Letter from Francis to Benjamin, who is in Egypt

December 30, 1204

My dear friend,

I labor in the sweat of the sun and the rain, rebuilding the walls of a few of the local churches. Do you remember a long time ago, it seems almost a century ago, so much has happened, when little Clara raised her arms in the heavy rain in Ancona, then made all of us dance in the rain?

What is the dance I do now? I danced in rapid circles then, moving in step with a five-year-old girl. Now, I am still dancing in longer circles, but I am a man, 22 years of age.

My life it seems is being lost with no purpose, than for me to be a rebuilder of walls. My father and mother told me this and asked of me "What will you do with your life—be a mason who does not get paid for his hire?" A hire which no one seems to care about. I am still mocked in the streets and the young urchins call me "crazy, crazy."

Yet, I console myself with the thought that God in his infinite mercy knows what he wants me to do. Thus, I heard this call from my Brother Jesus, it is astonishing to those near me that I have not become a Christian, doing all this work for nothing.

Again, the thought comes to me from our conversations long ago, that *Jesus was not a Christian. He was born a Jew and died a Jew.* So, why should my life or hopes be anything more or less than Him?

Write to me soon, for I miss your good counsel and friendship in these days of hard work in the daytime and long nights of doubt.

Francis (the crazy one) Bernardone

Post Script: I am truly sorry to learn about your loss. As you say, I will say "I hope my own life will not be any less" than this great man.

F. B.

Letter from Francis to Clara

San Damiani
December 30, 1204

My dearest Clara,

I cannot tell you how much your visit last week, with your Ortolana and your sister Agnes meant to me. Your mother like her noble and generous self brought a picnic lunch, which all of us shared with pleasure. Having Vollo bring you in the coach was a splendid idea. The poor man had not seen me in months and his happiness was best found in his bear hug which almost broke every bone in my body.

Vollo has known me, as has his wife Volla since the day I was born. In fact, I was actually born in their bed. She has cared for me with the same love as my mother Pica.

My life seems to be so empty of purpose now. Do you remember, a long time ago, when I told you of my ambition to become a great soldier? That one day I would become a great prince? All this seems so long ago. Where have all my dreams of doing important things gone? The Bible tells us that each life shall be three score and ten, already I have nothing to show for a third of mine.

After you left me, I missed your warm hands and loving smile. Did you know, dear Clara, that you have the warmest smile in all the world? Your round small face crinkles and your eyes dance with laughter for all the world to see.

Dear Ortolana let us wander away together, just so we could be alone for a while. Come to think of it, if your father had let me marry you, then I would not be here today, in an old church yard, fixing its walls like a poor inept mason, who is just learning his craft, then must correct his mistakes each day.

Do you remember how cold it was in the late afternoon? It snowed the next morning, but in my tiny hovel which I call my home, I tossed all night thinking about you.

God must be trying my soul during these nights, because it is only during these nights which are long and lonely ones, that memories come back to taunt me and demand to remain known.

One which comes back often it this one:

Do you remember the time I returned from Spoletto? I was on my way to the wars with Walter of Brienne. I was on my horse and a beggar came up to my stirrup asking for alms. I did a terrible thing. . .

I pushed him away from me with my foot. He went off into the dark night without a sound.

After he was gone, I was truly sorry for what I had done to the poor old man. This comes back to haunt me time and again. It wakes me from a peaceful sleep to taunt me as a human being of good intentions.

Somehow, I think God gave me another chance to prove to myself if I had any courage.

After I left the palace of the Bishop of Assisi, where I made myself look like the perfect fool, taking off my clothes in front of all those people and tossing them to my father! It is little wonder that my father calls me a play actor and a mime.

To everyone, including the Bishop, I was renouncing my parent's rule over me. Thinking back to that afternoon, I was just a big boy trying to show off. But, what was I trying to show?

On an impulse I had given a bag of coins to a deaf old priest for this church in San Damiani. My father wanted the bag of coins returned to him because they were his property. They were not mine to give away. When I gave the coins to the priest they became the property of the Bishop of Assisi. Ergo, if my father wanted his coins, only the Bishop could do that.

You were there. I remember your face, it was angry. As if you knew that I was making a fool of myself in front of your parents, my father and mother and brother Angelo and all our dear friends.

But, coming back to my story. When I left the palace of the Bishop, I was all alone in the world. The old Bishop had kindly loaned me some clothing which was clean but very old and worn. I was on my way to our old cave above Assisi.

On the way a leper came towards me on the road. As he came closer, I could see that most of his face was eaten away with this dread, which the crusaders had brought back with them from the land of Palestine.

As he came closer I could smell the horrible odor from his body like rotten meat left in the sun. I could have walked around him and held my nose to avoid his horrible stink. At that moment, a remembered thought came to mind of the advice Rabbi Jehudah Halevi had told me on my Bar Mitzvah day. "A man must be humble to walk with God."

Yet, how humble? The rabbi said that "man must walk with inner pride and dignity as a son is near his father."

So, here was the test of my resolutions, when I came near the leper. How far should I go with my humility for God. But, this man was one of God's poor creatures and he was all alone in the world. This man was forsaken by anyone who once knew him before this horror ate away his flesh.

To be humble, must I then be lower than the worm under the rock? Must I conquer every kind of revulsion and horror or stink and sight in my eyes? Must I bury all kind things about myself to reach the soul of this poor man?

I do not think that all these things went through my mind until long afterwards. I just walked up to this man and kissed him on the cheek in an act of friendship. For at this moment I too, was all alone in the world.

The poor man was so astonished that he fell on his knees, as if I were some angel from heaven come to change his life.

But, far more than anything else was the thought that in all the world was one single human being who cared enough about this flesh-eaten leper to give him a kiss of friendship. Since then, I have gone to the leper houses in several places. Did you know that there are almost 14,000 such houses in Europe since the Crusades?

I go to these leper houses to help write letters for them, read to those who cannot and give such help and comfort as I can. Many of them ask me to sing my troubador songs to them. This pleases them so much that they ask for my songs before I am inside the door.

"He that planted the ear, shall he not hear? He that formed the eye, shall he not see?"

I guess life has nobility only to those who make it noble.

But, as I had told you earlier, it had snowed near here, and I was in a turmoil of regret and self pity after you and your mother had left me. I had been awakened by this old dream about pushing the beggar and my thoughts turned to you and how much I missed you, dear Clara.

I am 22 years old and by all the normal kinds of life, I should by now have at least two children in my family and be enjoying the fruits and pleasures of a happy married life.

Instead, here I am, alone in my own turmoil of a lonely bed, trapped within the walls of a cold empty church. The inner torments were more than I could bear, so I ran out, half naked into the snow and rolled around on the ground, so it would cool the fires in my heart and in my body.

My body turned blue in color and I feared for my life, because my cough racked deep into my chest throughout the night. The old priest came in "poo pooing the devils around me to leave me in peace."

Clara, dear Clara, ours could have been such a wonderful life. Yet, our teachers tell us that we can hope for better things in the life to come.

I truly hope that in another age, in another time, we may return to this earth, that we may find each other and seek the true love which has not been ours in this world.

Your dearest friend
"Francie"

Reply to Francis from Rabbi Jehuda Halevi:

January 11, 1205

My dear young and unhappy friend,

You write in your letter that you have left the home of your parents. They did not drive you out. You made your own choice and as some elders would say, "you may lie in it."

This of course is of no consolation to you. Let me tell you a story of a young man who came to me and wanted to be ordained as a rabbi. I asked after his daily conduct and he told me that he dresses each day in white, drinks only water, rolled naked in the snow and tells the synagogue caretaker to beat him with forty stripes each day!

Just about then a horse came into the courtyard, drank some water, rolled in the snow and walked away. I told this young man, "Observe this creature is white, it drank water, it rolled in the snow and receives more than 40 stripes each day."

So much for asceticism, we Jews do not believe in such nonsense because it diminished the soul and the image of God. If people call you an ascetic then let it blow across your face like a flake.

The lot of the Jew in Europe becomes more difficult with the edicts from Rome increase, for us to change our faith. A Jew cannot join any of the guilds, have Christian workers or servants. They drive our people to the only means of support, that of money lending, which is the most hateful of any business and our *Torah forbids* it as a crime and the worst offense to people. (Exodus xx11:24)

It was the heavy contributions of the Jews which paid the ransom of King Richard the Lionhearted. Yet, on his coronation day, hundreds of Jews were massacred because a rumor was spread that the king wanted this. This was a vicious lie!

This is the price these Christians exact from us to merely live.

Your friend,

Jehuda Halevi, Rabbi.

Letter from Francis to Rabbi Halevi:

March 1205

Dear Learned Rabbi,

I thank you for your kind letter, which I have delayed answering. Some people have accused me of being an ascetic and wanting to hide myself from the world, from people and life itself. This is farthest from my dreams and thoughts. I love people too much and enjoy being with them to take the vows of some monks who indeed hide from the world and often take the vow of silence. To what avail is this?

Leaving my fine home and my parents and my brother Angelo to live this kind of life is not asceticism nor is there any mystery in what I do. For now, I labor like a common laborer, who wants no pay for his hire. I may be considered slightly crazy, but I am not an ascetic.

A while ago I heard a story which you may know, told by Philo-Judaeus in the first century. When God finished the world, He asked one of His angels if there was anything missing on land or the seas or in heaven. The angel replied that all was perfect; "only one thing was missing and that was speech to praise God's work."

So the Heavenly Father soon created man gifted with speech. God gives man the gifts of His bounty on land and sea. And man in return must give Him praise.

In a way I have tried this philosophy in begging stones for the church walls which I am repairing. Some people are cruel and throw water or garbage at me. Others curse me aloud as if I am some horrible leper. A few have been kind to me and given me food and some stones for the walls.

Yours for God's work,

Francis Bernardone

Reply of Rabbi Halevi to Francis:

May 15, 1205

Dear Francis,

Each one of us in his own way makes himself useful in the eyes of God. You must believe within your heart, what you do is just. There is doubt in your mind because, what you do is for a Christian Church? Let me then tell you two stories, the first one about our Father Abraham. When he discovered the One True God, he wanted to tell all the world about it.

One day two travelers came to his house and asked for food and lodging. He agreed and gave them food. While they were eating he tried to tell them about the One God. The men left in haste. The Voice of God came to Abraham and said, "These men have lived for over sixty years and I have abided their worship of false idols. Why should you in a few moments expect them to change?"

Abraham ran after the men, asked them to return and begged their pardon, and he would not bother them again.

The other story is one from the Talmud. Certain scholars asked the Jewish elders, "If your God hates idolatry, why does He not destroy the idols?"

The elders replied, "He would, if these objects worshipped were not needed in the world. Just because people worship the moon and the stars and the sun, should God destroy the world because of the fools upon it?"

The world goes on despite the idols. I have given you two parables which have no beginning and no ending. Each one must look at his own face in the clear waters of life.

Yours for better health and
life with God,
Jehuda Halevi, Rabbi.

Letter of Benjamin to Francis:

Fostat, Egypt
May 1205

Dear Friend Francis (who calls himself crazy)

I have learned a great deal from my late teacher, Moses Maimonides, may his soul rest in peace. One of the essays which he wrote has been translated into languages for the Moslems and the Christians of Europe to read. He wrote this in 1190:

"Fear the Lord, the God of your fathers and serve Him in love, for fear only restrains a man from sin, while love stimulates him to good. Accustom yourself to habitual goodness, for a man's character is what habit makes it.

"The perfection of the body is necessary for the perfection of the soul, for health is the key to the inner chamber. Measure your words, for by multiplying words you increase error.

"Keep firmly to your word, let your verbal promise be more binding than a legal contract or witnesses. Abhor inactivity and indolence . . . the cause of destruction of the body, of penury or self contempt!

"Glory in forbearance, for that is true strength and victory."

This essay in *Meditation* is for all the world to read and know. You have not written to me about your cough. I do know that the good clean air and the sun will reduce the lung infection. But, above all try to stay out of damp places.

Yours in truth and health,
Benjamin

Letter of Francis to his mother Pica:

May 1205

Dearest of all mothers,

I would gladly give my life to draw back your tears I have caused you. Each mother wants to share in the pride of a son who will achieve something of worth.

She wants the pain of her body and her womb to become something useful in this life and I have only caused you pain. All my life you have fed me the kindness and understanding which only a dear mother like you would feed an ungrateful son. With all humility, I am truly sorry.

As I write this letter, the strains of your favorite song, "My Beautiful White Roses" keeps running through my heart. In each tiny note, I can remember the anguish of your soul for the memory of your father and your dear Aunt Angela.

The mere fact that I am here, alone in this tiny hovel, in a tiny church, will hurt you still more. If you can find solace in singing this melody to yourself, I beg you to do so and remembering your unhappy son, who shares this memory with you.

I am returning this letter with our dear friend Bernard de Quintavalle who will, I am sure, deliver it to you with my heartfelt thanks for a lifetime of kindness and love.

Your humble son,
Francis

Letter of Francis to his father Pietro Bernardone:

June 1205

Dear Father,

The few times I visited our house in Assisi you were away on your travels across Europe.

Yes, you were right, I have no purpose in the work I am doing and am merely following the dictates of a voice which I heard in a small church more than a year ago. With time, the sound of that voice fades away into dull memory, like something which was in a dream.

I can remember the happy times we had together when I was a boy and you would walk with me in the fields around Assisi. You would tell me about the big cities across Europe and we would talk like a father and son should. And I remember the fine gifts you would bring back from your trips. We would look ahead to your return as a holiday. And the songs we sang!

That day at the Bishop's palace, when I threw my clothing at your feet, I could see from your face that you were ready to burst out laughing, thinking is was more of my buffooning. Mother did not appreciate this scene. Neither did my brother, the serious one. Angelo saw nothing funny about it. Are we the only ones in our family who can laugh?

I could see that everyone we knew was there, including Peter Cattaneo, Bernard, Count Offreduccio and Ortolana and of course little Clara and her sister Agnes. For a few moments I thought that she would burst into tears or throw something. She seemed to be angry *at my own shame*, not for anyone else.

You knew, of course, that I had asked the Count for the hand of Clara in marriage. Being a gentleman, he told me kindly that since I was a Jew, he loved Jews and pointed to his long friendship with you.

Yet he feared for the life and the future of Clara married to a Jew in these hardening times. So he found the excuse to tell me that Clara was already betrothed to marry some young fellow in Spain.

Would my life have been different had I married Clara? Only the good God in heaven will know the answer.

So I ask you to have pity for your eldest son, in these days of un-certainty and doubt in his heart. "For he who hath compassion on his fellow men may be considered to be a true descendant of Abraham."

Your ungrateful son,
Francis

Letter of Pietro to his son Francis:

July 8, 1205

My dear son Francis,

I thank you for your letter, which I read today. My heart is in truth heavy for your doubts and for the compassion which you ask of me. It seems strange to me, that I, who can talk to a thousand people in selling them woolens or silks, cannot talk easily with my own son. I was able to talk with you when you were a little boy. But, since you have grown up, somewhere in this time, you and I have lost each other. I think that this is a tragedy every father must find for himself.

First, let me assure you that my love for you, my tall handsome, golden son, has not diminished by one minutae. My greatest regret is that I could not be home the day you were born, so I could treasure it with that more affection. In the year 1182, your birth year, I had to fight my way over the mountains to free myself from brigands. So for a thousand years, (say closer to 700) the Christians have held full power in Europe and are unable to secure its main roads from thieves and make them safe for travelers.

What has Christianity achieved in the last thousand years? In all this time there has not been a single day without some kind of war either between cities or states and countries. There is poverty and starvation across Europe and still the wars go on. Yet the Christians still try to force us into joining them.

Look about you and ask questions. What great men have the Christians produced from their own ranks in the last 1,000 years? Any single one to equal the great men and the giants of the Old Testa-ment like Father Abraham, Moses, David, Solomon, Isaiah, Jeremiah or men closer to our age like Maimonides, or Rabbi Akiba or Rabbi Halevi, the elder?

Is there a single man who calls himself a Christian, could match any one of these or fifty more Jews I could name in a like period of time?

Can any man among them match the feat of Father Abraham, who was over 80 years old when he led a small army of 300 horsemen to recapture his nephew Lot, who was held for the army of five kings and numbered in the thousands? How he led his small army and attacked and defeated the larger force.

Can any man among them match the feat of Moses, who also was over 80 years old when he told Pharoah "to free my people." Then he led more than a half million souls, men, women and children and hundreds of animals out of Egypt. He led them for almost forty years against hostile nations and won? Moses also set up a system for government as an example for free countries which will be used for a 1,000 years from now?

Then again, why should you seek a copy, when you have the true original religion, which was *the faith of their own Jesus?* From our own ancient writings I must quote this. "They say that God had a Son. Behold, God would not permit Abraham to sacrifice his own son Isaac. Does it stand to reason that God would permit His own son to to be executed, like a criminal, without turning the world into Chaos?"

Your father,
Pietro Bernardone

Letter of Francis to Benjamin:

July 9, 1205

My dearest Friend Benjamin,

No, my cough has not left me. Often, in the most awkward time, I cough up some blood in my spittle. Then too, I feel as if a cruel knife has cut across my ribs and under my chest.

Once I sang to a small group of children who came to visit the "not so crazy man" and they asked me to sing some songs for them. Knowing me, the troubador of the church walls, with a lusty voice and much lamenting in my tone, I sang some melodies for them. Perhaps, in this way they will not throw stones and refuse at me as I walk through the streets of these towns.

I have come to the conclusion that each of these children is the true mirror of his parents. What they learn in hate and greed or falsehood and even love, they learn at home. Then each one learns better refinements from one another.

There is no spirit of life in this church in which I rest my bones. It is truly an empty shell which few people visit even on a Sunday. And I keep asking of myself, "what am I doing here?" I look at this little priest here in this church of San Damiani and learn that he can barely read or write! And this little man can minister to the aches and ills of people? How far downward indeed has the Christian Church fallen!

Again, like a true friend, I lay my doubts and tribulations at your feet, my dearest friend of my vanishing youth.

Your friend,
Francis

Letter from Benjamin to Francis:

August 6, 1205

My dearest friend and "troubador stonemason",

I do not like the *sound* of your cough. You need the hot dry air of the Egyptian lands to dry up that consumption of your lungs. It will not get beter and will become worse. Remember this is your personal physician telling you. There are many churches in Egypt and Palestine, why not come here?

For now, my advice to you, is to drink lots of liquid foods to ease the congestion in your lungs. Also eat honey and figs if you can, all these will help you.

Do not lose heart, my dearest of friends, Our Lord God has some noble use for all of us. Else, why should He waste His time with us tiny mortals, if He did not have a greater plan than each of us can know?

One of our Jewish poets in the Egypt community, who is a refugee from Spain, wrote a fine poem which is quite long, so I am writing only a small part:

> "As clay are we, soft and yielding clay
> That lies between the fingers of the potter
> At his will he molds it thick or thin
> And forms its shape according to his fancy
> So are we in Thy hand, God of Love.
>
> As cloth are we, as formless, graceless cloth
> That lies within the hand of the draper.
> At his will he shapes its lines and folds,
> Or leaves it unadorned to hang unseemly
> So are we in Thy hand, righteous God. . . . ."

I learn more of the practice of medicine, but I find how little we know of our own bodies, the blood vessels, the bones, the heart and the soul of man. It is a miracle we can ever help or save anyone.

It is becoming evident everyday that the human being can survive almost anything, in disease, starvation, wars and the art of killing each other.

Memory plays tricks upon us. I have become accustomed to the use of Arabic and almost forgot, or so I thought, my skill with translating Hebrew. This poem above, was written in Hebrew so I translated it into French and Arabic to test myself. Strange, that we can remember events from years ago and forget some of these from yesterday.

I would like to be around someday in a future age when we physicians will know more how memory works. Why do we remember the trivial from long ago and forget something which is recent? Someday, please God we will know.

Your personal physician
Benjamin Kolonymus,
Fostat, Egypt

Letter to Francis from Suesskind of Tremberg:

November 1205

My dear young friend,

I met your father Pietro Bernardone in the city of Calais one day on one of his trips to England and learned about your occupation to save the churches of Italy with your *own two hands*.

By some reasonable count this should take you about 3,000 years and is the kind of work which one can say has a *long future in it*. My own future as a Meistersinger is less secure. I travel too much and have not yet found a home life for a wife and children.

It is becoming more difficult for a Meistersinger to make a living in Europe today. It makes it more difficult if that man also happens to be a Jew. The ruling classes want their own form of entertainment, such as other men's wives, young boys and more often man sleeping with man. Europe is fast becoming a stinking pot of immoral people, stealing, killing and fornicating each other. We are entering a period of time which will one day be known as the *dark ages*.

Perhaps you are right to shut yourself off from the rest of the world behind your church walls. If I had the courage, I would buy myself a vineyard in Palestine and sing myself to sleep each night. But we are the substance which God created, for He said, "Each man shall have in him a portion of Myself."

I have enclosed a few songs for you, which I have heard in my travels.

Your wandering Meistersinger,
Suesskind of Tremberg

A SONG OF DAVID

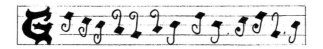

"The Lord is my shepherd: I shall not want.
He maketh me to lie down in green pastures:
He leadeth me beside still waters."
"He restoreth my soul:
He guideth me in straight paths for His Name's sake.
Yea, though I walk through the valley of the shadow of death,
I will fear no evil,
For Thou art with me. . . ."

"WORLDES BLIS NE LAST NO THROWE"
An Old English Melody.

"The world's joy lasts no time at all, it departs and fades away at once. The longer I know it, the less value I find in it."

Letter from Pica to Francis:

December 11, 1208

Dear Son,

It is with heavy heart and sorrow that I write this letter to you. You may have heard that the Provence that I knew and loved, the land of my birth, is dead. All by the orders of Pope Innocent III, who for years has demanded that the Dukes of Provence "use any means they can" to destroy the Waldensians and the heretics. This would include any Jews who get in the way.

After all, are we not heretics too? We refuse to bow our heads to any scepter of the Holy Roman Church. The rulers of Provence were willing to let the people, Waldensians and the Jews live in peace. But, this Pope insisted he must have his way. So he ordered in tens of thousands of his soldiers, the Dominicans, to kill and burn Holy Books and the writings of centuries. All the music and poetry and great thoughts went up in flames.

Not only was there death, there was unspeakable mangling of women and children. Most of these people only wanted to free their church from slavery created by the power of the Roman Popes.

Innocent III gives his own Christians no choice, either death or full obedience to his own rule. As Jews we do have a freedom of choice. It started with our Father Abraham, when he wanted to sacrifice his only son and was forbidden by God. The Almighty wanted to find out what was in Abraham's heart and did not order him to kill his only son. *God gave him a choice.*

There is a story being heard in many cities of Europe that Pope Innocent III was asked by one of his captains before the slaughter of Provence, "How shall we know the good Catholic from the heretic?"

The reply was, "God will find his own."

My heart is heavy in sorrow for all my friends, many of them Christians and my relations who are dead in Provence. I hope the Eternal God will punish those who did this and keep them in the fires of purgatory forever.

Your sorrowful mother
Pica Bernardone.

Letter to Francis from Rabbi Halevi:

March 1209

My dear young friend,

These letters to you seem to be a long distance method of a teacher talking with his pupil. Do you remember on your Bar Mitzvah day, when the Lady Pica asked me to give you one final word of advice and I spoke to you of being able to "walk humbly with your God?"

In the Pirke Avoth (The Sayings of the Fathers) you could find many comments, such as: 'A necessary ingredient for self discipline is the trait of humility. It is basic to all virtues.'

You mentioned to me that you ask for charity and contributions to your cause, then you must remember that, "He who does charity and justice is as if he had filled the whole world with kindness. For great is Charity if it uplifts the soul."

A friend of mine, the Rabbi of Coucy, sent me a letter, from which I quote many times in my sermons to young people: "Because man is half brute and half angel there is a struggle between such unlike natures. The brute demands sensual joy and only things in which there is only vanity. But, the angel resists and strives to make him know that meat, drink, sleep are only means for the body to be efficient for the study of truths and doing the will of God."

Have I burdened you with writings of other people, then I must add one more written by my relative Rabbi Jehudah Halevi in the year 1140, may his soul find eternal peace (in part):

"O Lord where shall I find Thee?
　　Hid in Thy lofty place:
And where shall I not find Thee
　　Whose glory fills all space?

Who says he hath not seen Thee?
　　Thy heavens refute the word;
Their hosts declare Thy glory,
　　Though never voice he heard.

Dare mortal think such wonder?
　　And yet, believe I must,
That God the Uncreated,
　　Dwells in this frame of dust. . . ."

The evil spirit of Innocent III rules over the lives of the Jews of Europe. I hear that he has a vile temper and bursts his anger at even those around him in Rome. The conduct of daily affairs and religion cannot be mixed together. For where does one end and the other begin? This is what this Pope has done. He now has the power of the Church and the Governments in his hands.

Jesus was a radical who did not like the state of things with Rome ruling the Jews. He was against the power of the Romans. People wanted to follow Him as a new spirit in Judaism, *to make it alive*.

About the year 400 the religions of the Romans had begun to die and they sought a new one to fill the void. They then took over the upstart religion of Christianity and made the Jews the scapegoats for all crimes they never knew about, built new temples of stone and found a new God to replace their idols of old.

I repeat again, that in a good Christian world the Jew can live in peace. In war and turmoil, he becomes a pawn for their spoil.

Yours for peace,
Jehudah Halevi, Rabbi

Assisi 1209

It was a warm afternoon in March 1209, when Francis had gone into the square of Assisi and noticed a crowd standing near San Giorgio. There seemed to be an argument going on about religion. (In the late 12th and 13th centuries people would argue and talk about God, religion and the hereafter much as we do today about some recent shows or television.)

Someone in the crowd shouted "God is dead, His son died on the cross" and another long argument ensued. One of the men approached Francis and asked him what he thought about the subject.

"Is God dead?" he asked of those near him. One of the people then asked him to get up on a stone bench and speak so all could hear his words.

"Is God dead?" he asked again. Some of the people in front of him nodded their heads. A few remained sullen and silent. "Is God truly dead?" his voice carried, holding all of them, ready to listen.

"Everyone of us carries God near his heart. The evil one drives him away from all of us. Those who are good and see in this world of ours, all around him God's handiwork, can only know that God is very much alive. You," he pointed at a small sullen-faced man, "you planted seeds last spring for your vegetables. They grew did they not? You," he pointed to another, "you mated your cow and your bull, did not the cow give you a small heifer?"

With his arms outstretched, he looked towards the sky, "all of you, did not the full rain come upon this town of Assisi only two days ago?

"Did any of you create these miracles? Let one man raise his hand and say that he made the rain, or the grapes to grow or the greens to flourish on the field and the trees. Did all this come, like 'Pooph' with the snap of the fingers?

"God is everywhere, he may even be listening to us grumble and complain, if you would only let him near you. Is it not a strange fact, that each one of us in this way is perhaps greater than God? He could force himself upon us, but He waits for each one to need Him."

"Yes, but we cannot see him," shouted a man from the rear of the crowd.

"That is true," replied Francis, "but do we have to see him? Think of that for a moment. Here, strike at the air above you with your hand. You feel the rush of air. You know it is there, because you just felt it. But can anyone of you see this air?

"Not one of us can. Look yonder to the East. All of us know good Brother Sun comes up every morning without fail, not over there in the Western sky but always from the East. You will not see our Brother Sun after dark. Does anyone think that the Sun is not there, when he goes to bed?

"It is truly said in the Zohar, 'He who receives enjoyment in this world without blessing God for it, robs both the Lord and the Congregation of Israel. For he who blesses the Lord is likewise blessed'."

From the crowd came the voice of someone. "Give us a song about God, Francis boy. Be a good lad and sing for us . . ."

Someone handed up a short-necked lute to Francis. He strummed a few notes across the strings, searching in his mind for words and music.

"A song reaches up the ladder to the throne of God. Ah yes, here is a song my mother, Pica, taught me. Did you know that my mother's name in Hebrew means 'fresh and flowing like a spring?' "

A little later, after Francis sang several songs, the crowd broke up arguing among themselves. Some of the men and a few women became loud and voluble. He stood at the edge of the crowd smiling at the eagerness with which some of the people adopted his arguments to use against the non-believers.

He felt a strong arm around his shoulders and turning, saw it was Bernard de Quintavalle and near him was Peter Cattaneo. They had stood at the edge of the crowd listening to him.

Bernard kept his arm around Francis as they walked away from the square. He turned and hugged the older man much as he would an older brother. Francis then moved to Peter and gave him a bear hug, until the man shouted aloud, "Francie, you don't know your own strength, you are crushing my ribs. Those long years moving bricks and stones made you into a man of iron." All three laughed in good fellowship with each other.

"Perhaps you have found your true calling after all," Bernard suggested suddenly to Francis.

Francis pointed behind them, "A preacher must have something to sell, like eternal damnation if you sin and eternal happiness if you don't. Is this justice?"

"You are a Jew," Bernard told Francis. "Your lineage goes back to Moses the Law Giver and to Father Abraham. Your people by every law in your Torah speak of justice for everyone, poor man and rich man, king or slave."

"We speak of God and justice so loosely," Francis told them. "For the word God itself means justice. Yet, these people can have no voice in their own destiny, as people. Your Roman Church has decreed that they are as low as dust and it has built huge structures of stone but lost the spirit of my Brother Jesus. They cannot and dare not reach God, but must speak through that man in Rome we call 'not-so-innocent' I have labored long hours and with much vigor in repairing the walls of the Church in San Damiani, San Pietro and the Portiuncula. I have had many letters from my friends Benjamin Kolonymus and Rabbi Jehudah and my parents to give me food for thought.

"They have by no means satisfied my own hunger for knowledge of what I am to do. My Brother Jesus asked me to 'save his Church'. I have discovered to my deep chagrin, and I have a hundred calluses in my hands to prove it, that He did not want me to be a mason and a layer of bricks. Not with my stumbling hands."

"I am certain that such a call must have a deeper meaning," said Bernard, "than the building of some old walls."

"Perhaps," Cattaneo suggested, "he meant the wider application to the Roman Church. All of us know that the Church is slowly dying of its own power and greed. This is as inevitable as the tides of the rivers."

"With the power of Innocent III," Bernard said slowly, "he is crushing all opposition to his voice and his Bulla. The free and open-hearted religion envisioned by Jesus Christ has truly begun to die."

"Perhaps like a small candle in the darkness," Francis replied quickly, "I can show people the way to God. But, in the name of all that is holy, how can I do it alone?"

The two older men were silent as they looked into the earnest face of the young man near them. Bernard nodded his head to Peter and they both said quietly to Francis, "We will help you. Yes, *both of us.* Then others will follow to join us."

"You know," Francis told them, "that preaching is just talk like empty winds fanning into the leaves of the trees. We must live lives of such art that people will want to follow our example. I am no priest and cannot reach them in a church. How many squares will be open to me to tell them? The noble priests would have us in chains and in a dungeon, before we have spoken ten words.

"My Brother Jesus said to His Apostles, 'Sell thy possessions and give the proceeds to the poor and come follow Me.' This is the kind of precept we must follow to the tiniest letter. There can be no single exception to this Rule.

"The Roman Church stands for audacity and avarice and the accumulation of wealth. Money and gold has become the only worthwhile and useful things in this world of ours. Then, we must show all people, Pope or priest, poor and rich, that a simpler and more fruitful life is through humility and love of our fellow man."

"Let us be practical, if we are not wise," Cattaneo said. "If we sell all our possessions, how shall we live? Are we to be beggars in a world of plenty? This, in essence is our protest . . . in a world of plenty the rich get richer and the poor have less and less."

The three of them were silent held by their own thoughts, overturning every instinct for survival by the loss of their personal life and dignity.

"We cannot, like the monks in a hundred monasteries lock ourselves from what *they* see as a *sinful world*," said Francis." God made the world and it is a good one. The people are good, the earth is kind and feeds us in plenty, the rivers are full of living fish for man to use freely. He is a merciful God and if we do His work, then He will feed us."

"We must have the courage of the holy angels," Bernard shook his head in wonder at his own decision to lead the life of a beggar. He had a home full of art and beauty, his life was rich with promise and long inherited wealth and position in the entire valley. Suddenly he put out his hands, with his palms upwards.

The other two placed their hands on top of his, "So be it," he said gladly. "Poor we shall be, beggars we are, we can do no less. Then in God's name, let us call ourselves the Lesser Brethren. We can go no lower than the lowliest. For no man can say we are above him in worldly goods of any kind."

"If we are indeed the Lesser Brethren," said Peter, "then we will be lower than the priests and the monks. Do you know that some of these monks are the worst criminal dregs, who pay their way by paying good hard coin for admission into a monastery to avoid imprisonment by the law? Priests buy their own way to own a church and then leave their wealth and their priesthood to their own begotten sons as an inheritance?

"The priesthood seems to have become the safe haven for bastard sons not only of priests but of lords of the realm who buy them good positions in the Holy Orders," Peter went on. "The Archbishop of York, the Bishop of Salisbury, the Bishop of Leon are all bastard sons. The Bishop of Le Mans is the son of a priest. King Richard of England, of blessed memory, gave the Bishopric to Master Mauger, who was his personal physician and an illegitimate son of some housemaid. Richard gave him the position of Archdeacon of Evreux.

"I have no quarrel with bastard sons of any woman; they have the right to live as well as anyone, but why must they crowd into the Holy Orders? What kind of dignity or respect can ordinary people like ourselves have for a Church which will only accept so many of them?"

"I guess that they are the unwilling victims of events," Francis said. "As the Lesser Brethren our philosophy must accept all people as being good."

They agreed to meet again on the first day of April at the Church of the Portiuncula, after Bernard de Quintavalle and Peter Cattaneo had sold their homes, horses and all their possessions. They again repeated their resolve to start with nothing, *work* for their daily bread and *yet beg* for it.

On April 16, 1209, Bernard had completely sold all his belongings and finally joined Francis as his First Companion. On that same day Peter Cattaneo, Doctor of Laws from the University of Bologna, canon of San Rufino Cathedral of Assisi, member of an old Roman family of Gualdo Cattaneo, became the third member of the Lesser Brethren and the Second Companion of Francis.

On April 23, 1209, Francis was called from the fields where he was working to meet an old friend, Gilles. They greeted each other as two lost brothers hugging and walloping their backs in a happy reunion. The younger man, who was only 18, told Francis that he too wanted to be one of the Lesser Brethren, asserting that "anywhere that Francis went he would follow."

So Gilles, the son of a farmer, whom Francis loved as his younger trusted brother, became the Third Companion.

They dressed in simple gray robes which the priest of Portiuncula gave them, wearing only a cord and sandals on their feet.

One day, as Francis walked on a side street of Assisi, he met his brother Angelo full face. The two brothers stared at each other almost like strangers. The pain across the younger boy's face, at the sight of the garb of his brother, seemed to twist his face into contortions. They stood facing each other for a moment. Each stood the same height and tall with their blond heads meeting the sun's golden fingers in their hair.

Suddenly Angelo turned and ran towards an alley of a house and retched aloud in his anguish. Francis ran towards him and held his brother in his arms as the boy stopped his torture.

The older one asked after their parents and learned that they were well and would likely move back to Lucca soon.

"Are my parents so deeply hurt by the things I have done?" Francis asked slowly.

"Why the Church? Why the Church?" the boy repeated. "Look at you, you are dressed like a monk." He shook his head, as if in desperation and walked away quickly from his brother.

He turned when he had gone a few steps and said aloud, "*You* Francis a beggar . . . *you* of all people . . . Oh, Francis." He walked away, tears trailing down his cheeks.

That first month and the next few months were difficult for the new Order. They met old friends of long standing and their neighbors. At first there was a mutual embarrassment shared alike by each one. Some of the people insulted them calling them "Pazo, Pazo, you crazy ones, do you want to upset the world?"

Several times they were forcibly stopped from preaching in the streets by priests who told them that they could only preach inside a church and *with their permission.*

Finally, one day they received a message from Bishop Guido of Assisi, who wanted them to visit with him at his palace.

There, he told them that they could not preach in the streets.

"But, we ask for nothing," was the reply of Francis.

Bishop Guido bent closer to Francis as he told them confidentially. "That is just the point. All my clergy need money and gifts to the church and its welfare. Since, you ask for nothing, you therefore will deprive our church of its tithes. For our people can justly reason, 'why should I pay to the church when I can hear and be comforted by Francis and his Companions for nothing?' "

"Your excellency knows," Peter Cattaneo said, "that people who wish to contribute to the church will do so out of the fullness of their hearts. Those who do not, will find any excuse, no matter how trivial, to refuse."

"Such is the nature of 'Homus bestialus'," the Bishop told them. "I heard one of my people, some old crow, bitten by her miseries, threw a plate of hot soup into your face, my son," the old man turned towards Francis.

"Francis was more concerned with the fact that she had soiled his clean robe." Bernard laughed as he told them, "So Francis did not mind the hot soup so much as the fact that he had no other robe to wear, while this one was drying in the sun."

"Do they still throw mud and stones at you?" the Bishop asked.

"My brother Jesus said it most aptly, Bishop Guido," Francis replied with a smile. " 'Forgive them Father, for they know not what they do . . .' Perhaps one day, they will deal with us more kindly."

"I pray for that day with all my heart," the old Bishop said, "When people will deal kindly with each other in God's name. Was it not the Prophet Isaiah who demanded of the rich,

'What do you mean by crushing my people,

By grinding the face of the poor

He who gives to the poor will not want.'

Or from Proverbs, 'He who hides his eyes will

get many a curse'."

"With no disrespect to you," Peter inquired, "We have the right of appeal to a higher authority? We believe that our cause is just, the benefits to the Roman Church will be many, not in material things but in the eternal spirit of man becoming more enobled."

The Bishop thought for several moments, then agreed that they could appeal to the Pope in Rome, Innocent III.

The Bishop perked up his head in surprise, at the slight involuntary groan from the throat of Francis. "I can arrange for you to meet with Cardinal Hugolin, who is at the right hand of his uncle the Pope. Yes, you will be surprised to learn that the Cardinal who is approaching more venerable years is the nephew of our Pope. He is the Bishop of Ostia and Velletri."

"What kind of reception can we expect from his Holiness?" Bernard asked. "His reputation for believing in non-spiritual things are known in all of Europe, his temper is short and his language is most expressive."

The Bishop laughed softly, "I know that the reputation of our young 'Wonder of the World' has gone before him. But, Cardinal Hugolin soothes him with words of wisdom and kindness. Deal openly with him and you will find in the Cardinal a man wise in the ways of the world and could easily become a good friend in the highest of places."

The old Bishop told them he would arrange an appointment with the Cardinal. It would take several months, because frequently the Cardinal went on long journeys into Germany and northern Italy on business for the Pope.

It was in 1210 that an appointment had been arranged by the Bishop of Assisi, through the secretary of the Cardinal.

Francis had no opportunity to see Cardinal Hugolin who was to become his best mentor and friend in the highest Papal circles.

Rome *1210*

Innocent III sat at his ease on his white and gold throne in a large hall in the Vatican. Around and above him hung the splendor of 500 years of accumulated wealth and entrenched power. On the walls were huge tapestries and a few Greek statues which gave some warmth to a coldly depressing room.

There was a pervading chill in the room, soaking into the walls which the soft Roman sun could not reach and warm away.

As Francis walked into the audience room, with Peter Cattaneo on his right and Bernard de Quintavalle on his left, Francis caught the chill of the room and reacted with a deep spasmatic cough. The year in the prison of Perugia suddenly demanded payment.

The Pope had been talking to the Cardinal at his side. He turned when the three entered the room and was annoyed by the sudden cough. His eyes rested on the newcomers and suddenly became hard and intense. He noticed that the older man (Bernard) had put his arm around the shoulders of Francis.

Innocent nodded his head, surveying this gesture of fellowship to the younger man. For a brief moment he remembered that no one had ever shown him such warmth. He had been told, how this boy, the son of a woolen salesman, gathered people around him like flies to honey.

He remembered that this Quintavalle had given up wealth and all he owned to join this lean hungry boy. Peter Cattaneo on the other side, wasn't he a brilliant student of the Law? He, too, gave up this fine career for an idle dream. (Such were the vagaries of men.) This man might have been a fine Bishop and useful in canon law. With all these damn sects springing up every day, he would need a good lawyer near him.

Innocent kept thinking to himself that this boy must have something people want. Look at that intense face with the set of the dark eyes. These were the cheekbones of the fasting mystic, with the skin as tight and smooth as carrara marble.

On that head was the golden hair of brass, and that chin! Here was no limping beggar. Here was a man! His eyes softened for a moment. These mystics thought they had the back door to God Almighty. Where would the Church be, where would *he Innocent be*, there would be no force or strength in the Church . . . the Church came before all else . . .

Well, he was determined to deal kindly with this intense young man. Let us see what he can offer for our day's joy.

He nodded his head in consent, as Francis moved forward, closer to the throne. His sandals clap-trapped on the hard marble floor. Francis knew that he had to make a quick decision. The Pope's silken foot was outstretched. There was something in that gesture which made him remember the Pope's nickname, "The Wonder of the World."

He would have to kiss that foot in the supreme gesture of obeisance to this man.

They looked at each other, the one high up in the councils of the world, the other a lowly man close to the ground and the people. For years Francis had been pleading of others that they obey total poverty and complete obedience in humility.

In this philosophy each man would think himself lower than his fellow man. Francis, who had kissed a leper and bathed the jagged wounds of the lepers a hundred times, the Francis who would go begging from door to door without shame or degradation. In this one perverse moment he decided he would *not kiss* the foot of *this man*.

Instead he bent his head and slid his fingers over the silken shoe, his eyes hung over the thick, bloated veins on the calf of the heavy leg.

There was a slight and sibilant sound above him and near him, at this gesture. One of the courtiers tapped his staff impatiently. Francis held his bowed head for about the count of five, then raised his eyes to that of the young Pope.

There was a challenge, met and decided between them. The Pope saw no fear in the eyes of this young man. The Pope cowed kings, bishops and a thousand eyes of men greater than this country lout. Francis saw the heavy lips knit a simple pattern across the man's mouth under the round full face.

"What is it you want of us?" the Pope's voice was imperious as he reached into his sleeve and dusted his face with a perfumed lacy handkerchief. At least, Francis could have bathed before the audience. He smelled like a country barn. Perhaps one day he could have people sprayed before they entered the Royal Audience. Happy thought!

Francis waited, knowing that the other man's mind was elsewhere. Then Innocent nodded his head.

"We wish permission to preach in the cities and far afield. We wish people to join the Brotherhood of the Poor."

"You mean you don't want to see the rich prosper. Is it your thought that all wealth and property be extinguished? This is madness."

"No, your excellency. It is *not* our wish to destroy the ownership of property. Ours is a Brotherhood of Choice. We force our will on no one."

"What makes you think your group could last any longer than the thousand other sects which flare up, like a bolt of lightning across the sky and in a moment is lost to view?"

"Ours is no Brotherhood of coins or property. Ours is one of the Spirit. The Spirit which enlivened the heart of my Brother Jesus."

"I've heard about this," the Pope raised his voice. "You call God your brother and perhaps the Virgin Mary is your sister?"

"We all come of one blood. They were Jews as were my people," Francis answered mildly.

"Then why have you not converted to the One True Church?" the older man asked him.

"Because I can do better work as an outsider, a foreigner," Francis replied. "In any event, a short while ago, in the Church of San Damiani, my Brother Jesus told me to 'Save my Church'."

The Pope stood up, in all his white, silken and bejeweled majesty. In this one gesture, 1,000 years of Church power stood towering above them on the dais.

"Do you think our Lord would ask salvation of a stinking, country bumpkin like you?" Suddenly the silence of the room held a promise of more to come. The audience and the courtiers waited for another rage of temper from the "Wonder of the World."

Francis smiled as he looked again at the eyes of the young Pope. I'll be obedient to my Brother Jesus *not to this man,* his mind raced. His voice was low, soothing the anger in the other.

"Jesus was a man of the people. He was a poor man and he worked as a carpenter," he reminded the Pope.

"Oh, get out of my sight, you stinking country lout," the Pope commanded him. Francis bowed his head. Slowly, he turned away sad that he had failed the others in the Brotherhood of the Poor.

As Francis turned away, walking slowly with his two companions, the

Pope gave Francis credit for courage, audacity and especially his own brand of impertinence. This boy would not turn to the left nor to the right.

The young Pope's eyes followed the three men, Francis, Cattaneo, and Bernard, as they left the room. Good family that Bernard de Quintavalle. Now, why should a man of wealth and sound culture give it all up. With it the fine food, the good clothes and decent dwelling, give this up and live like a common serf? How could he, Pope of this Roman Empire, do things for his people, when they were such simpletons?

The Pope's mind wandered in reverie as he thought of these men leaving the room. Every waking hour, every working moment, he gave without stint to *his Church* and to be flouted by such buffoons!

He must preserve our Holy Church despite such people. They know no better. He turned to his Cardinal Secretary at his right and inquired, "Who is the next one to await our presence?"

As they walked away from the Papal Palace, Bernard, Cattaneo and Francis talked about their audience with the Pope.

"He wouldn't listen to me," cried out Francis. "I have seen failure for all of us in our Brotherhood. Do we need this . . . man's consent . . . to do our work?"

"Yes, we do," Peter told them. "This is the Holy Roman Empire and that man rules on top of the roost. There is nothing that anyone does which he cannot destroy at will. There is more power in this man than any of the ancient Roman Emperors of Rome. At least there was once a Roman Senate which could prevent any excess of power. Pope Innocent III need answer to no one for his acts."

"This man is so hungry for power that he will stop at nothing." Bernard said. "When the King died and Frederick II was to rule, our Wonder of the World threatened the young queen out of her wits. She then gave up the guardianship of the boy king to the Pope in Rome. Now, the Pope is king of all Europe and all the Holy Church."

"We must tread carefully," Cattaneo said. "Look what happened to the Waldensians with Peter Waldo. At first they were granted the right to organize under Alexander III. Then Pope Innocent III overruled this and accused them of heresy. Most of them died in fire and torture. This we must prevent at any cost to ourselves. I have no liking for the stake."

"Neither have I," laughed Francis. "I understand it raises quite a sweat in the early stages." He then shuddered as his mind reached back in empathy for the horror of those tortured people.

A messenger from Cardinal Hugolin stopped them on their way out of the papal grounds and asked that they return to an anteroom of the palace.

There, Francis and his two companions met Cardinal Hugolin, a tall man with a long graying beard capped by two bright searching eyes. He had the manner and dignity of inner nobility and a man who had found peace within himself.

Francis and the older man held each other's eyes in gentle submission and caught a message of friendly knowledge, quickly passed and just as quickly accepted. They would be friends for the rest of their lives.

The Cardinal excused himself for not being able to see them before the meeting with the Pope, but the business of the Holy Church was most demanding. He slyly referred to the dismissal by his superior as he explained "the Pope has not been well lately due to a surcharge of the blood in his vessels."

He invited the three men to be seated and join him in having a new drink introduced by Venetian travelers who had brought back certain dried leaves from the land of China. The leaves were brewed slowly in boiling water and was called "tea."

He questioned Francis at length about his purposes in forming the Lesser Brethren, the reasons for complete poverty and the denial of ownership of property. This last, he thought, would meet with the greatest objections from the Pope, who was a firm believer in more ownership of property by the Church to keep itself alive in this world.

"Strange, strange, it was a Jew who founded our religion and another comes along to help it." The Cardinal was thoughtful. "I have been reading the Clementin Letters, which were those written by Saint Peter to Saint Paul in which he says, that 'Christianity is Mosaic teaching purified, with the addition of preaching to the heathen and baptism.' Now, you want to preach Christianity to the Christians."

"If your excellency remembers," Peter added, "there is nothing in those letters which mentions any kind of resurrection of Christ. The death of Jesus does not mean salvation. God is one, but he is a personal God. The devil is always seducing men and the 'True Prophet' teaches them how to serve God."

"If evil comes from freedom," the Cardinal told them, "the letters say that eternal punishment comes. They also command that all property is sin, eating flesh is sin and frequent bathing are commanded."

"Then we can conclude," Francis suggested, "that the foundation of the Roman Church is in Judaism and its system of priests is the same as that of your church today."

They chatted about a few other matters and the Cardinal asked that he be remembered to Bishop Guido of Assisi.

He promised them that if the three men would return the next day just after noon, they would have another audience with the Pope.

Francis would have been interested in hearing a conversation later in the day between the Pope and one of his most confidential advisors, Cardinal Hugolin, who *was his nephew* and 16 years older than the Pope.

"Why can't we use this young man?" the Cardinal asked his uncle. "Our goals in the Third Lateran Council (of 1179) were a greater effort for restraint upon those who wander away from the Holy Church. That young Jew can do something like that for us."

"That Brother Jesus idea . . ." the young Pope ruminated. "It has a catchy name to it and the masses of our good people would eat it like their daily bread, with salt on it," he laughed.

"Our past experiences with Jew converts to our Holy religion have not been successful ventures," the bearded Cardinal suggested. "These converts hate their own religion from fear and think they can find a haven of safety in their petty lives within the bosom of our church. They are then hated by the Jews who neither respect nor trust them or their motives.

"In the mind of the Jew the most hateful person is he who tries to convert him. These converts bring their own kind of terrors and shortcomings to us. As if their own failures within the mother of all religions, Judaism, can offer them any more surcease in Christianity. All we acquire is these fresh Jew converts who are indeed half people, troubled in spirit and no value to us as missionaries."

"Is it then your thought," surmised the Pope, "that this Francis can perhaps act as a new kind of missionary. That chin of his tells me that he will not go to the right nor to the left. He asks people to live in poverty, yet he comes from a wealthy home. Strange people these Jews. It's little wonder our Roman forbears called them a stiff-necked people. We must bend them to our will. Yet, my predecessor Pope Gregory the Great, issued the Sicus Judaeus, which protected the Jews from conversion by force. I must abide by this Bull of my noted friend who sat on the hard rock of Peter." Innocent laughed at his own humor.

"We must find more facile methods," Cardinal Hugolin suggested. "Perhaps this young Francis has something of value to all of us. It is worth a trial. The Church has nothing to lose and more to gain."

"Very well," the young Pope agreed, "Let's have this young man back to see us again. But make certain that he has no country odors about him. I am a city child and these country smells make my blood course with greater speed across my head and my chest."

His mood suddenly changed and he turned to his nephew, "Why isn't he a Christian or a priest like everyone else?" he demanded.

"It is far better, this way," the Cardinal soothed him. "This Francis Bernardone, what a name . . . a 'big bold bear' and a French one at that . . . supposing his mother came from the north . . . she would have named him 'Germanicus Bernardone' . . . . ."

"Lord help us in such a disaster." The young Pope laughed with his nephew.

"The Church is like an open bosomed woman," Cardinal Hugolin said. "She can welcome another child at her breast . . . all in due time."

At the audience the next day, Pope Innocent III told them he had a dream that night of Francis "holding up the walls of the church from falling down into ruins."

He granted them the right to preach, to form the Order of the Lesser Brethren. He also granted Francis' wish: they could bear no arms, no individual friar could own anything more than his tunic, a pair of breeches and in dire necessity a pair of shoes. The Brethren could earn their food only with their hands, not the labor of others.

Then as if in an afterthought, "How about a cord for his waist?" The young Pope laughed, "He could then hang himself if he did not like this kind of a life."

He then agreed to Francis' request that the Order could own no property and their houses must be poor and mean.

He bent his head closer to Francis, who could see the wide, protruding eyes and the heavy, fleshed face, mounted over a thick jowled neck. His ringed hands were thick and smooth as silken cloth.

"You people must be drunk, like the Jews of old to our Lord Jesus, to ask this kind of life for yourselves. And I must be drunk to grant this kind of foolishness." He looked over towards his nephew, Cardinal Hugolin, and shook his head in mock despair. Then seeing some sign in the other's eyes, raised his open palms and dismissed them, the audience was over.

After they left the Papal Palace, the three men were walking down a street in Rome when a fine carriage stopped alongside them and a woman's voice called to Francis from inside the vehicle.

He came closer and recognized Jacopa . . . he had not seen her and Father Bellas in seven years. She remained in the carriage and spoke to Francis. She was dressed in the conservative fashion of a noble Roman lady.

He returned to the others and told them it was Jacopa, whom he had known many years ago in Spello. He wanted to visit with her and would meet them later at a given place.

Jacopa then invited all three to visit with her at her home. All three got into the carriage with her and rode to her home. She had her servants provide refreshments for all of them.

Then she told Francis the story of events which occurred after he had left them about seven years ago. Father Bellas, as Francis well knew, was critical of the local priests for some time. He became more outspoken when an old couple wanted to bury their son, who had died fighting for the Pope, in the local church cemetery.

The priests of the church had set such a high price for the sacrament of burial that the old couple would have to sell their pitiful, small farm to pay for it. Which they did, to a relative of the priest.

A week later several hooded monks came to their house and arrested Father Bellas in the name of the Inquisition. She never saw him again.

The monks tried to bind Jacopa's hands, one of them threw her child Gloria to the floor when she started to cry at the mistreatment of her mother.

When Old Isaac tried to interfere and help, one monk beat the old man on the head and the back with a cudgel. As he fell to the floor they tied him with ropes in the form of a cross.

As one of the monks beat Isaac's chest with a stick, he shouted, "Die you old Jew, die like my Lord Jesus died on the cross." He continued to beat him until the old man died. They left him tied with the ropes on the floor, spread into an eternal symbol of death.

Jacopa was taken to a monastery and then for some reason she could not understand, she was released without harm. She then found a position in the home of a Count Settesoli, a widower with two small grandchildren. His daughter and her husband were dead.

She was able to bring Gloria to this household, where the child found companionship with the other two children. After two years in this household, she married the Count, who was her senior by about 30 years. He had died about six months ago and had left her his house and provided amply for her and the care of the children.

What happened to Father Bellas? They concluded that he, like thousands of others, just disappeared in the caverns of the Inquisition.

Assisi *1211*

One day a message came to Francis that his mother, Pica, wanted to see him. When he got to his home, he found it was in a turmoil. Vollo and Volla, their house servants, had been arrested by the monks!

Several weeks before, Volla had told Pica that one of the local priests had ordered them to leave the employ of the Bernardones, giving her many reasons. The monk warned her she and Vollo could not work for the Bernardones because they were Jews!

They went away for several days to a rabbi in Viterbo, the nearest Jewish community, where he circumsized Vollo and had Volla repeat some prayers, which made her into a Jewess. Almost childlike, Vollo had shown the monks his bandaged organ as proof.

When they returned to Assisi, they were again approached by the same priest and Vollo naively showed him his bandaged organ as proof that he was a Jew and could now work for the Bernardones. They were arrested by the Inquisition monks and were being held in a monastery for execution. It was heresy punishable by death for a Christian to become a Jew!

Francis remembered how childlike and simple these two had been in their love making. They had the large warehouse room downstairs and they used a corner of it for their own. It had no partitions and he and Angelo would often see them making love in their bed. They knew the boys were watching them and they would laugh aloud.

Once when Angelo was fourteen he asked Volla if he could have her. She was openhearted and invited him in her bed. As Francis and Vollo watched, Angelo had his first experience with a woman. Volla also invited Francis to use her, which he politely refused.

Francis long ago had learned that Volla was barren. She had been a servant girl in a castle in Germany. The son of a baron had made her pregnant. She had been whipped across the abdomen to make her abort the fetus. As a result, she had bled profusely. There was such damage, that now she could no longer bear a child.

She and Vollo had tried to get married, but a priest had demanded so much money, far beyond their meager means, that they lived together as man and wife ever since. Neither could read nor write. They were devoted to every whim of the Bernardones. Pica several times tried to teach Volla simple words to read and write, but the woman preferred to remain as she was.

As a pair of house servants they cooked, shopped, cleaned and cared for the bales of goods in the warehouse. They were loyal and loved the Bernardones as their own family. To them, the act of circumcision and becoming Jews was just another instance of loyalty to their friends. They knew little or nothing of religion.

Francis remembered that it was Vollo who had tried to carry Pica up from the basement when she was in labor with his birth. Ever since he was born, these two were like a second pair of parents to him.

Now, Pica was without help in the house and to cap her troubles, Pietro was away on one of his long journeys to northern Europe. Since she could not employ another Christian, she had to do all the cooking and cleaning herself. She had done no such work in all her life and it was much too late to start now. She was frantic with work and worry about the two servants.

Then she called Francis. He knew that he could not resolve this problem alone and the advice of Peter Cattaneo was needed, since he had been a canon and a lawyer. The older man suggested they first see Volla and Vollo in the monastery and decide upon other legal actions for the trial before the Inquisition.

Francis and Peter walked into the somber room and they waited for their old friends to appear.

Volla hesitated as she came into the room, when she saw Francis she cried out volubly, "Francis, my Francis, you came to see your Volla, you did not forget her, ma cherie."

She folded her ample arms round him, hugging him close, holding him with the love of her own barren years. In her arms were the countless nights when she was up with him as an infant, rocking him to sleep in her lap.

He, too, was held by the love this woman bore for him, as a boy growing up in the house of his own parents. The affection and love was there for both of them to share.

She held him away from herself, looking over his simple threadbare gown and the cheap sandals on his feet.

A look of consternation came over her face. "Where are the 'so beautiful' clothes?" she wanted to know. Her face was twisted with distate, "these are priest's clothes, and no fancy leather boots."

"Yes, Volla," he nodded. "This is the kind of life I must lead now. But, come now, I came to hear about you. Are they treating you well?"

She looked around and behind her to see if they were observed. "Vollo my husband works in the field today."

"Oh, this is my friend, Peter Cattaneo," Francis told her. She nodded and half curtsied to the older man. His ugly face crinkled in a friendly smile.

"We came to hear about your life here," the older man said, "and how we can help you."

A grey-shrouded monk came into the room silently and stood near them.

Volla looked full into this man's face and shrugged her Gallic shoulders with disdain.

She quickly lifted her skirt showing Francis and Peter one of her bare buttocks. They moved back quickly in surprise, yet their eyes were caught by the cruel marks on her bare skin.

They were an angry red, with bluish tinges, strangely, there was a pattern to them. Each of them was exactly like the other! As if one marker had made them all in a motley array over her clear white skin. They looked like four-leafed flowers.

The grey-robed monk looked at them, still saying nothing.

She then told them a story which made Francis writhe with bitterness.

It seemed there were about seven women who "worked" in the monastery. Each of them had a husband employed on the grounds. There were about fifteen children born to these women.

Each of these women and their husbands were there for some petty crime imposed by the clergy. In one instance a woman broke a sacred vessel in the church and her punishment was life imprisonment in this monastery. In another, the husband was drunk had leaned on a church trellis and it broke. In both cases the wife *and the* husband were sentenced to life imprisonment here.

Volla went on in her voluble French, telling how the monks would at first threaten the wives with death to their husbands if they did not submit to regular intercourse. Some were forced against their will.

The arrangement was such that the husband had one night a month with his wife. In the event there were any children, the husband would be the father of the pregnant women, not the monks.

Cattaneo asked Volla if she knew who the men were who had intercourse with her. She told him that they darkened the room so that the woman would not know who was there. In fact, when she would come into the room it was pitch black and always at night. No woman would ever know who her lover was.

In her case, the man would come into her room, would attempt to have intercourse with her, fail to enter, then whip her with his hand on her bare buttock.

"Such a selfish man," she said sadly. "He would light the fire of my passion then leave . . . I would have to finish with my fingers what he started." She shuddered in distaste.

"To make such marks," Francis observed, "this man . . . this beast must turn his ring around on his finger to make these marks on her skin."

"I agree with you," Peter said.

"Don't you women resist these men?" Francis asked her.

"Yes, we do," Volla told them. "But, these religious are shrewd ones. They tell us that our husbands are under an interdict for burning at the stake. Or they tell some of them that their children will be taken away and they won't see them again. So they have us. This is how life is, we pay for it." She shrugged her shoulders. "We are truly simple women with a few needs."

Cattaneo watched as Francis twisted one hand in the other. The look of pain and horror on the young man's face were studies in the lines on his flat cheeks.

"All the monasteries aren't bad," Peter told his friend. "Many of these men are spiritual in their personal outlooks and thoughts. Many do much useful work writing the Bible and the history of these times."

"Then how can we account for this kind of life?" asked Francis opening his arms in a gesture taking in the entire building. "These men are not doing God's work. They are messengers of darkness.

"I cannot in truth defend them," Peter said slowly. . . .

"We knew many good padres in Paris and in Arles," Volla told them. "They were honest men who did not try to cheat us or tell us lies."

"Yet two of them burned down my mother's house in Arles and killed her father . . . my grandfather and his own sister," Francis said quickly as if the saying was bitter ashes in his mouth.

"And Pica would always sing and cry about her white roses," Volla reminded them.

"You know this story," Francis turned to Peter Cattaneo. The older man nodded his head. "She would think she was alone and hum little songs to herself about her 'beautiful white roses,' lost in the fire."

"When you were a little boy, Pica would sit in the rocking chair and sing you some sweet songs from Provence," Volla mused aloud. She hummed a short melody then she repeated it. "Oh it was too sad."

"My mother long ago buried her father and his sister, my aunt," Francis told them. "But, she never forgot her song of the white roses."

"This was in Arles?" Peter's face was shrouded in sympathy. He pursed his lips, "Perhaps one day we shall visit Arles in Provence. It is a beautiful city, I have been there. It has many large trees and big forests near by."

"And the beautiful Rhone River near the house, with all the children making their small boats and swimming and splashing in the river. The water is like the clean sky above," Volla remembered for them.

The monk moved near them, interrupting their reveries. He nodded to the door and pointed to Volla. They must leave. Volla hugged Francis in her big motherly arms. She started to cry. He, too, held her close to himself, this woman who was a second mother to him.

"Don't worry Volla," he soothed her gently with his voice and touch. "We will not leave you here too long."

"You have my word on this too," Cattaneo promised.

Away from the monastery, Francis turned to Peter. "These are monsters the Roman Church hides behind these walls. Is this the kind of church my Brother Jesus told me to save? Is this the sort of life to which we will come ourselves, like them?"

"It all starts from the top," Peter told him. "The Pope himself thinks and acts like his cut-throat relatives in Venice. Did anyone stop to think that it was Venetian gold which elected the youngest Pope in history. It was a sad day for all Christians when we got ourselves the 'Stupor Mundi', seated in the chair of Peter."

"I remember, so many years ago," Francis said, "I stopped off at the house of a Cardinal, who bought himself the job of being a Prince of the Church. Yet the man had three children."

"There is no secret about all this," Peter informed him. "Some of the Princes of the Church bought their jobs with gold and the influence of their rich merchant cousins. These jobs would go to the ones paying the most into the papal treasuries. They always are hungry for gold and property."

"There is one man who is honorable and not corrupt, like the others. . . ." Francis started to say.

"Hugolin?" finished Peter.

"Cardinal Hugolin, we can trust him and he will help us." Francis said. "He is a good man."

From several sources they learned that the Cardinal was visiting with a nobleman named Spadalunga in Perugia. They went there walking many heat-filled miles across the hot Italian countryside.

The old Cardinal was glad to see Francis and told him so, with an affectionate hug. His beard was shredded with silver cords as it hung low on his chest. Peter Cattaneo he knew long before, as a canon lawyer pleading cases before his court.

When Francis told him the purpose of his visit, the Cardinal nodded his head sagely. Yes, he knew of many such malefactors in the country. But, the Church worked slowly to cure its ailments. In cutting off the limb, it is wise to make certain one does not sever a large blood vessel.

As for the Inquisition, this had been set up by his uncle, Pope Innocent III, to "inquisitio veritatis" the truth of a man's thoughts about his religion and God. Since the Pope was the Supreme Pontif and the only Vicar of Christ on this earth, then all of them must obey his every edict without question. "It is unfair," the old man admitted. "In many cases, all of us, from the Cardinal to the lowly servant, must obey this man. You know Peter," he pointed to the man, "you are a lawyer. All of us must first obey the law.

"Since we are dealing within the framework of the law," the Cardinal continued, "then let us examine the facts which may alter the interpretation of this law. From my understanding of this case, your servants Volla and Vollo will come up for a second hearing before the Inquisitor Fra Baccione. You may challenge the authority of the court in this matter. Where is the proof these two are Christians?"

"Indeed your excellency," Cattaneo smiled. "These people have never been married and are living in sin. Therefore, they could not be good Christians. They could be infidels or Cathari. That court cannot try any but Christians."

"Where's the proof of their marriage or that they ever attended any church?" Francis added.

"Just so," the Cardinal advised them. "The Inquisitor Fra Baccione is known to us. His morals and his philosophy are a corruption to the Church. But, he is a stickler for the precise interpretation of canon law. This is where you can trap him.

"As for you, young Francis Bernardone, you are doing God's work and without the sanction of being a priest or a Christian. You wear no breviary nor a cross, yet you make all of us remember that we need symbols. Yes, I remember, you do this for your Brother Jesus, who was indeed born a Jew and died on a Roman cross."

The Cardinal paused, looking kindly at his young friend, "Are you happy in the work you do for God and your people?"

"I am still searching for my true direction," Francis answered slowly. "Often time, I believe that my Brother Jesus leads me down many paths to find myself at the end, wondering where I've been. This I have learned. He does not want me to be a layer of stones and a builder of poor church walls."

"Remember the fifth commandment, my son," the Cardinal told him. 'To honor thy father and mother and thy days may be long.' Go see your father and your mother often, they love you."

"I will remember that, your excellency," Francis bowed his head.

"The rabbis of old tell us," the Cardinal said, "that God gives wisdom to those who have wisdom. God willed that this fifth commandment is the last of those concerning Him and leads to those concerning your fellow men. Honoring your parents comes ahead of murder, adultery and stealing."

"God knew," suggested Peter Cattaneo, "that if people honored their parents, they would in turn honor God and never need to murder or be adulterers or steal."

"Very well said," the Cardinal said. "I will have to use that in one of my sermons some Sabbath morning." He had been holding a book in his hands, with a finger inside the pages. He opened it and they could see it was an ornate book in Hebrew. He started to read in Hebrew, explaining that it was the 40th chapter of Isaiah.

"This is a beautiful language, much more alive than our stilted Latin, which is more for soldiers than for worship in a house of God. You understand Hebrew, Peter Cattaneo?"

The other nodded his head.

"And you young man," he turned to Francis, "have had your education neglected. You know your French, but no Hebrew or Latin."

"I grew up in Assisi," Francis replied, "there were no teachers in Hebrew."

"Pity, it's a pity, more young people should learn Hebrew. It rings with the majesty of God. After all, this was close to Aramaic, which was the language of our Lord Jesus." His silver beard caught some reflection of light. "I would like to read and translate what I'm reading from Isaiah. What a giant of a man this was. We have none like him today, a pity, a pity."

Then he began to read in Hebrew, translating as he went along,

"Loh'mo sohmar yachov, oosdabaer yisroel . . ."

'Why sayest thou O Jacob, and speakest O Israel My way is hid from the Lord and my right is passed over from God'.

Hast thou not known? Hast thou not heard that the everlasting God, the Creator of the ends of the earth, fainteth not, neither is weary? His discernment is past searching out.

And they that wait for the Lord shall renew their strength

They shall mount up with wings as eagles;

They shall run, and not be weary;

They shall walk and not faint."

"Isn't this a beautiful thought and words of majesty and glory?" the Cardinal asked. "But here in the next chapter is one of my favorites, When the prophet says, 'I the Lord who was the first, and with the last am the same. The isles saw and feared, the ends of the earth trembled: they drew near and they came.

" 'They helped everyone of his neighbor and everyone said to his brother: 'Be of good cheer'.

"Then later this great man writes on, 'Fear thou not, for I am with thee, be not dismayed for I am thy God, I strengthen thee. Yea, I uphold thee with my right hand.

" 'Behold, all that are incensed against thee, shall be as nothing and shall perish.'

"There is much more to this chapter," the old Cardinal went on, "but I will not burden you with my readings. Cherish these words as I do." He nodded his head with his long grey beard folding on his chest.

Francis and Peter thought the interview was at an end. They rose to leave. He shut the book gently and fondly like the caress to a good friend, to be met again.

He looked up at them, "I bid you a good day gentlemen and good fortune on your journeys. And Francis," he paused, "Come to see me again . . . and soon."

Later Francis commented, "There is truly a man of God."

On their long walk back to Assisi, Cattaneo spoke bitterly about the legal effects of the Inquisition begun by Innocent III. "If a man disagrees with the tenets of the Church, that man is a heretic. Legally, under the Inquisition, the Church may search into that man's innermost thoughts. He can be imprisoned and all his property become forfeit to the Church. By whose right? By what God given or legal right can they do this?

"What Innocent makes legal today remember if anyone else says something like this it bears little weight . . . but, written and ordered by the

Pope in Rome, then it becomes a law forever. All those who come after him must follow his edict.

"One day, perhaps a year, perhaps a thousand years from now, men will search for one single reason for the beginning of the Inquisition and they will place it at this man's head. For he made *it legal and the law* of the Church.

"Upon his head will rest the calumny of the ages of Christians to be born, for this master stroke of their Pope. Just as the Jews for ages have suffered for the acts of one man named Caiaphus. Do not misjudge this man of ours in Rome. He has one of the most brilliant and literary minds in Europe. But his own personal ambitions for a greater and stronger church have corrupted him.

"For hundreds of years the Jews and the Christians will say to the Roman Catholics, 'you have burned our people at the stake, flayed us alive to death, broken us on the torture rack, only because your Pope said it was legal.' Now, all the world will ask again and again, you Christians, tell us why you obeyed this horrible edict?"

* * *

A week later, Francis learned from the office of the Bishop Guido of Assisi that the official trial of Volla and Vollo would be held the next day at the monastery and that he could attend.

He and Peter were stopped at the entrance gate by one of the monks who requested their credentials to enter. They convinced him that they were emissaries from the Bishop to *help the Inquisitor*, at the trial, with new evidence.

They came into the large, cold and depressing room where the poor woman and her husband sat on chairs with their hands tied behind them facing a high wooden bench, behind which sat three monks.

The one seated in the middle asked them who the visitors were. Francis replied that they were of the Lesser Brethren and came there to be of assistance to the Inquisitor, whose name they had learned from Bishop Guido was Fra Baccione.

Francis and Peter came closer to the high bench.

"I recognize you sirrah," the man pointed to Francis. "You are that crazy beggar going around the streets of Assisi trying to fix walls of churches. When you are done, you must come here. We have sufficient work for a lifetime of hard labor," he laughed.

"Yet," he again pointed his finger at Francis, "you spoil it for the rest of us religious, who want to make an honest living of this holy work for our Lord

Jesus." He made the cross over his chest with two open fingers of his right hand.

Francis caught the glint of jewels on the ring the man wore. As the man moved his hand it was caught by the dancing lights it reflected and its strange design. Where had he seen this design before? Francis wondered.

"We have come to aid your excellency in making a worthy decision in this matter, based on justice," volunteered Peter.

"How could you aid us in making such a noble decision of law?" asked a heavy-set monk in the middle. The other two on the bench beside him nodded in agreement.

Peter informed them, "I am a graduate scholar and a Doctor of Laws from the University of Bologna and one time canon of San Rufino in Assisi."

"These defendants are in a court Christian of the Inquisition," Fra Baccione said, "and the civil laws of the city of Assisi do not apply here. This is a clear case of heresy and we have taken full jurisdiction of the matter."

"Yes, we only seek justice for these two defendants," Peter's voice was mild and soothing.

"The common law of England has no application here," the Fra's voice rose in anger.

"Quite true," replied Peter slowly, "The laws of justice were founded, in fact had their roots, in the ancient Norman lands of France. Can we deny these laws exist, when we are so close to their birthplace?"

"We create the needed justice by each situation," the Fra reminded them. "Our power is granted under the Inquisition through Pope Innocent III, 'to inquire into the truth' and we may use any means at our disposal to obtain this truth. Heresy does not lie upon the skin so all men can see it. Our power enables us to reach under that skin and probe the devil further."

"No one denies the power you have vested and your jurisdiction in this matter," Peter replied, "Yet, no less an authority on canon law, than Cardinal Hugolin informed us . . ."

"Who did you say?" the monk asked.

"Cardinal Hugolin," the lawyer told him.

"In that case, we would be pleased to hear what . . ." the monk's voice caught a pitch of anxiety.

"I wish the permission of this court to interrogate the two defendants, named Vollo and Volla," Peter asked. Francis nodded his consent.

"Vollo," Peter turned to the seated man writhing in his bondage. He tried to give him a brave smile of recognition. "Were you and this lady, Volla, married? Please tell us where and by whom?"

The man shook his head in dismay. "We have never been sanctified by any priest."

"When was the last time you went into a church to pray?" the lawyer went on.

This time both Vollo and Volla replied volubly, "Never."

"You mean not lately?" was the next question.

"Never," Vollo replied. "We have never been in a church to pray."

"Don't you believe in God, the Almighty God?" he asked.

"Oh, sure, Oh, sure," they both answered quickly. "We have fear of God in heaven and eternal punishment in hell for our sins. Sure we believe in God."

"I may take it therefore," Peter continued, "that you two have not observed at any time in your lifetime any of the tenets of true Christianity?"

"Eh, what," Vollo started to say.

"We have observed nothing," Volla told him. "We have never learned to read or write, so how could we learn anything?"

"Ignorance of the law," Fra Baccione intoned, "as you well know Mr. Lawyer, is no excuse for breaking the law. Say, come to think of it, you both look familiar to me. Where have we met once before?"

The faces of both husband and wife became blank. For Volla's memory had suddenly tracked Fra Baccione to that inn in Arras, so many, many years ago.

"Ignorance of the law is no valid excuse," Peter began to address the monks in a louder voice, to distract them to his questions. "Yet, the defendants admit that they cannot read nor write. Therefore, your excellency must concede that they would have no possible knowledge of the existence of the law as propounded by the Third Lateran Council of 1179, namely that no Christian may change his religion to another, without suffering the hell fires and torture of this court."

"Very well said," the Fra inclined his head.

"Since these two cannot read, nor have they in all their lives, acted or been true Christians," Peter went on, "then they cannot be condemned in this court or any other for straying from their religion. In truth they probably had none of any significance for this court to bother its time and energy. In fact they may be Jews, how are we to know? For with this type of ignorance, they may have known little or nothing about their own rites of circumcision in their own faith."

"Yes," the monk suddenly nodded his head, "it is within our power to assume that they were Christians."

"Agreed," the lawyer said, "but the purpose of the Inquisition is . . . er' . . . prime justice . . . and this court must determine if it is 'legis pura' and whether indeed a crime has been committed against the church. Since no crime has been proven. . . ."

"This man showed his private parts, that he was circumsized just recently," argued one monk on the end.

"As I pointed out earlier," the lawyer answered smoothly, "the defendant cannot read or write and was not aware of the existence of such law in his own faith. Many men are circumsized late in life. This is part of the ancient history of the Jews from biblical days. Many of their kings were cut late in life."

The three monks bent their heads closer to each other, whispering into their cowls, as they talked for a few minutes.

Peter waited in silence in this time, then added, "In the event there is doubt in the heart and soul of the Inquisitor, then the edge of innocence must accrue to the accused."

The three monks seemed to ignore this admonition.

Francis reached over and untied the ropes holding Volla. He said something, in a whisper to Peter, who nodded his head. Francis again whispered to the woman, who arose, lifting her skirts high showing her bare buttocks, to the three monks. She moved closer to them so they could see her skin.

Peter then pointed to the bruises on her skin and the pattern of tinged flowers. "We have seen these brutal marks of Cain upon this innocent woman," the lawyer's voice rose in anger. "Cardinal Hugolin is also aware of the brutalities in this monastery and has promised us that only fire will clean these Herculean stables."

"We do not fear any Cardinal," Fra Baccione replied angrily. "We do God's work in these hallowed walls of God. We supply food and sustenance for many churches and the poor of this town. As long as we do this work honestly and without fear of favor, we in turn have nothing to fear of anyone, in any high places. This monastery is a safe haven for those who want to flee from a world of cruel passion and greed. Here, they can come and find peace and quiet, in God's name."

Francis and Peter remained silent under this harangue.

"In view of the circumstances of this case," the monk's voice grew calm, "we will give the defendants the assumption of doubt in this case. Pope Gregory the Great issued the Sicut Judaecus that no Jew can be forced into our glorious faith in Jesus Christ. Yes, they may go in peace, with you both."

Francis bent over and untied the ropes around Vollo. The four of them hastened out of the gloomy chamber, as if death itself lurked on its walls and fearing the monks might change their minds.

Strangely, the man and his wife were silent as they walked back to the Bernardone house in Assisi. Francis had expected some Gallic hugging and kissing from Volla. For a moment he was disappointed, then he realized that the shock of the past months had aged this pair. These events were now indelible patterns on their souls.

All the way home, the pair said little. For the rest of his life, Francis did not remember seeing either of them laugh or sing again.

Assisi 1212

One afternoon, Francis stood upon a bench in the center of the square in Assisi, with Gilles, Bernard and Peter just below him, facing the crowd which had gathered to hear him.

He raised his arms towards the sky, in a gesture older than man. His voice was vibrant, reaching upwards as he spoke.

"You are now and will ever be the One God in Heaven. Help all of us this day to find strength within our own hearts to walk humbly with you dear God. In Psalm 103 the words, "Bless the Lord, Oh my soul," is said five times by King David. As God fills the entire world, so does the soul fill the whole body. As God sees and is not seen, so with the soul of man. As God nourishes the whole world, so does the soul nourish the whole body. As God is pure, so is the soul pure. As God dwells in secret, so does the soul. So let the least of us, who have all these things praise the Lord God to whom all these five attributes belong.

"Oh, God and God of my fathers, teach me to walk humbly with you as free men, not what others tell us. We will walk humbly with You as men and not as slaves. Teach me to be humble, though I am oppressed; teach me to have courage, when my strength fails me. Teach me to love all your creatures because they are all your own."

He saw Clara and her mother Ortolana standing at the edge of the crowd, both of them wearing purple colored lace mantillas, which the women of Assisi had recently adopted. Francis raised his hand in a mild salute to them. In turn, Clara moved her hand upward across her face, to let him know she had seen his gesture. His words seemed to carry more depth as he continued.

"Help me Oh Lord. . . . teach me to love your greatest creation . . . my fellow men and their people."

Francis looked down from his bench at his listeners and could see that he was holding their attention. He was talking and they were listening . . . as if they had waited a lifetime for something, they knew not what. They

234

could see that he was poorer than the lowliest among them. He wore a meagre robe held by a simple cord around the waist and his feet were bare. Many of them remembered the time when he wore the rich clothing of the town dandy, with fancy leather shoes and expensive coats. Now, not one of them could truly say that Francis wore better clothing than he.

"My Brother Jesus opened His arms and enfolded all people . . . . the Jew as well as the Gentile . . . the white and the colored. He said to them, as I now say to you . . . . . "Follow me and I will show you the way to God . . . not in the life to come . . . . but right now . . ."

"The greatness of God is infinite, for man with a single die can make many of the same coins. Our God can make every one of us in the image of Adam, yet not one is like his neighbor. So each can say, 'for me the Universe was created.'

"For God said, 'I did not create Man for you to hate each other and destroy one another . . . for each one of you carries a part of Me . . . your God . . . love one another . . . .'"

At this moment, there was a distraction just below him. One of the men had started to hiccup and could not stop. He made a movement to leave the crowd. Francis stopped and jumped down from his bench and stood behind the man tapping him soundly on his back. The man continued to hiccup and the crowd began to laugh at the red face of the poor man.

There was a water wagon nearby and Francis asked for a cup of water. He made the man with the hiccups insert each forefinger deep into his ears and hold down the lobes, while he held the water for the man to drink continuously. In a few minutes, the sound of the hiccups stopped and the crowd clapped its hands in collective appreciation.

On the bench once again, Francis went on, "People believe that God left unfinished the most northern part of the world. But, there was a purpose, for God said, "Whoever believes he is equal to God, let him come and finish these icy wastes, so that all may know that he is equal to God!

"Then I say to all of you, come live a full life of service . . . without violence . . . a life of humility and courage. From being humble, you will find a mighty strength. It is in Isaiah that we find the great prophet cry out, 'The spirit of the Lord is upon me, to bring good tidings to the *humble!* He did not say to the 'Saints' or the arrogant . . but to the humble . . . so it means that humility is the greatest of all human values.

"Speaking of Isaiah, he once said, 'If thou draw out thy soul to the hungry, if you have nothing to give him, *comfort him with words.* Say to him, 'My soul goes out to you because I have nothing to give you.'

"A rabbi once told his wife, 'When a beggar comes to the door hand him bread, so that the same may not be done to your children.' She cried out, 'are you not cursing your children?' The man replied, 'The world is like a wheel, the man who is rich today may be poor tomorrow and the poor may be richer soon.'

"Whoever among you will practice charity and justice is as though he filled the whole world with love and kindness. Like the waves of the oceans it spreads on and on to far distant shores. Remember, far more than the owner of the house does for the beggar, the beggar does for the owner. For the door which is not opened to charity, will one day be open for a doctor.

"When a man appears before the Judgement throne, the first questions asked of him will not be, 'have you believed in God, or have you prayed and performed daily ritual acts,' but, 'have you dealt honorably and faithfully in all your dealings with your fellow man?'

"When the Jews of old wandered in the desert after leaving Egypt, Moses sent out men to look at the lands beyond them. They were gone for forty days and came back with lies about giants who lived in those lands and they would eat people. They said, 'We are like grasshoppers in their sight and in ours.' The people believed these false tales and became afraid.

"For this act of fear, they had to travel in the desert a year for each day, or forty years. But, for *every day* in a like manner, he who helps his Maker well, will be repaid a full year in payment.

"Look about you, the 'earth is the Lord's,' say the Psalms, yet another Psalm says that God 'gave the earth to the children of men'. This means that everything belongs to God. Yet, He his given all these bounties to men to be enjoyed.

"Man was created on the sixth day, so if he is ever filled with pride at himself, in this world, he must remember that the lowliest insect came before him on earth.

"The soul of man was created on the first day of creation, and He created the Angels on the second day. If man keeps the spirit of God always near him, then 'he is greater than the angels.' "

For a few minutes, Francis was silent. Like tiny echoes his voice danced across the square. The people, lulled into a respite by his voice, were now released and free again, by his silence.

"Someone asked me if I should help the wicked man as well as the good one? I say to you it is our duty to show the wicked man the correct way, for the wise to help the unwise; for the rich to aid the poor. Each one of us should help his brother according to his talent."

"Who among you has the courage to raise his hand and make a vow to follow me . . . . in humility and poverty and service . . . Who among you will cast off the garments of this world and live like my Brother Jesus in a spirit of humble poverty . . . *to live among people* . . . . not shut up behind some stone walls of a monastery . . . ? This will be our service to the sick, the poor and the leper among us.

"Who among you will vow never to bear arms, in anger or in war against his fellow man? Who among you will venture into a new world of peace, of such inner strength that it will shine from your face, like a bright star in heaven?

"Do not think this will be a life of ease and luxury in demeanor or in thought. Each one must work and earn his bread by the sweat of his own hands . . . .

"There is an ancient story, which my mother Pica once told me. There was a wide river . . . it was swift and strong. On the other side was a land where *all people could find true wisdom*. There was no bridge to cross this river and on the edge stood a lonely man, wondering how he could cross.

"Then a voice came from the other side of the river: 'Each person must be part of a bridge leading to the other side . . . . each one of you must be a chain of arms and hearts . . each one of you must serve the other. You dare not let go, lest the chain break . . . for one single break in the chain and the entire bridge is lost. Who shall be the first to start the bridge?' the voice asked, 'to build a bridge to the land of wisdom?'

"Who among you will raise your hands to help me?" Francis' voice carried across the square. A few men in the crowd raised their arms and moved toward him. They came closer to Bernard and Gilles who spoke with them.

At the edge of the crowd, he saw Clara raise her arm slowly, then in a single motion, she hugged her mother, Ortolana. Francis could see tears on the faces of these two women. Within himself, he felt an outgoing emotion of warmth and love for both of them. They waited on the edge of the crowd, until it had moved away.

Ortolana then drew her strong motherly arms around Francis. She held him close to her for a minute, the tears were still on her face. Then she slowly walked away from them, leaving Clara and Francis alone. They walked to the archway of the city gate.

"Once again we come to this spot," Clara said, "as if in this one place, we know so well, will remind us of so many things that are past."

"What is past is forward," laughed Francis. "And perhaps this too is the parting of the ways for us," he said slowly.

"I remember, it seems ages ago, that I promised . ." Clara started to say.

"No, dear Clara it was I who promised," Francis said. "Now, our paths have gone in different ways, never to meet again."

"Hold my hand," Clara begged. "You and I will not share our lives as husband and wife. Nor, the closeness which children would bring into our lives. Oh, Francis, we could have made such wonderful parents to our children."

"This man in Madrid . . . .?" Francis inquired.

"My father says that he betrothed me when I was very young," she told him. "This is the way of all our modern parents. But, Ortolana always wanted me for you and only you, Francis."

"I know this," he replied, "Your mother, God bless her, is an understanding and noble woman."

"What shall become of us?" she asked.

"My paths of poverty and humility are not for you, Clara," he said. "For men to live this kind of life, we can and we do. But, for women, the hardships are too many. But, the worst part, could we ask our women to beg? This would degrade them in the eyes of the world and the beholder . . . greedy men would take advantage of this . . . you know what I mean . . . . ."

"You said that people could serve others," she said "to serve the sick and the leper. If men can do these things then women can do them as well."

"It would be such a hard and cruel life for you," he said. "Is this what you truly want to do? Give up your life of comfort and beautiful clothes, to live a simple life of austerity and want?"

"You gave up your life of ease and luxury, in doing this," she pointed to his meagre robe and bare feet.

"Perhaps the will to do these things came from God, I don't know," he replied.

"Then you be my father and teach me how to reach God," she said. "Let me know the paens of glory you must have within yourself . . . . ."

"Is this what you want?" his voice was incredulous in disbelief.

"Ever since you threw your clothing in front of your father almost eight years ago in the Bishop's palace," she told him. "Somehow, I knew that we would find a path down life together, not as man and wife, but in truth . . . . we are married in the spirit of doing God's work for His creatures. Is this not so?"

"When we were children, we had so many noble plans," he remembered. "Are dreams only the things children can have for nothing?"

"But the stuff of childhood dreams are the bones to make us into grown people," she said.

"We must return now," he told her. "The world has many unhappy and wicked tongues . . . we must never be alone together again."

"Is this, how we end our life together?" she asked. "With a faint handshake and a farewell? No, I will come to you tomorrow night at the Church of the Portiuncula and you "will induct me . . . you are the Lesser Brethren, then I will be the Poor Sister . . ."

"Of Clare," he added.

She nodded her head. "This is the kind of life I want to lead, only if you Francis tell me it is right for me to do this. Please Francis, let me help you."

Once again Francis heard, from dim memory, the child's voice, before the walls of Assisi, almost ten years ago, 'Let me help you Francie'.

"Very well," he nodded his head. "On your way home, you go . . . no, I will go to see our friend Vollo. He will find a carriage and bring you to me. We will make the start."

It was almost midnight, on March 18, 1212, when the carriage rolled up to the heavy wooden doors of the Portiuncula and Francis with Gilles and Bernard admitted her into the Church. They had no sooner shut the doors when the clatter of a horse troop, came raking the night with their heavy noises.

The soldiers banged heavily with their swords on the doors demanding entry. Francis knew that Clara's father, Count Offreduccio, was there demanding the return of his daughter. They could not enter, because of the sanctity of the building. At this point, the world of arms and the soldier had to remain outside.

Inside, Francis made Clara take the vows of poverty and meagre living and service to all beings. This she vowed to do, as his three companions, Peter, Bernard and Gilles stood nearby. Thus was sworn in the first of the Poor Sisters of Clare.

The room in the Portiuncula was deep in the gloom of night. Only the two candles, held by Peter and Bernard, glimmered their faint light, to give the room some warmth and trim the shadows forming around them. The walls were brutal, in their stark, cold lines.

"Francie, let me help you," whispered Clara, once again.

Francis then raised his hands over Clara's bent head, with his fingers outspread, in the gesture of the ancient priestly blessing. Outside could be heard the pounding of the soldiers on the heavy doors, insisting their power over all beings. Its sounds rebounding with vigor across the yards.

Inside, Francis recited the ancient blessing over Clara, "May the Lord bless thee and keep thee."

Almost like a faint whisper, across the centuries, could be heard the priests in the Temple in Jerusalem blessing the children . . . the voice was so much like that of his Brother Jesus . . the voice he heard in the cave above Assisi . . .

"Y' voreh . . heh . . hoh Adonai v' yish mor eh ho"
"May the Lord make His countenance to shine upon thee and be gracious unto thee,"

"Yo ayer Adonai poh noff ail eh hoh v' hoo neh hoh"
"May the Lord turn His countenance unto thee and give thee peace."

"Yiss oh Adonai poh noff ail eh hoh v' yo saym l' hoh sho lom"
The two candles flickered, then held dimly.

Arles 1213

It was late in 1212 when Francis asked Gilles and Bernard if they would join him in a preaching tour toward Arles in Provence. They would first visit the cities of Rome, Florence, Lucca, then on to Nice, Montpelier, Marseilles and Arles. This tour Bernard estimated would take them about six months. He suggested that, from Arles, they then could go on to Spain and visit some of the large cities.

When they finally reached Arles, Francis asked that they go to the monastery called Cordeliéres.

There Francis stood on a platform and looked down on the men seated on the rough benches waiting for him to begin. Suddenly he felt a chill chase through his bones and he coughed deeply. The constant reminder that he was not to forget that year in the Perugia prison.

He looked around him holding his listeners with his eyes, making them wait as he searched for the words to begin. The heavy masonry walls of this monastery at Cordeliéres were cold and bare. The heavy timbers across the roof were black with time and the dampness of many winters.

"I would like to talk with you about Ezekial, one of the great Prophets in Israel, when he talks about the 'dried up bones of people, waiting in the desert of death for rebirth.'

"Today, this is where the religion of Christianity lies in death. It is only a bag of bones, drying and would remain forever in death. And like a small star across the night skies, Christianity would have lived its brief time and died in the night. It would die together with a hundred other religions which have long since been forgotten in the desert sands of Assyria and Persia.

"My Brother Jesus did not die to build great churches of stone for rich bishops and priests. He did not die to have men use his name to murder and steal and defy all the laws of God."

As he said this, Francis looked full into the faces of the two monks seated on the benches, their faces turned towards him. One of them known as the 'Arab' and the other as the 'Sicilian.'

His eyes held them in a grip of silence, as he continued to speak almost directly to these two men. "My mother, her father and his sister lived in the house next door to these walls," he pointed in that direction on his right.

"One night two men set fire to the house. One of those men wearing the robes of a monk pushed that fine old man into the fire to his death."

There was a gasp of dismay from the others in the room. A look of understanding passed between Gilles and Bernard. They now knew the reason why their steps led them to Arles. Francis wanted to come back and see where his mother had lived in her youth. They followed his looks at the two olive-skinned monks and realized that this address was meant for them.

Francis continued speaking, his voice reaching around the heavy walls. "In Job, the Prophet cries out to God. 'He who has clean hands will increase his efforts' and the eternal cry of my Brother Jesus, For what shall it profit a man if he gain the whole world and yet lose his soul; will that soul be lost in the eternal damnation of hell fires?" Francis asked the monks. He again looked fully at the two men in front of him.

"To all of you," he raised his head higher, his voice reaching, "In the writings of the Zohar, written by Rabbi Jehudah the Pious one, 'there is a divine quality in all of us, that we reach closer to God by doing charity in God's Name.'

"This charity must come from our own labor. By doing this we ourselves become divine. Although a man give no more than a fifth part of that help, this fifth part carries the other four fifths up to God.

"My friend Rabbi Jehudah taught me long ago that we must offer praise to God and give thanks in his name every morning and to say aloud, 'Happy are we! How goodly is our portion, how pleasant is our lot and how beautiful is our heritage.'

"Just as a person rejoices and is happy when an inheritance of an immense fortune, for which he did not toil, falls to him, how infinitely more should we rejoice over the inheritance our fathers left us, namely, the true unity of God.

"Look about you my friends in Cordelière," Francis' arms swept them in. "God is here with you. He is here and everywhere. He rewards in this life those who do good and will punish those who do evil."

Later, when all the others had left the room, the 'Arab' and the 'Sicilian' remained seated on the bench, waiting for the hand of doom to fall on them. They waited for Francis to say something to them.

He glanced at the two men and left the room without saying a word. Gillies and Bernard were beside him as he walked out the door to the garden on the outside of the monastery.

Francis noticed that a short stone wall had been built around the area where his mother's house once stood. He walked towards the heavy oak tree at the far corner. He looked up into its huge heart above him and saw there were a few cross branches and cut timbers spiked together in the form of a large box.

The men behind him could see the covered scars of the tree, which the years had dwelt over the fire more than 33 years ago.

"See," he turned to Gilles and Bernard, "this is the tree house my mother told me about. There," a note of joy rang in his voice, "my mother's childhood lives in that tree."

The others came closer to him they loved, then saw him place his arms part way around the gnarled trunk, hugging it to his bosom.

His golden head bent upwards into the branches. "God is indeed good to me. He has given me a look into my mother's happy days as a girl. She spent many happy hours, dreaming her girlish dreams in that treehouse. Here, give me a lift up," he beckoned to the men.

They helped him slide up the trunk into the old treehouse. He stood over them as he smiled down at the two men. They smiled in return and then sat down at the base of the tree like two silent sentinels guarding his solitude.

He looked down at the field leading to the broad, glimmering delta expanse of the Rhone River. Turning slightly, he could see the deep lush forest above Arles.

He leaned back against the cool tree trunk, his fingers gentled the rough edges of the pieces of timber making the tree box.

In his mind's eye he could visualize his mother standing here, seeing and sensing the details and sounds his mother saw, so many years ago.

He could imagine his Grandfather Jacobs, walking around, near the animals, talking to them in a bold voice, yet soothing their fears of him. There was strength and firmness in that voice. The same kind of strength which Pica had told him many times he had inherited from his gran'pere.

His grandfather was a strong man, with wide shoulders and a round heavy face. His hair was once blond and was now almost gray. He had such strong hands he could set the bones of an animal without using any leather straps.

Pica had told Francis once about the female lion from Arles Zoo. Actually it was not a zoo, but they kept the lions in cages in the city because the symbol of Arles was a lion. Some wealthy landowners had bought the lions and had them placed in an open field owned by one of the men.

It seems that a female lion had been mauled by another jealous lion. The animal was very valuable and the Directoire wanted to save the big cat. He had admitted that the lion would die, with such large cuts on its shoulders.

Another fact to complicate matters was that the lioness was about ready to have her cub. This had not happened before in the city of Arles. The Directoire had wrung his hands in gloom because this would be the first lion cub born in captivity of a direct mating.

And if Doctor Jacobs could save the mother he would have the honor of bringing this cub into the world and greater glory of Arles and to him the Directoire.

At this point in her story telling, Pica would imitate the anguish and the mannerisms of the man. Both she and Francis would go into gales of laughter at the imagined sight.

Then like a curtain quickly opened and as quickly drawn, her face would become shadowed with gloom, as she remembered her father. She would look at her tall son, fondly remembering the days of her own youth and freedom.

Gran'pere Francis had given the hungry lioness some raw meat mixed with finely ground corn and a good dose of strong liquor. Pica told Francis how Vollo had tried to eat the mixture in front of the lioness, making all kinds of pleasant faces, as if to please a small child. Telling the lion that it was better food than Volla made. Slowly, the lioness became drowsy and quiet.

Doctor Jacobs then cleaned the wicked cuts and sewed them up. The animal lived and the doctor did get to deliver the first lion cub in the history of Arles.

Thereafter, he was established as the Doctor for Animals for the Arles Zoo. Many farmers came to him with their animals despite the fact he was a Jew. They were more concerned with the well being of their precious animals than any ideology.

Francis' mind wandered on dwelling on the simple stories his mother had told him . . . all brought back to him by standing in this treehouse.

Francis looked to the river which was washing, in slight swells, the abutting stone wall, now part of the monastery. Yet, once his mother had trotted along its top. He could hear across almost 30 years, the cries of boys and girls playing and swimming in the clear river waters. And the shouts, as they guided their small boats and rafts near the shore, playing naval war games.

Once again, Francis looked down on the scene below him, in the monastery garden, now barren, sparse and unloved. Love and affection must be a daily seed to keep a fine garden in bloom. Here all was austere and friendless.

Lost forever were the girlish shouts, the murmurs of animals and birds and gone were his mother's *beautiful white roses*.

Francis slid down from the treehouse as the two men below him stood aside, waiting for him. The three men walked slowly around the garden. He kept looking on the ground along the wall.

"What are you searching for?" asked Gilles. Francis shook his head.

"I want to find something," he replied, with a sheepish grin. "I don't know *what* it is."

They walked along with him for about a quarter of an hour as he roamed the large garden, probing with a stick and his toe. They were all silent waiting for Francis to say something.

He came closer to one stone wall and stopped, bending down close to the earth.

The hearts of his two friends stood still, as Francis suddenly dropped to his knees and started to dig into the ground with his bare hands. He scratched into the dirt along the wall with his fingers.

"What is it, Francis?" Bernard asked the youth, bending down close to him.

Francis shook his head slowly. He cropped out some more weeds and high grass, tossing them along the wall, away from him. He kept on digging with his hands, refusing the stick which Bernard held out to him.

Then he slowly began to draw out a thin, yet long vine about as thick as his thumb. The men could not see what Francis was doing because his body blocked their view.

He turned to them and almost shouted, "Here is proof that God is always with us."

They looked at the small bush he had drawn from under the wall and was gently bending upwards. The three bent closer to look at the two white rosebuds growing on the end of the small bush.

"It must have been growing on the other side and under the wall." Bernard said.

"My mother's white roses," Francis cried out. He was still on his knees as he made a crooning sound over the small bush. "My mother would sing to me when I was a young boy about these white roses. This garden was her own and she grew these roses from some shoots her relatives brought over from across the seas.

"She tended them with all the love a gentle girl could give without stint to these speechless flowers. When the house was burnt to the ground her flowers as well as the animals and the birds died here."

Still on his knees, facing the wall, he hummed the old Provencal melody his mother sang to him, reaching into his memory with affection, holding the two rosebuds tenderly in his palm.

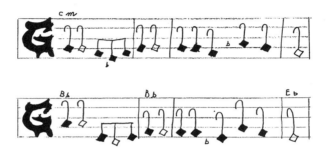

"My beautiful white roses each like a heart
With precious fragrance its petals part
Bring all lovers a breath of life
Points new beauty in its sight."
"Each rose with gentle color rare
Dips this glory from the earth
The petals float as soft as air
From far away its land of birth."

Francis bowed his head low to the ground before the vine with the two rosebuds. In this one gesture the men behind him knew he was paying homage to the love for his mother and the God who had shown him His love too.

The men moved closer to the boy. Bernard gently lifted him on his feet, "Let us not remain here too long," the man said.

They started to walk back to the monastery building.

The two men placed their arms around their young friend and started to sing an old familiar walking song they had sung many times together. Suddenly, de Quintavalle turned from them saying.

"I have left something near that tree. I will meet you later," he swung away from them walking quickly. The two continued on to the building.

Francis turned slightly as they entered the building and saw Bernard standing near the huge tree looking up at the treehouse, his arm holding the trunk.

Later, Francis spoke to Bernard looking full into his eyes, "You love my mother, do you not my dear friend?" he asked.

De Quintavalle nodded his head. "For a few moments in this life I could hold the same things she touched and held. So I could hold them gently. One day I will tell her about this day. We will speak of this day with gladness and hope and good friendship. Does this answer your question?"

Francis put his arm around the older man kindly and pressed his shoulder with his strong fingers.

Now, Francis could understand the readiness with which Bernard de Quintavalle had been the first to join his Brothers of the Poor. He had loved his mother, Pica, with a hopeless devotion. Perhaps he saw in Francis the son of his own he would never have. By tramping the streets of the world with him was the way he would be close to the son of the woman he loved.

Francis told Gilles and Bernard the story which the 'Arab' and the 'Sicilian' had played in the death of his gran'pere and his aunt.

"These men are safe behind these monastery walls," Bernard told them, "and no civil justice can reach them, except that of a Bishop. Only he could drive them out like two vicious rats. Hanging would be too good for them."

"There is so much villainy in the heart of the Church. Is this the Church we are trying to save?" he mused aloud as if talking to himself, "I wonder how many times ten are those incidents we saw in Montpelier, where the priest convinced that poor peasant that the pig's shank bone was really the fingers of Goliath, the giant killed by David?"

"To cheat this poor man out of his life's savings is an infamy beyond the knowledge of men. If men who do God's work act like this where is it all to end?" Francis said.

"Let us pursue this matter further," suggested Bernard. "There are two factions in Rome struggling for control of the Church. Once the Ghibellines ruled with the power behind Frederick the Second. Now the Guelphic faction is in power through their boy named Pope Innocent III."

"This Pope, through every device, is trying to control the church as well as the kings of Europe. He has excommunicated King John of England, who is himself a worse rogue, demanding that he, John, become a vassal of the Pope.

"Innocent will not be satisfied until he has bathed the streets of Europe

Giotto   ST. FRANCIS APPEARS AT ARLES   (Alinari-Art Reference Bureau)

in blood not only of those he calls the heretics, or anyone who disagrees with him. Thousands of Jews and Christians will be murdered in the name of the Prince of Peace."

"I will say this for our young Pope," Gilles interjected. "He may not want the wealth of those about to die, but he wants the glory of the single power in his hands over one church both Greek and Latin."

"Come to think of it," Francis said, "I hear that young Frederick the King of the Holy Roman Empire is not easily led by the ears. One day he may kick up his traces and boot the Pope nearest him."

They were all silent for a short while. Then Francis said, "Then we return to my talk at Cordeliére, is the Christian Church indeed a bag of dried bones? Are the roots of death sown too deeply? Is there nothing to save?"

"What is the philosophy of the Holy Christian Church?" asked Bernard. "Is it the mumbo jumbo of reciting a few Latin prayers on Sunday morning, with the smell of incense and the beating of gongs and bells. Or some illiterate priest standing up before a mob and haranguing them about hell and the hereafter?"

"I've never learned any Latin," Francis admitted, "So any kind of prayer could be strange to me. In fact I have never attended a mass in any church."

"Yet all this started," Gilles laughed, as they joined him, "with your going into a church on the way to Foligno."

"I will have to admit," Francis replied quickly, "that I wanted to get out of the hot sun and cool off. Any place could have done just as well."

The others joined him in friendly appreciation.

"Coming back to our Christian philosophy," Bernard's voice was cool, "is indeed, based on its most simple terms, on a poor Jewish carpenter getting himself hung on a Roman cross. The man was a radical, stirring up trouble for the Romans. That's what the Romans were always after, peace at any price, even if they killed you for it.

"Don't forget it," Bernard went on, "Jesus was a radical and the Romans never liked any radical thoughts. The rulers who are *now in Rome* have not forgotten it to this day." He paused for a few moments, searching his thoughts.

"Then for about 150 years people just talked about this poor Jewish carpenter who died to save all the other Jews from the power of the Romans. There was little or no talk about being born of a Virgin and being the Son of God or flying up to heaven. It took another Jew named Herodotus of Alexandria 150 years later to write the first known book about his fellow Jew who had died in Jerusalem."

"There is pure simplicity in the religion of being a Christian," Francis suggested to them. "My Brother Jesus was a simple man with simple needs. It is said that he was born in a stable. As a matter of fact so was I. We kept the horses and the donkeys in our cellar. My mother Pica went into labor and Vollo could not carry her up the stairs soon enough. So, I was born in the stable in our cellar."

"I remember is quite well," smiled Bernard, "I remember that night well. Vollo came to my house because we could not find the doctor in Assisi and I had to ride into the country to find a mid-wife."

'We could take this birth of my Brother Jesus and make it into a scene with sheep and donkeys near the manger." Francis was excited with the idea. "Then people could see how simple was the beginning of the life, which made Christianity."

(The first crèche was built by Francis, showing the birth of Jesus in the simple stable. The idea in its utter simplicity catches the imagination of people to this day.)

"Come next Christmastide," said Bernard, "We can play with this idea in some town."

"We have made a complicated mass out of a simple belief," Francis went on. "There are many of the Cathari, who say that Jesus was never born. That religion is based on the imagination of a couple of fast talkers named Peter and Paul."

"It is a fact," Bernard said, "that the story of Jesus waited almost 150 years for a Jewish historian named Herodotus to actually put it into writing. There was nothing before him. I think that the concept of the Virgin birth is a chain on the souls of men. No man of intelligence would accept this kind of belief. Nor that Jesus was the son of God. He was a simple human being who had great faith in His own Jewish religion. He did not want to start a *new* religion. He only wanted to save the one He was in at that time."

"Where has all this led us?" asked Francis. "Thousands of people all over Europe are now worshipping stone idols, the moon and the sun and everything but the One God. They have indeed lost faith in God. For four hundred years the Romans murdered and crucified Christians and made sport of them in the animal arenas. Now, for the last 800 years the Christians have been killing each other and everyone who does not believe as they do. I am no prophet but these wars of Christians against Christians will continue on for another 1,000 years."

"No, my dear friends the end is not in sight," Bernard said. "The rumors still persist all over Italy that our Pope Innocent truly wants to be known to posterity as the 'Wonder of the World.' The only way he can attain this is by making one Church in the entire world."

"With the Latins ruling everywhere?" suggested Francis.

Bernard de Quintavalle nodded his head. "Now, there is something that taxes the heart and soul with the horror of its telling. Namely, the Children's Crusade."

"Yes," Francis agreed solemnly. "These poor, innocent children came by the thousands from across France and the Rhineland to Provence, to Marseilles and Italy. Across the land, the priests filled their hearts with stories that the sea, like that which opened for the ancient Israelites, would allow them to walk across dry land to Jerusalem! They believed, these innocents, that they could capture the city without any weapons."

"There is a greater shame upon the face of our young Pope and upon all Christians," Bernard added, a note of horror in his voice." Christian merchants shipped these children to Egypt by the boatloads and thousands of them were sold into slavery by the infidels."

"Could not the Pope have known this?" asked Francis.

"Who can tell?" the older man replied. "This Pope knows where every 'sparrow falls in the Holy Roman Empire'; it would not profit him to do this. Yet, I have not heard of a single merchant who was engaged in this horror who was punished."

They remained silent, watching the workers and monks slowly sawing the trees in the edge of the forest above the monastery in Arles. They could see the men, like silent wraiths, moving among the trees.

"Our work is with people," Francis mused aloud. "Even those out there." He pointed to the workers. "They need us, not the high and mighty ones in their marble palaces, dressed like Persian Shahs. The worth of all the oceans is with people outside these walls and not in the shallows which roar aloud in their dying gasps."

The three men nodded in agreement. Once again, the Brotherhood of the Poor had resolved another question to allay their early doubts.

Later, in the day, in the hot afternoon sun, they went swimming in the Rhone River, splashing each other like three young boys, let free with no cares in all the world. Francis swam strongly into the river, his muscled athletic shoulders plunging his powerful arms into the clear waters as he moved swiftly across the surface, to the admiration of his two friends.

Some heavily laden merchant ships passed them in the center of the river. They had loaded their cargoes in Arles and these goods would find their way to the marts of Paris and England. One of them passed close to Francis in the middle of the river. A few sailors stood in the stern and waved to him. He drove himself out of the water, waving his arms in greeting. As the water cascaded down his face each drop trapped, for a moment, the light of the warm sun.

Epilogue and Notes

In 1219 Francis went to Egypt on the advice of his friend Benjamin Kolonymus. For the hot, dry climate of this land would relieve the racking cough and the persistent pain in his chest, (the tuberculosis was draining his life) It was Benjamin, the friend of his youth, who enabled Francis to appear before the Sultan of Egypt, Al Kamel (the nephew of Saladin) and translate his French into the Egyptian-Arabic language.

It was Benjamin who acted as his translator for Francis when he preached "humility and love of mankind" to the Moslem troops outside of Fostat (now Cairo). Later Francis preached to the Crusaders at Damietta. Historians say that "Francis made a good impression on the Moslem troops and with Al-Kamel."

SOME NOTES ABOUT THE MUSIC NEUMES AND THE CLEF:

The modern treble or "G" clef is an outgrowth of an ornamental letter "G".

The neumes shown, are those the author saw on some ancient manuscripts and is a contraction of the old German "hofnagle" neume. I believe these were the neumes Francis knew and used.

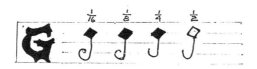

For 2000 years, Jews turned their prayers and poetry into melodic songs. The words to the Hebrew songs in this book were known long before Francis was born.

Much of the same music could have been passed from generation to generation before the 12th century.

THE LEGACY OF FRANCIS

Francis died from tuberculosis, on October 3, 1226. Holding his hands in death was Clara. In 1228, Pope Gregory IX (Cardinal Hugolin) made Francis a Saint of the Christian Church.

Clara died August 12, 1253, and she was made a Saint in 1253.

This was the legacy Francis left behind him:

1. In 1226 there were more than 260,000 people in Europe who followed his precepts of poverty and humility.

   In 1258, there were more than 1,585 Houses of the Grey Friars.

   (In an age without any modern communications of printing, radio or television, this was an achievement for all the ages.)
2. In 700 years more than 1,000 million people have been of service to others, in a choice of poverty and humility.

Francis left us one of these prayers:

"Lord, make me an instrument of Thy peace.
   Where there is hatred, let me sow love;
Where there is injury, pardon; where there is doubt, faith;
   Where there is despair, hope;
Where there is darkness, light;
   Where there is sadness, joy."

THE LEGACY OF POPE INNOCENT III

Pope Innocent III holds a signal and unique place in the history of Western Civilization. Here was a brilliant, literary and trained mind, corrupted by his search for power. "Less than God, but greater than man, judge of all men and judged by none" . . . His Vicar on earth above all kings." (Quote from his first sermon after consecration as Pope.)

In 1199, he wrote the decretal "VERGENTES in SENIUM" which created the legal means and legislation to search into people's minds for their religious beliefs. This led to the horrors of 650 years of the Inquisition, which followed this order.

He alone, wrote and read to 1,500 priests and bishops, (no one could object or suggest any change) his own edict to the 4th Lateran Council of 1215. Among other things, it deprived the Jews of Europe the means for a livelihood; every Jew over 13 had to wear the hated yellow badge of shame; no Jew could live near or work with a Christian, nor could a Christian work for a Jew . . . . all this led to 700 years of the Jewish ghettos; the shame and degradation of a people; the successive pogroms through the centuries and then to the gas chambers of the 1940 period.

In April 1198, he issued this Bull to the Archbishop of Auch in Gascony . . . . " We give you a strict command that, by whatever means you can, you destroy all these heresies. If necessary, you may cause the princes and the people to suppress them with the sword."

In 1208, on his orders, the Dominicans were sent into Provence, to 'use any means' to murder and torture tens of thousands of Waldenses and Jews. An entire civilization of music, art and writing more than 1,000 years old, died in flames.

In 1201, he encouraged the formation of the 4th Crusade, to capture the Holy Land from the infidel. Instead, in 1203, the Venetians and the Crusaders attacked Constantinople and Latin Christians murdered more than 30,000 Greek Christians. Then, on the coronation of Baldwin of Flanders as Emperor on May 16, 1204, the Pope sent a letter of congratulations to the victors with . . . . "now we have One See and One Shepherd."

In 1212, he knew of the creation of the Children's Crusade. In the cold light of history, could he possibly have remained silent when *Christian Children* were sold by the boatloads, by *Christian merchants* to the slave markets of Egypt? There is no indication that he ever punished any of these men.

On August 24, 1215, this Pope excommunicated every baron in England who had signed the Magna Charta! This was on the principle that they were depriving *him*, the Pope, of his ownership and fee of England!

The Christian world now has the opportunity to examine the trauma source of its infection of hates and internal ailments; its perpetual wars for the past 750 years . . . A physician could suggest . . . now that you know the source . . . . "HEAL THYSELF".

OTHER NOTES ABOUT PEOPLE IN THIS BOOK:

Ortolana, the mother of Clara joined her in the Poor Sisters of Clare in 1226.

Agnes, in 1212 joined her sister as did another younger one, Beatrice, in 1229.

Rufino Offreduccio joined the order in 1210, as did *John (The Hat) Capella* a little later.

Pietro, Pica and Angelo Bernardone . . . .there is no record anywhere in history, where this family went after Francis' death. There is much controversy, as with everything else about Francis' early years, between historians in Lucca about the family Bernardone.

I have a strong suspicion that the Bernardone family could not *exist in Italy* after Francis died. *At this time,* the Barons of Poland *invited* Jews from all over Europe to come to that country, since it needed them for commerce and for their economy. It is my belief that the Bernardones did migrate to Poland and many of their descendants are in Europe, Israel and the United States.

It is interesting to note that the name Bernardi, a contraction of Bernardone, is a common Jewish name through the world today!